# DIESEL & ELECTRIC ME

# BASINGSTOKE TO WEY

COLIN HALL

The aim of this book is to portray the line from Basingstoke to Weymouth, including the branches to Fareham, Fawley, Hamworthy and Swanage over a 25 year period from 1970 to 1995. We show a selection of the ordinary and not so ordinary as the corporate image crumbles, sectorisation passes and privatisation beckons. Much that we see has been superceeded and lost. REP's and TC's, 07's and 71's. We cover the fall and rise of the Swanage branch. Special events, railtours, preservation and livery changes. Although produced as part of our "Diesel and Electric Memories" series steam has been included. Rules are meant to be broken. Two working narrow gauge lines in close proximity to the lines covered are also shown.

Colin Hall *January 2000*

*Photographs:*

*Front cover:* A Waterloo to Weymouth express formed of 2x4TC units propelled by a 4REP passes the Freightliner container terminal at Millbrook. The connection to the then new Maritime Container Terminal can be seen in the foreground. 15/4/72

*Frontispiece:* BR standard 4MT 2-6-4T 80104 awaits restoration at Swanage in the early days of the attempt to rebuild the Swanage branch. Cosmetic restoration belies the actual state of the locomotive. 8/88

*Back cover:* The next generation. The first class 442 EMU is unveiled at Bournemouth depot. 26/3/88

**COLIN HALL PUBLISHING**
**GODSHILL**
**FORDINGBRIDGE**
**HANTS**

1. In the late 80's an attempt was made to revive the "Bournemouth Belle" Pullman train which ceased running in 1967, using the VSOE "Orient Exprees" coaches. It was short lived. 33111 is seen approaching Basingstoke returning to Waterloo with the train. 26/9/87

2. One of the most spectacular rail events to take place in the area was staged at Basingstoke over a weekend in September 1987. The "Basingstoke Rail Event" brought together a large collection of locomotives for display in the former goods yard with some running special services. Here class 40 D200, restored to its original green livery, departs on a circular trip via Southampton and Andover. In the background a class 73 creeps into the up yard on an engineers train. 26/9/87

3. As part of the Basingstoke event newly restored class 45 D100 is officially named "Sherwood Forester" by the regiments CO looked on by Gerald Daniels who as the local BR area manager made this event possible. D100 was 45060.

4. Other "Peak" class locos on display are class 44 D4 "Great Gable" restored to original livery and 46 97403 "Ixion" in research deparment colours.

5. Class 24 97201 "Experiment" in the livery of the Derby Railway Research Centre. Formerly this loco, built in 1959, carried the numbers D5061 then 24061. 26/9/87

6. Another view of 97403 "Ixion". This loco formerly carried numbers D172 and 46035.

7. Class 40 D213 “Andania”. Built in 1959 it also carried 40013.

8. Class 55 “Deltic” D9000 “Royal Scots Grey”. Built in 1961 for the East Coast main line. It also carried number 55022.

9. Modern motive power was represented by class 56 56085. These locos were regular performers to the area on stone trains particularly from Whateley Quarry in Somerset.

10. The future was represented by American built General Motors Class 59-59003 used on stone trains operated by Yeomans from Merehead Quarry, Somerset. This was an important first as these locomotives were owned and maintained by a private company for use on BR main lines.

11. Electric traction was represented by Class "77" 27000 "Electra" built in 1953 for the then newly electrified service from Manchester to Sheffield via the Woodhead tunnel. On the withdrawal of passenger services on this route the class were sold to the Dutch railways for further use. It had not long been repatriated and still in Dutch railways livery as their 1502 when seen at Basingstoke. The "Dutch" livery became a common sight here when it was adopted by the engineers department of BR for their assigned locos on sectorisation.

12. Another electric loco on display was Class 86 86401 showing newly applied "Network South East" livery for its role on Euston to Northampton commuter trains.

13. Preserved Western region hydraulic diesel loco D7018 is of a class seen regularly on Southern Region lines in the 1960s and early 70s. This loco was built by Beyer Peacock in 1962 and were known as "Hymeks". 26/9/87

14. Just west of Basingstoke the Salisbury and Exeter line swings off under a flying junction. The line separated at Worting Junction with the up-line from Weymouth elevated over the diverging lines known as Battledown Flyover. Here we see Class 74 E6105 coming over the flyover with an up Southampton Docks to Waterloo boat train. 09/70

15. One of the thrills of the 4TC/4REP formations was standing where the cabs joined and watching the controls, especially the speedo.Here 4REP 2003 is clocked at 104 mph south of Worting whilst working the 1745 Waterloo to Poole. 4/5/88

16. Restored to Southern Railway livery for special duties was 4SUB EMU 4732. It is seen passing Shawford bound for Winchester.

17. Eastleigh has always been noted for the variety of motive power seen there due to its importance as junction, freight yard, loco depot and railway works. Here 33103 speeds through on the 1410 Waterloo to Salisbury diverted due to a tree on the line near Overton. 1/2/88

18. Another 33 this time 33025 enters the station with a defective coach bound for the works. 20/9/90

19. An interesting sight at Eastleigh for many months was the Channel Tunnel test train. This was formed of specially adapted Class 73, 33 and 4TC. The Class 33 was fitted with special bogies and electrical pickups which were to be fitted to the Eurostar power cars for working on the third rail. The test train is seen entering Eastleigh hauled by 73205. 20/9/90

20. Close-up of the test locomotive converted from a Class 33 Diesel and numbered 83301. This shot shows clearly the bogie and pickups under test.

21. Inter-City trains from Poole and Bournemouth to the north pass through Eastleigh. Here Class 47 47851 passed at the head of the 0825 Glasgow Central to Poole. 20/9/90

22. Another Class 47, this time 47121 on a freight heading for the Marchwood Military Port off the Fawley branch. On the right a Class 33/1 takes to the Fareham line via Botley. 14/9/89

23. Class 37 37074 stabled at Eastleigh. This signals the beginning of the end for BR. The livery is that of "Mainline", one of the 3 proposed privatised railfreight companies. In the end the whole lot was sold as one to EWS. 1/10/95

24. A bevy of 47s, 47277, 47503 and 47123. 20/9/90

25. The first class 60 arrives at Eastleigh. 60011 "Cader Idris" on the stabling point between crew training runs. 20/9/90

26. The new order at Eastleigh by 1995 as 60076 "Suilven" is seen with a Class 58 behind. 1/10/95

27. Preserved Southern Railway EMUs 2HAL 2090 and 4SUB 4732 (nearest camera) leave Eastleigh depot for Winchester from where they will form a special working to Southampton. 8/85

28. 2HAL EMU 2090 at the rear of the special working from Winchester to Southampton passing Eastleigh depot.

29. 3 Car Hampshire DEMU 1111 runs into Eastleigh on a Southampton to Alton working. This will run over what is now the Mid Hants Railway between Alresford and Alton. 11/7/70

30. Class O7 D2997 and Class 71 E5011 stand at the back of Eastleigh depot. The red carriage behind the 07 is part of the Eastleigh breakdown train and a former LSWR "Ironclad" coach. 11/7/70

31. D2991 is a restored Class 07 kept at Eastleigh works built in 1962 to replace the "USA" tanks in Southampton Docks. This Class has always been a familiar sight at Eastleigh. 27/9/72

32. Class 08 shunter 08642 was re-painted in a special livery including the LSWR coat of arms for duties as works pilot at Eastleigh. 14/9/89

33. Forlorn sight at Eastleigh. 33013, 33031 and 33059 in the scrap line. 14/9/89

34. Inside the works 33006 receives attention. 27/9/92

35. Resplendent in new railfreight livery 33203 stands in the works yard. This is one of the slimmer members of the Class specially built for the narrower tunnels of the Tonbridge to Hastings line. 27/9/92

36. Also ex-works in a new livery 33035 in "Network South East" colours, stands outside the engine testing house. 27/9/92

37. 33008 restored to original livery as D6508 for special duties. 27/9/92

38. 50021 "Rodney". The Class 50s finished their days on the Waterloo to Exeter line and became regular sights at Eastleigh where they came over from Salisbury for refuelling and running maintenance. 27/9/92

39. Class T9 120 stands in the works yard in Southern Railway colours. Built in 1889 at Nine Elms works before the LSWR moved their works to Eastleigh to make the town what it is today. 27/9/92

40. De-icing Unit 002 converted from 2x 2HAL motor coaches to keep the third rail clear of ice in winter. 27/9/92

41. From Eastleigh a line goes to Fareham with an intermediate station at Botley. Here we see 50044 "Exeter" heading the 1410 Waterloo to Exeter St David's. This had been diverted via Havant and Eastleigh due to engineer works. 1/3/87

42. More usual power at Botley is 3 Car Hampshire DEMUs working 1508 Portsmouth Harbour to Reading. 1/3/87

43.

43 and 44. Very unusual motor power in the shape of Midland Region DMMUs passing through Botley on an excursion returning to Spring Road, Birmingham from Portsmouth Harbour. 1/5/89

45. Heading south from Eastleigh we are soon in the large conurbation of Southampton. A short branch from Northam Junction served coal wharves on the River Itchen. For many years after the end of steam on BR an ex-LSWR B4 0-4-0T 30096 was to be found shunting Dibles Wharf. 1970

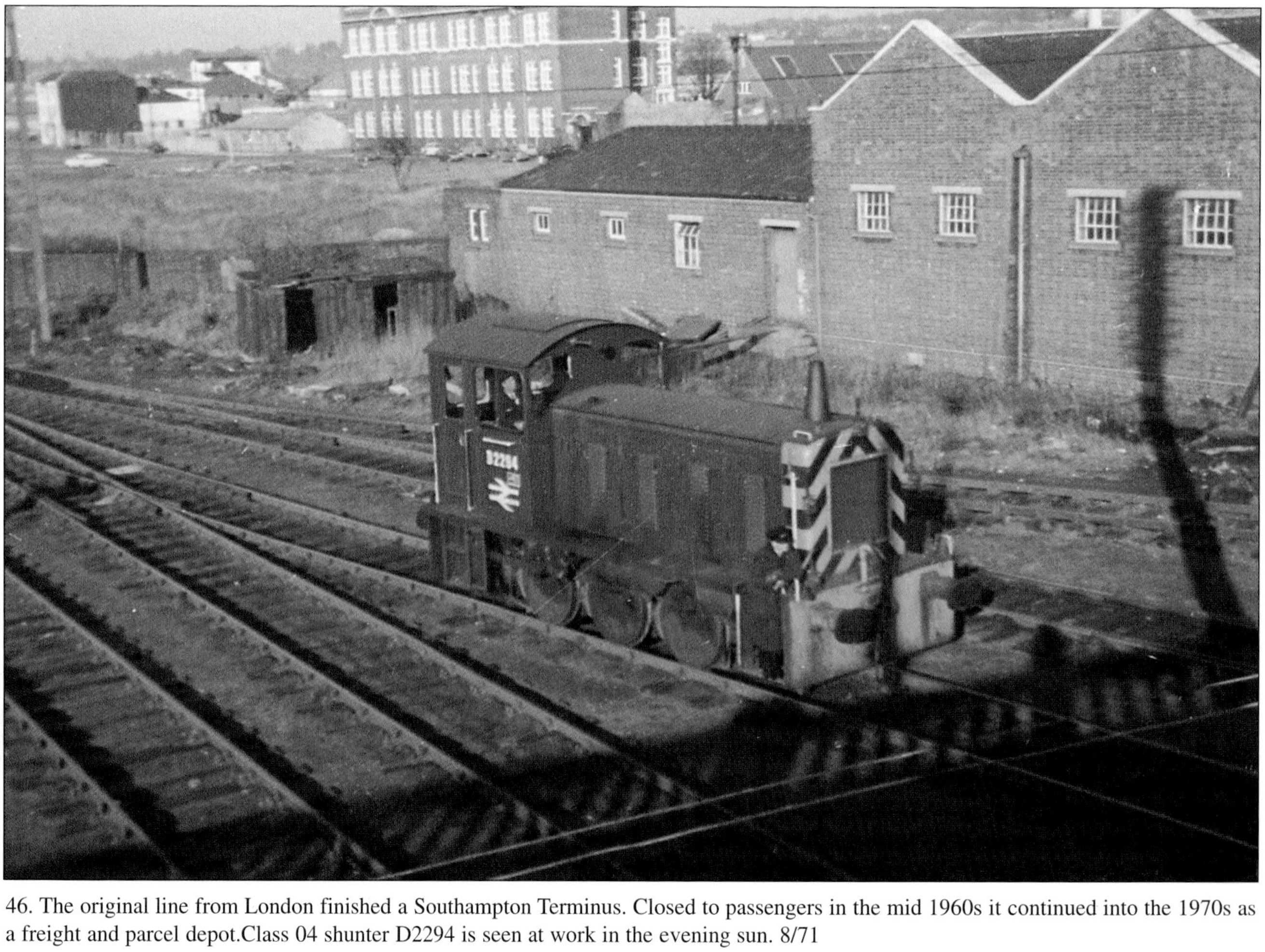

46. The original line from London finished a Southampton Terminus. Closed to passengers in the mid 1960s it continued into the 1970s as a freight and parcel depot.Class 04 shunter D2294 is seen at work in the evening sun. 8/71

47. Shortages of 4REP Units in the early 1970s, particularly on summer Saturdays, saw Class 33s on Waterloo to Weymouth trains. Here 6529 arrives at Southampton Central hauling two 4TCs. 8/71

48. Class 47s were frequently seen in Southampton in all sorts of roles. 47814 enters Southampton on a York to Poole Inter-City train. 1/5/91

49. 47481 passes light engine bound for Eastleigh depot after bringing in a Freightliner train. 1/5/91

50. 47564 "Colossus" heads a track testing train of the Derby Railway Research Centre. 13/9/88

51. One of the original batch of Class 73s 73005 stands in the down siding at the entrance to Southampton tunnel. 4/7/86

52. A pair of 73s 73105 and 73126 leaves Southampton Central at the head of a Poole to Waterloo semi-fast train. 13/9/98

53. Class 74 E6103 passing through Southampton Centrals platform 4 with an "Ocean Liner Express" probably for one of the ships in the background whilst a 4VEP sits at Platform 3 on a stopping service to Bournemouth. 15/4/72

54. 4REP 3011 stands at Platform 1 at the head of a semi-fast working to Waterloo. 15/4/72

55. Class 50 50020 "Revenge" stands at Platform 3 on the 1438 Waterloo to Exter St Davids diverted due to engineering work at Andover. 16/3/85

56. 33114 departs Southampton propelling 4TC ECS to Eastleigh. This combination had worked in from Salisbury deputising for a failed Hampshire Unit. The 4TC had been restored to its original all-over blue livery. 13/11/91

57. 4REP Unit 2003 departs Southampton at the rear of the 1745 Waterloo to Bournemouth. 4/5/88

58. In the siding alongside Platform 5 stands Class 09 shunter 09025. Unofficially named "Victory" it was used for trip workings between Central Station and the Post Office Parcel sorting office in the Western Docks. 4/5/88

59. 4CIG Unit 7415 passes the Freightliner Terminal at Millbrook on a Waterloo to Bournemouth stopping service. 15/4/72

60. The four original Class 59s are hauled past Millbrook Station by a Class 47 after being unloaded from a ship in Southampton Western Docks.

61. 47339 runs into the Freightliner Terminal at Millbrook to pick up its train. 18/9/96

62.

62 and 63. 45106 passes through Redbridge Station to pass over the River Test Causeway as it approaches Totton on a railtour from Manchester to Weymouth. 5/11/88

64. Taking up the rear of the 45106 railtour are 33102 and 33104. This top and tailing was to enable the special to run over the Fawley branch. 5/11/88

65. 47224 runs wrong line out of Totton over the Causeway to Redbridge with an oil train from Fawley refinery. 20/9/83

66. A 2x4TC and 4REP formation heads away from Totton as the 1400 Bournemouth to Waterloo. 20/9/83

67.

67 and 68. Top and tail on the Manchester to Weymouth railtour as it traverses the Fawley branch, leaving Marchwood with 45106 leading and 33102/114 at the rear. 5/11/88

69.

69 and 70. Returning back up the branch from Fawley to Totton passing through Hythe now with 33114/102 leading and 45106 coming up at the rear.

71. A short railway line in Hythe worth visiting is the pier tramway. This 2' gauge electric railway runs out onto the pier where ferries cross to the Town Quay in Southampton. This picture shows the pier head station with its overall roof.

72. This tank wagon takes fuel oil out to the ferries.

73.

73 and 74. Two third rail electric locos redundant from a World War I munitions factory provide motive power with one in service as seen at the pier head and one spare outside the workshops. They were built in 1917 and originally ran on batteries being converted to 3rd rail for use on the pier.

75. Back on the mainline 45106 continues on to Weymouth through Lyndhurst Road station. This station has since been re-named Ashurst, New Forest after the village in which it is situated. 5/11/88

76. Beaulieu Road station is next down the line in the middle of the New Forest. Restored 4SUB 4732 passes bound for Bournemouth and an open day at the depot there. 25/3/88

77.

77 and 78. 2x4TC propelled by 2xClass 73 pass through working the 1140 Waterloo to Bournemouth. 25/3/88

79. 47475 heads through Beaulieu Road with the 1238 Poole to Manchester. 25/3/88

80. 2x4CIG Units pass with the 1300 Bournemouth to Waterloo. 25/3/88

81. 47836 heads out of Brockenhurst with the 0915 Wolverhampton to Poole. The photograph was taken from the trackbed of the old line to Ringwood and Wimborne looking across the site of the former junction. 13/1/91

82. 33114 approaches Christchurch hauling preserved LMS "Black 5" 4-6-0 5305 en route to an open day at Bournemouth depot. In the background is the former goods shed alongside the trackbed of the old line to Ringwood via Hurn. 26/3/88

83. LMS "Black 5" 5305 stands in Branksome station. 33114 had acted as pilot from Salisbury. 26/3/88

84. 5305 seen later the same day on display at the Bournemouth depot open day.

85. 4 Car "Hastings" DEMU 203001 on display at Bournemouth depot. It had been re-painted in near original livery for special duties.

86. A very unusual visitor at this open day was Thameslink 4 Car EMU 319030.

87. The shape of things to come! A then brand new Class 442 on display at Bournemouth depot. 26/3/88

88. The shape of the past! Departmental EMU 002 at Bournemouth depot. 11/7/86

89. The original station serving the Poole area was at Hamworthy. It was relegated to goods only following the opening of the direct line through Poole to Bournemouth. Here we see the "Wessex Wanderer" railtour from the Midlands to Weymouth as a rare visit of a passenger train to Hamworthy Goods. 3/4/88

90.

90 and 91. The "Wessex Wanderer" railtour heads on west at Rockley Point. It is formed of LMR DMMUs. 3/4/88

92. Class 47 47371 approaches Wareham station with oil empties for Furzebrook sidings. On withdrawal of passenger services from Swanage, Furzebrook became the end of the line. 6/7/89

93. View of the driver of 2H DEMU 1121 as he picks up the token for the single line to Swanage at Worgret junction. 8/70

94.

94 and 95. Halfway down the remains of the Swanage branch the line passes near the village of Stoborough. Here the "Wessex Wanderer" heads towards Furzebrook. 3/4/88

96. Another view of 47371 as it approaches the oil terminal at Furzebrook. Oil is now shipped out by pipeline but LPG still goes out by rail. 6/7/89

97. Before closure to passengers, 3 Car Hampshire Unit 1125 passes Furzebrook working the 1241 Wareham to Swanage. 8/70

98. On the same day Class 33 D6549 arrives at Furzebrook.

99.

99 and 100. Two further views of D6549 at Furzebrook as it shunts clay wagons before departing with a loaded train. A network of narrow guage lines originally brought clay to the works but even at the time these pictures were taken they had long gone. The oil traffic took off when the clay stopped.

101.

101 and 102. Nearer to Corfe Castle a 2' gauge clay tramway continued into the 1970s. However, this in its final years was to dispose of spoil rather than to ship out clay by rail. At Norden a Simplex diesel lies derelect whilst an Orenstein & Koppel diesel is still in good working order. This O & K loco supposedly came from a V2 rocket site in Germany after the war. 8/70

103. Seen near the former exchange sidings between the Norden system and the Swanage branch at Eldon sidings, is this tank wagon for the transportation of diesel fuel. This sytem was originally built to 3'9" gauge and this wagon clearly shows it was originally built to this guage and has been converted to 2'.

104. On the Norden system an old wagon turntable lies in the grass.

105.

105 and 106. The clay mines at Norden continue and some narrow gauge tracks were still in use in the 1980s. Wagons were hauled up by ropes from the mines, then manhandled outside to be tipped into open lorries.

107. As the Swanage Railway re-built its way to re-joining the national network at Furzebrook, Norden became a temporary terminus with park and ride facilities. Arriving at the original intermediate station at Corfe Castle on a Norden to Swanage train is Bullied Pacific 34072 "257 Squadron". In steam days this class of locomotive were regular visitors to Swanage on through trains from Waterloo. 26/5/97

108. A new station built as an earlier temporary terminus is Harmans Cross. Seen here is visiting GWR 0-6-0 pannier tank 7752. 6/7/89

109. Newly returned from the USA and awaiting return to working order M7 0-4-4T 30053 is seen at the buffers at Swanage. The M7s were the mainstay of local services on the Swanage branch for many years until the early 1960s. 8/88

110. BR Standard 2-6-4T 80104 is returned to steam after restoration outside the engine shed at Swanage. This represents the last steam class to work the line before diesels took over in 1967. 26/5/97

111.

111 and 112. Diesel memories of a preserved kind. Two views of an ex BR Gloucester Twin DMMU being shunted at Swanage in the early days of reconstructing the branch. This unit is no longer at Swanage. 8/86

113.

113 and 114. Returning to the mainline we continue to Wool station. Here two views see the 1530 Weymouth to Waterloo arrive and depart. 4TC 8103 is propelled by 33114. 3/4/88

115. 33106 arrives at Wool on the 1244 Waterloo to Weymouth. These push-pull workings ceased shortly after these pictures were taken when full electric services were extended to Weymouth. 3/4/88

116.

116 and 117. Two views of the "Wessex Wanderer" railtour passing through Wool on its way back from Weymouth to the Midlands. 3/4/88

118. Weymouth is the end of the line. 3 Car Hampshire DEMU 205033 stands at the buffers having worked a special from Salisbury via Yeovil. 6/8/87

119. During the first two months of 1992 several special trains ran from Waterloo to Weymouth using unusual motive power. ARC 59103 is seen arriving at Weymouth alongside a Class 442 which is about to depart to Waterloo. 5/1/92

120. 20007 draws to a stand at Weymouth on a special from Waterloo. 23/2/92

121. 37107 and 33052 arrive double heading. 19/1/92

Bitesize



# Bitesize Pearson Edexcel GCSE (9-1) MATHEMATICS

## REVISION WORKBOOK

## FOUNDATION

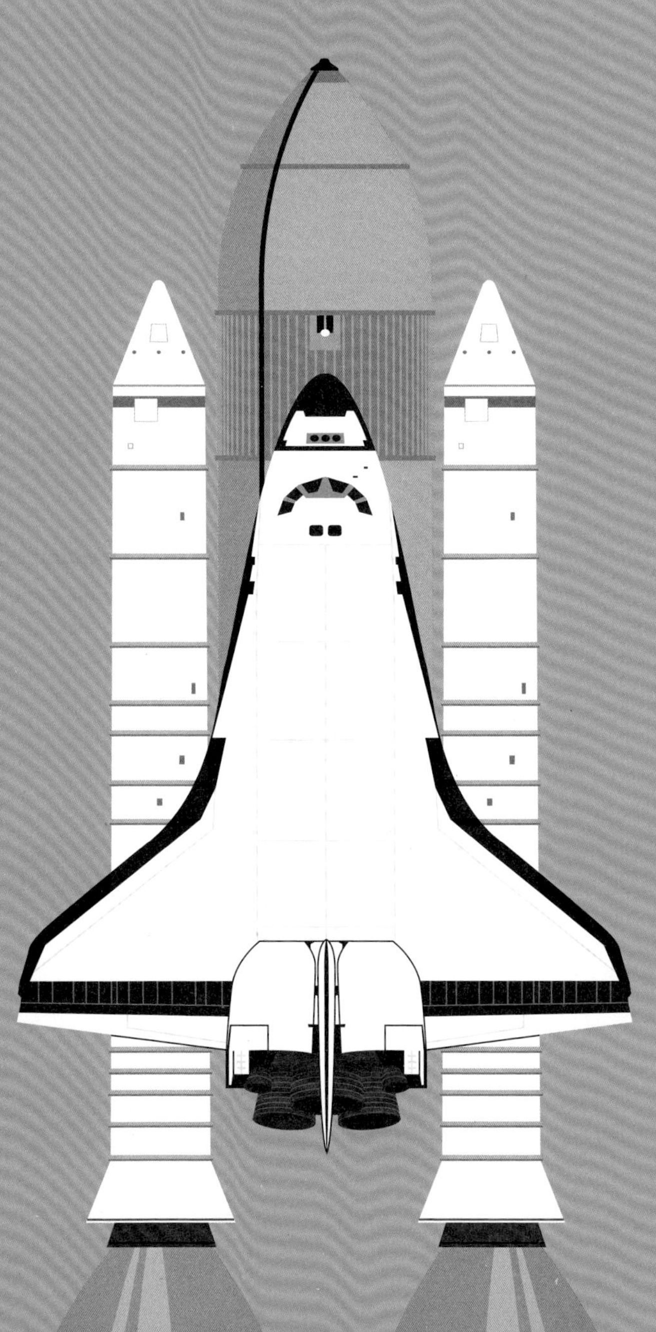

**Series Consultant:**
Harry Smith

**Author:**
Navtej Marwaha

# Contents


## Number
- Place value 1
- Negative numbers 2
- Adding and subtracting 3
- Multiplying and dividing 4
- Order of operations 5
- Decimals 6
- Operations with decimals 7
- Rounding 8
- Fractions 9
- Operations with fractions 10
- Mixed numbers and improper fractions 11
- Factors, multiples and prime numbers 12
- Prime factors, HCF and LCM 13
- Estimation and outcomes 14
- Indices and roots 15
- Standard form 16
- Error intervals 17
- Exam skills: Number 18

## Algebra
- Function machines 19
- Algebraic substitution 20
- Collecting like terms 21
- Simplifying expressions 22
- Writing expressions 23
- Algebraic formulae 24
- Algebraic indices 25
- Expanding brackets 26
- Expanding double brackets 27
- Factorising 28
- Linear equations 29
- Rearranging formulae 30
- Inequalities 31
- Solving inequalities 32
- Solving sequence problems 33
- Arithmetic sequences 34
- Factorising quadratics 35
- Solving quadratic equations 36
- Simultaneous equations 37
- Gradients of lines 38
- Drawing straight-line graphs 39
- Equations of straight lines 40
- Parallel lines 41
- Real-life graphs 42
- Quadratic graphs 43
- Using quadratic graphs 44
- Cubic and reciprocal graphs 45
- Recognising graphs 46
- Algebraic reasoning 47
- Exam skills: Algebra 48

## Ratio, proportion and rates of change
- Ratio 49
- Direct proportion 50
- Inverse proportion 51
- Percentages 52
- Fractions, decimals and percentages 53
- Percentage change 54
- Reverse percentages 55
- Growth and decay 56
- Compound measures 57
- Speed 58
- Density 59
- Proportion and graphs 60
- Exam skills: Ratio and proportion 61

## Geometry and measures
- Angle properties 62
- Solving angle problems 63
- Angles in polygons 64
- Constructing perpendiculars 65
- Constructions with angles 66
- Loci 67
- Perimeter and area 68
- Areas of 2D shapes 69
- 3D shapes 70
- Volumes of 3D shapes 71
- Surface area 72
- Circles and cylinders 73
- Circles, sectors and arcs 74
- Circle facts 75
- Transformations 76
- Enlargement 77
- Bearings 78
- Scale drawings and maps 79
- Pythagoras' theorem 80
- Units of length, area and volume 81
- Trigonometry: lengths 82
- Trigonometry: angles 83
- Trigonometry techniques 84
- Time and timetables 85
- Reading scales 86
- Symmetry 87
- Quadrilaterals 88
- Plans and elevations 89
- Similarity and congruence 90
- Similar shapes 91
- Congruent triangles 92
- Line segments 93
- Vectors 94
- Exam skills: Geometry and measures 95

## Probability
- Introduction to probability 96
- More about probability 97
- Relative frequency 98
- Venn diagrams 99
- Tree diagrams 100
- Exam skills: Probability 101

## Statistics
- Averages and range 102
- Pictograms 103
- Line graphs 104
- Pie charts 105
- Stem-and-leaf diagrams 106
- Scatter graphs 107
- Frequency tables 108
- Two-way tables 109
- Sampling 110
- Analysing data 111
- Exam skills: Statistics 112

## Problem solving
- Problem-solving strategies 113
- Solving number problems 114
- Solving graphical problems 115
- Solving geometric problems 116
- Solving algebraic problems 117
- Solving statistical problems 118
- Non-calculator practice paper 119
- Calculator practice paper 122

Answers 125


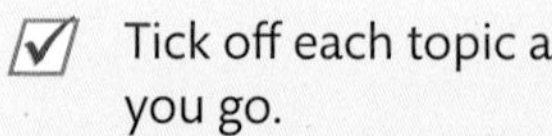

Tick off each topic as you go.

Each bite-sized chunk has a **timer** to indicate how long it will take. Use them to plan your revision sessions.

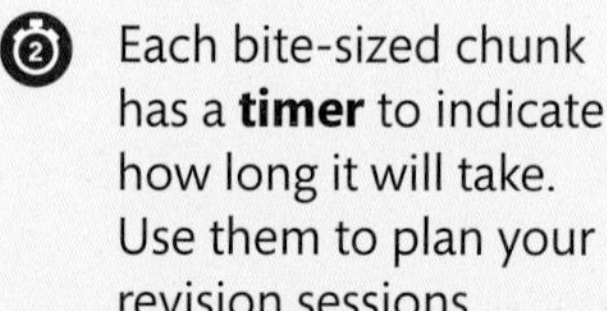

Scan the **QR codes** to visit the BBC Bitesize website. It will link straight through to revision resources on that subject. You can also access these by visiting www.pearsonschools.co.uk/BBCBitesizeLinks.

# Place value

## 2 Quick quiz

1. Write these numbers in words.
(a) 20 ..............................
(b) 100 ..............................

2. Write these numbers in figures.
(a) fifteen ..............................
(b) one thousand ..............................

## 10 Numbers and words — Grade 1

**1. (a)** Write the number four thousand six hundred and three in figures. **[1 mark]**

Write out a place value table.

| Thousands | Hundreds | Tens | Units |
|---|---|---|---|
| 4 | 6 | .................... | 3 |

Write 0 in the empty tens column.

**(b)** Write the number 7235 in words. **[1 mark]**

Seven thousand, ........................................ and

..............................................................................

**2. (a)** Write the number three thousand and eighty-four in numerals. **[1 mark]**

..............................

**(b)** Write the number 9002 in words. **[1 mark]**

..............................................................................

..............................................................................

**(c)** Write down the value of 8 in the number 3856 **[1 mark]**

**Exam focus**
You can write your answer in words or digits.

..............................

## 10 Ordering numbers — Grade 1

**3. (a)** Write the following numbers in order of size. Start with the smallest number. **[1 mark]**

6 18 3 24 9

3 6 .......... .......... ..........

**(b)** Write the following numbers in order of size. Start with the smallest number. **[1 mark]**

6587 6578 6758 6857 6775

6578 .......... .......... .......... ..........

If the first digit is the same, then look at the second digit, and so on.

**4. (a)** Write the following numbers in order of size. Start with the smallest number. **[1 mark]**

14 34 47 21 5

.......... .......... .......... .......... ..........

**(b)** Write the following numbers in order of size. Start with the smallest number. **[1 mark]**

8569 8965 8595 8956 8659

.......... .......... .......... .......... ..........

## 5 Applying place value — Grade 1

**5.** Here are four digits: 7 4 6 8

**(a)** Write down the largest three-digit number you can make, using three of these digits. You may use each digit only once. **[1 mark]**

..............................

Here are the four digits again: 7 4 6 8

**(b)** Write down the three-digit number with a value closest to 700 that you can make with three of these digits. You may use each digit only once. **[1 mark]**

..............................

Made a start

Feeling confident

Exam ready

# Negative numbers

## Quick quiz

Write down whether each calculation will have a negative or positive answer.

**(a)** positive × positive .............................. **(b)** positive × negative .............................. **(c)** negative × positive .............................. **(d)** negative × negative ..............................

## Simple negative numbers

Grade 1

**1.** Work out

**(a)** −5 − 4 **[1 mark]**

= − ..........

..............................

**(b)** −12 ÷ 4 **[1 mark]**

= − ..........

..............................

**(c)** −9 × −5 **[1 mark]**

= + ..........

..............................

If you multiply two negative numbers the answer will be a positive number.

## Using rules

Grade 1

**2.** Work out

**(a)** 7 − −6 **[1 mark]**

= +7 + 6

= ..........

..............................

**(b)** −7 − 5 **[1 mark]**

= −7 − 5

= − ..........

..............................

**(c)** −8 + −4 **[1 mark]**

= −8 .......... 4

= − ..........

..............................

**(d)** −10 + −18 **[1 mark]**

= −10 − ..........

= ..........

..............................

**3.** Write these numbers in order of size. Start with the lowest number.

**(a)** −8 4 −10 −1 2 **[1 mark]**

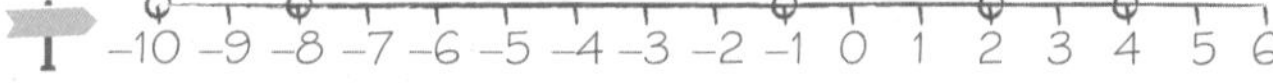



.......... .......... .......... .......... ..........

**(b)** 40 −32 −14 −15 28 **[1 mark]**

.......... .......... .......... .......... ..........

## Using negative numbers

Grade 1

**4.** At 8 a.m., the temperature was −5 °C. By 4 p.m., the temperature had gone up by 12 degrees.

**(a)** Write down the temperature at 4 p.m. **[1 mark]**

..............................°C

At 10 p.m. the temperature was −2 °C. By midnight, the temperature had gone down by 8 degrees.

**(b)** Write down the temperature at midnight. **[1 mark]**

..............................°C

**5.** Gemma recorded the maximum temperature and the minimum temperature on each of six days in December. The table shows information about her results.

| Day | Monday | Tuesday | Wednesday | Thursday | Friday |
|---|---|---|---|---|---|
| **Maximum temperature (°C)** | 1 | 3 | 2 | 0 | −3 |
| **Minimum temperature (°C)** | −6 | −7 | −4 | −3 | −10 |

**(a)** Write down the lowest temperature. **[1 mark]**

..............................°C

**(b)** Work out the difference between the maximum temperature on Wednesday and the minimum temperature on Wednesday. **[1 mark]**

.............................. degrees

The minimum temperature on Saturday was 5 degrees higher than the minimum temperature on Friday.

**(c)** Work out the minimum temperature on Saturday. **[1 mark]**

..............................°C

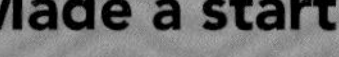

Made a start Feeling confident Exam ready

# Adding and subtracting

## Quick quiz

Work out

**(a)** $3 + 8$ ..............................

**(b)** $42 + 16$ ..............................

**(c)** $18 - 5$ ..............................

**(d)** $67 - 32$ ..............................

## Column addition and subtraction — Grade 1

**1.** Work out

**(a)** $163 + 286$ **[1 mark]**

```
  163
+ 286
.....9
```

**(b)** $2489 + 6571$ **[1 mark]**

```
  2489
+ 6571
......0
     1
```

**(c)** $65\,842 + 6532$ **[1 mark]**

..............................

**2.** Work out

**(a)** $789 - 42$ **[1 mark]**

```
  789
-  42
.....7
```

**(b)** $6395 - 4523$ **[1 mark]**

..............................

**(c)** $8000 - 6451$ **[1 mark]**

```
 ⁷8̸ ⁹0̸ ⁹0̸ ¹0
- 6  4  5  1
..............
```

## Problem solving with addition and subtraction — Grade 2

**3.** There are 150 people on a train.
At the first stop:
10 people get off the train
25 people get on the train.

At the next stop:
5 people get off the train
16 people get on the train.

**Problem solving**

Write down your method, step by step.

How many people are on the train now? **[3 marks]**

..............................

**4.** Miraan sells onions in bags.
There are 8 onions in each bag she sells.
On Thursday morning Miraan has 115 onions.
On Thursday afternoon she sells 11 bags of onions.
On Friday morning Miraan gets 85 more onions.
On Friday afternoon she sells 8 bags of onions.

Work out how many onions Miraan has now. **[4 marks]**

..............................

**5.** Lee passed these two signs, at different points of his journey, at the side of the road as he was travelling. The road is between Dudley and Glasgow.

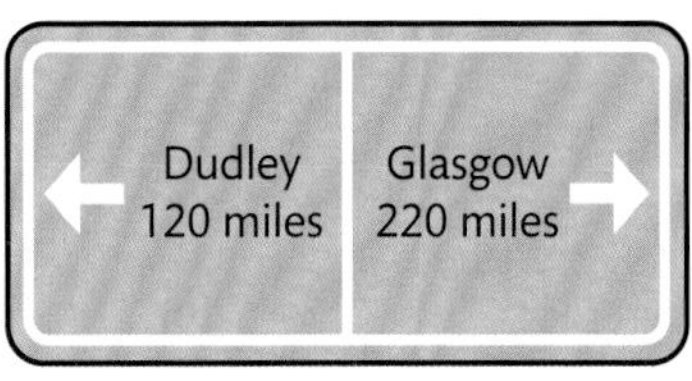


Dudley 244 miles | Glasgow 96 miles

**(a)** Work out the distance between Dudley and Glasgow along the road. **[2 marks]**

..............................miles

**(b)** Work out the distance along the road between the two signs. **[2 marks]**

..............................miles

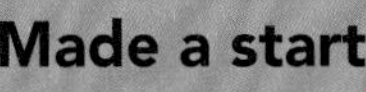

Made a start | Feeling confident | Exam ready

# Multiplying and dividing

## Quick quiz

Work out

(a) $6 \times 7$ ..............................

(b) $8 \times 9$ ..............................

(c) $24 \div 6$ ..............................

(d) $63 \div 9$ ..............................

## Column multiplication and division

Grade 1–2

1. Work out

(a) $426 \times 4$ **[2 marks]**

```
  4 2 6
×     4
.........
```

(b) $789 \times 53$ **[2 marks]**

```
  7 8 9
×   5 3
.........
.........
.........
```

(c) $384 \times 89$ **[2 marks]**

```
  3 8 4
×   8 9
.........
.........
.........
```

2. Work out

(a) $425 \div 5$ **[2 marks]**

5)4 2 5

(b) $288 \div 8$ **[2 marks]**

8)2 8 8

(c) $3429 \div 9$ **[2 marks]**

9)3 4 2 9

## Problem solving with multiplication and division

Grade 2

3. Davit is going to make some sandwiches.
He has 4 packs of bread.
There are 19 slices of bread in each pack.
Davit wants to make 36 sandwiches.
He will use 2 slices of bread to make each sandwich.

Does Davit have enough bread to make 36 sandwiches?
You must show your working. **[3 marks]**

**Problem solving**
Work out how many slices of bread Davit has in total and then how many he needs to make all the sandwiches.

..............................

4. 146 people are going on a school trip.
Each person will travel by coach or by minibus.
Gus gets 3 coaches for the trip.
Each coach has seats for 36 passengers.
Gus also needs some minibuses for the trip.
Each minibus has seats for 12 passengers.

Work out the smallest number of minibuses Gus needs.

**[3 marks]**

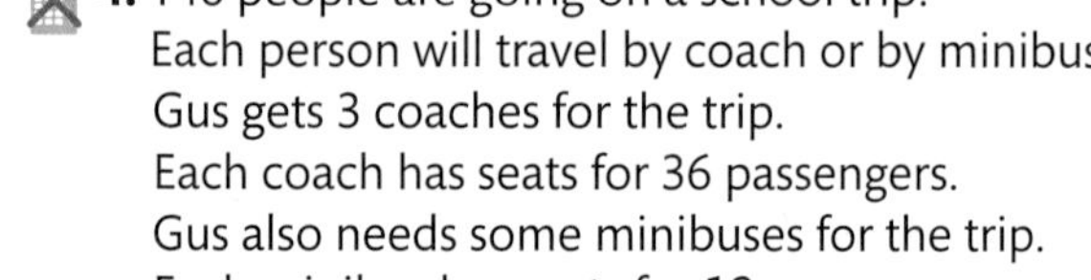

..............................

5. Nalla is going to make some trousers. She needs 525 cm of thread for each pair of trousers.
Nalla wants to make 7 pairs of trousers. She has 45 m of thread.

Does Nalla have enough thread to make 7 pairs of trousers? You must show how you get your answer. **[3 marks]**

..............................

 Made a start  Feeling confident  Exam ready

# Order of operations

## Quick quiz

Write down the name of each operation.

| B | I | D | M | A | S |
|---|---|---|---|---|---|
| ........ | ........ | ........ | ........ | ........ | ........ |

## 15 BIDMAS — Grade 2

1. Work out the value of each expression.

(a) $3 + 5 \times 2$ **[1 mark]**

(b) $4 + 3 \times (9 - 2)$ **[1 mark]**

$9 - 2 = 7$ (B)IDMAS

$3 \times 7 = 21$ BI(D)MAS

$4 + 21 =$ ..........

**Exam focus**

Write down BIDMAS and ring the first operation that must be done in the calculation.

.................................   .................................

2. Work out

(a) $2 \times (8 - 3)$ **[1 mark]**

(b) $3^2 + 4 \times 5$ **[1 mark]**

(c) $(13 - 6) \times 2$ **[1 mark]**

.................................   .................................   .................................

3. Complete these statements by adding in brackets to make each statement true.

(a) $5 + 3 \times 2 - 1 = 15$ **[1 mark]**

(b) $12 - 2 \times 3 + 1 = 4$ **[1 mark]**

**Problem solving**

Try some different options:

$(5 + 3) \times 2 - 1$  $5 + 3 \times (2 - 1)$

4. Complete these statements by adding in the correct operations to make each statement true.

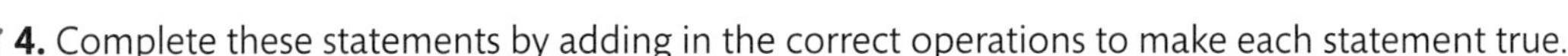

(a) (7 ☐ 9) ☐ 1 = 64 **[1 mark]**

(b) 32 ☐ (5 ☐ 10) = 480 **[1 mark]**

(c) (7 ☐ 2) ☐ 13 = 18 **[1 mark]**

## 10 Word problems — Grades 2–3

5. Avi says $20 - 4 \times 3 = 48$

Brian says $20 - 4 \times 3 = 8$

Who is right? Give a reason for your answer. **[2 marks]**

.................................................................................

.................................................................................

6. Don says that $30 + 10 \div 2 = 20$

Don is wrong.

Explain why. **[2 marks]**

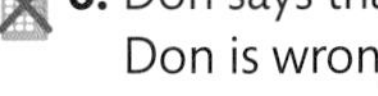

.................................................................................

.................................................................................

7. Ntombi organised an event for a charity.

The tickets sold for £20 each.

Ntombi sold 560 tickets.

She paid costs of £5000.

She gave all of the profits to charity.

Write down a calculation that Ntombi can use to work out how much money was given to the charity.

You can only use the numbers that are given. **[2 marks]**

.................................

Made a start   Feeling confident   Exam ready

# Decimals

## Quick quiz

Circle the larger decimal in each pair.

**(a)** 0.7 1.3 **(b)** 0.6 0.7 **(c)** 0.84 0.89 **(d)** 0.4 0.41

## Place value

Grade 1

**1.** Write down the value of

**(a)** the 4 in 6.423 **[1 mark]**

**(b)** the 8 in 47.5896 **[1 mark]**

**(c)** the 2 in 143.962 14 **[1 mark]**

**(d)** the 7 in 100.279 **[1 mark]**

............................... ............................... ............................... ...............................

## Ordering decimals

Grade 1

**2.** Write the following numbers in order of size.
Start with the lowest number. **[1 mark]**

**(a)** 4.7 3.62 0.9 11.3

4.7 3.62 0.9 11.3

The whole number parts are all different so you don't need to consider the decimal parts.

.......... .......... .......... ..........

**(b)** 0.25 0.2 0.4 0.75 0.5 **[1 mark]**

0.25 0.20 0.40 0.75 0.50

Decide on the place value of each digit. 0.2 is the same as 0.20 – write out the 0s to help make your decision and then order them.

.......... .......... .......... .......... ..........

**3.** Write the following numbers in order of size.
Start with the lowest number. **[1 mark]**

0.801 0.86 0.79 0.838

.......... .......... .......... ..........

**4.** Write the following numbers in order of size.
Start with the lowest number. **[1 mark]**

0.754 0.7 0.65 0.745

.......... .......... .......... ..........

**5.** Write the following numbers in order of size.
Start with the highest number. **[1 mark]**

0.6 0.666 0.66 0.606

.......... .......... .......... ..........

**6.** Which is higher, 0.44 or 0.404?
Use < or > in your answer. **[1 mark]**

..........................................................................................



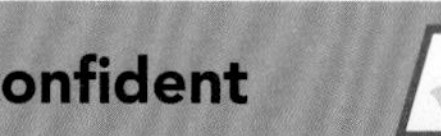

Made a start Feeling confident Exam ready

# Operations with decimals

## 2 Quick quiz

Work out

(a) $1.2 + 2.4$ ..............................

(b) $1 - 0.5$ ..............................

(c) $1.5 \times 4$ ..............................

(d) $10 \div 2.5$ ..............................

## 10 Basic operations with decimals — Grade 2

**1.** Work out

(a) $12.8 + 6.93$ **[1 mark]**

```
  12.80
 + 6.93
 ......
```

(b) $7.2 - 5.48$ **[1 mark]**

```
  7.20
 -5.48
 ......
```

Write in 0s so that all numbers have the same number of decimal places.

(c) $5.49 \times 2.6$ **[1 mark]**

First work out $549 \times 26$. There are 3 decimal places in total in the calculation so put 3 decimal places in your answer.

..............................

(d) $9.63 \div 0.3$ **[1 mark]**

**Exam focus**
Check your answer makes sense. The number you are dividing by is between 0 and 1, so the answer will be larger than 9.63.

..............................

## 15 Operations in word problems — Grade 2

**2.** Dunia and Bella are in a gymnastics competition.
Here are their scores.

Dunia: 14.2 10.6 12.4
Bella: 13.4 11.4 12.2

Work out who got the higher total score, Dunia or Bella.
You must show your working. **[3 marks]**

..............................

**3.** While at the grocery store, Anika noticed that there were two different-sized bottles of tomato sauce. One bottle was 17.8 ounces and the other bottle was 33.56 ounces.

Calculate the difference in weight between the two bottles of tomato sauce. **[1 mark]**

..............................ounces

**4.** A ticket for a show costs £36.
Gill has £210 to spend on tickets.
She buys as many tickets as possible.

Calculate how much money Gill has left. **[3 marks]**

£..............................

**5.** Callum uses an oil heater for 6.5 hours each day.
The oil heater uses 0.75 litres of oil each hour.
He has 280 litres of oil.

Work out whether Callum has enough oil for 70 days.
You must show clearly how you got your answer. **[4 marks]**

..............................

# Rounding

## Quick quiz

Circle the correct answer.

**(a)** 18 is nearer to 10 or 20

**(b)** 124 is nearer to 120 or 130

**(c)** 1425 is nearer to 1400 or 1500

**(d)** 5.7 is nearer to 5 or 6

## To the nearest 10, 100 or 1000

Grade 1 

**1.** Round

**(a)** 34 to the nearest ten **[1 mark]**

..............................

**(b)** 5643 to the nearest hundred **[1 mark]**

Is 5643 nearer to 5600 or 5700?

..............................

**(c)** 197 458 to the nearest thousand. **[1 mark]**

Is 197 458 nearer to 197 000 or 198 000?

..............................

## Decimal places

Grade 1 

**2. (a)** Write the number 15.46 correct to 1 decimal place. **[1 mark]**

..............................

**(b)** Write the number 34.567 correct to 2 decimal places. **[1 mark]**

..............................

**(c)** Write the number 8.5689 correct to 3 decimal places. **[1 mark]**

..............................

## Significant figures

Grade 2 

**3. (a)** Write the number 421 correct to 2 significant figures. **[1 mark]**

..............................

**(b)** Write the number 78.46 correct to 2 significant figures. **[1 mark]**

..............................

**(c)** Write the number 7.5284 correct to 3 significant figures. **[1 mark]**

..............................

## Using rounding

Grade 2 

**4.** Use your calculator to work out $\sqrt{800} - 13.4$

**(a)** Write down all the figures on your calculator display. You must give your answer as a decimal. **[1 mark]**

..............................

**(b)** Write your answer to part **(a)** correct to 1 decimal place. **[1 mark]**

..............................

**5.** Use your calculator to work out $\dfrac{\sqrt{80.36}}{10.6 - 7.2}$

**(a)** Write down all the figures on your calculator display. You must give your answer as a decimal. **[2 marks]**

**Exam focus**

You might need to use the S⇔D button on your calculator to get your answer as a decimal.

..............................

**(b)** Write your answer to part **(a)** correct to 4 decimal places. **[1 mark]**

..............................



Made a start  Feeling confident  Exam ready

# Fractions

## 2 Quick quiz

Find

**(a)** $\frac{1}{2}$ of 40 ..............................

**(b)** $\frac{1}{3}$ of 60 ..............................

**(c)** $\frac{1}{4}$ of 80 ..............................

**(d)** $\frac{1}{5}$ of 120 ..............................

## 5 Shapes — Grade 1

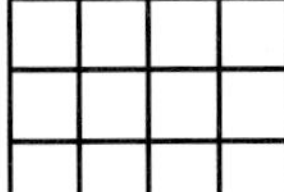
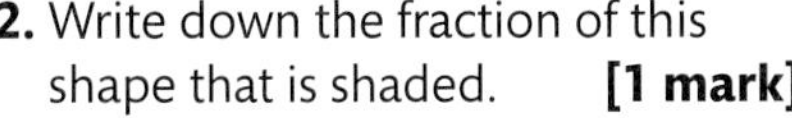

**1.** Here is a shape.

Count how many squares make up the shape.

Shade $\frac{2}{3}$ of the shape. **[1 mark]**

**2.** Write down the fraction of this shape that is shaded. **[1 mark]**

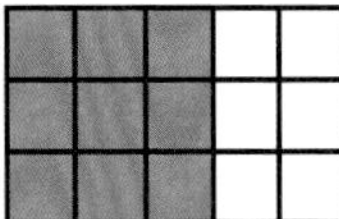

..............................

**3.** Write down the fraction of this shape that is shaded. Give your fraction in its simplest form. **[2 marks]**

..............................

## 5 Simplifying fractions — Grade 1

**4.** Simplify $\frac{2}{4}$ **[1 mark]**

..............................

**5.** Write the fraction $\frac{18}{24}$ in its simplest form. **[1 mark]**

$\frac{18}{24} \xrightarrow{\div 6} \frac{\square}{\square}$ ($\div 6$)

..............................

**6.** Write $\frac{8}{12}$ in its simplest form. **[1 mark]**

..............................

**7.** Write 15 as a fraction of 75 in its simplest form. **[1 mark]**

..............................

## 10 Finding a fraction of an amount — Grades 1–2

**8.** Find

**(a)** $\frac{2}{3}$ of 15 kg **[2 marks]** ..............................kg

**(b)** $\frac{4}{5}$ of 12 g **[2 marks]** ..............................g

**9.** A piece of string is 84 cm. Riku cuts off $\frac{7}{12}$ of the piece of string. Work out the length of the piece of string that Riku cuts off. **[2 marks]**

..............................cm

**10.** Ezriel has £480.
He spends $\frac{3}{5}$ of the £480.

Work out how much money Ezriel has left. **[3 marks]**

£..............................

**11.** In a box, there are 120 counters.
$\frac{1}{4}$ of the counters are red.
$\frac{2}{5}$ of the counters are green.
The remaining counters are blue.

How many blue counters are there in the box? **[3 marks]**

..............................

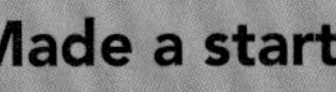

Made a start | Feeling confident | Exam ready

# Operations with fractions

## Quick quiz

Match the operations to the methods.

| Adding or subtracting fractions |
|---|
| Multiplying fractions |
| Dividing fractions |

| Multiply the numerators and multiply the denominators |
|---|
| Invert the second fraction then multiply |
| Find equivalent fractions with the same denominator |

## The four operations

Grades 3–5

**1.** Find the answers to these calculations. Give your answers in their simplest form.

**(a)** $\frac{3}{7} \times \frac{5}{6}$ **[2 marks]**

$= \frac{1 \times 5}{7 \times 2}$

When multiplying fractions, always see if you can cancel first.

..............................

**(b)** $\frac{3}{10} \div \frac{11}{20}$ **[2 marks]**

$= \frac{3}{10} \times \frac{\square}{\square}$

$= \frac{3 \times \text{.......}}{\text{.......} \times \text{.......}}$

..............................

**(c)** $\frac{8}{9} \times \frac{3}{4}$ **[2 marks]**

..............................

**(d)** $\frac{3}{8} \div \frac{15}{16}$ **[2 marks]**

..............................

**(e)** $\frac{3}{7} - \frac{1}{6}$ **[2 marks]**

..............................

**(f)** $\frac{5}{6} - \frac{3}{4}$ **[2 marks]**

..............................

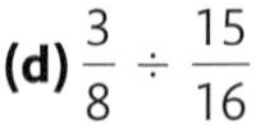

## Working with fractions in context

Grades 4–5

**2.** 120 children compete in a charity race. $\frac{1}{4}$ of the children don't complete the run.

Work out the number of children who complete the race. **[3 marks]**

..............................

**3.** A headmaster collected information about 225 Year 11 students.
$\frac{1}{3}$ of the students wanted to go to college and $\frac{2}{5}$ of the students wanted to do apprenticeships.
The rest of the students wanted to stay on at school.

Work out the number of students who wanted to stay on at school. **[3 marks]**

..............................

**4.** Mischa is cutting a cake. She gives $\frac{1}{3}$ of the cake to Lyron and $\frac{1}{4}$ of the cake to Olivia.
Mischa keeps the rest of the cake. Olivia only wants half her slice and gives the rest of it back to Mischa.

What fraction of the whole cake does Mischa now have in total? **[4 marks]**

..............................

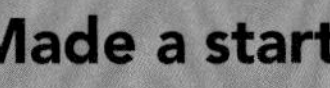

Made a start

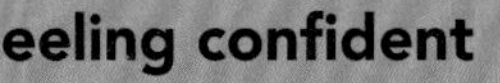

Feeling confident

Exam ready

# Mixed numbers and improper fractions

## 3 Quick quiz

**1.** Write down the remainder from each division.

**(a)** $30 \div 4$ ...........  **(b)** $17 \div 3$ ...........  **(c)** $42 \div 5$ ...........

**2.** Work out these. Give your answers as improper fractions.

**(a)** $\frac{2 \times 7 + 1}{2} =$ ....................  **(b)** $\frac{5 \times 4 + 2}{5} =$ ....................  **(c)** $\frac{4 \times 6 + 3}{4} =$ ....................

## 10 The four operations

Grades 4–5

**1.** Work out the answers to these calculations. Give your answers as mixed numbers in their simplest form.

**(a)** $3\frac{1}{2} - 1\frac{3}{5}$ **[3 marks]** **(b)** $7\frac{1}{7} \times 8\frac{2}{5}$ **[3 marks]** **(c)** $3\frac{1}{2} + 2\frac{4}{5}$ **[3 marks]**

$= \frac{(3 \times 2) + 1}{2} - \frac{(5 \times 1) + 3}{5}$

$= \frac{\square}{2} - \frac{\square}{5} = \frac{\square}{10} - \frac{\square}{10} =$

..............................  ..............................  ..............................

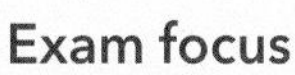

**Exam focus**

Make sure you clearly show your working out when dealing with fractions.

**2.** Find the answers to these calculations, giving your answers in their simplest form.

**(a)** $3\frac{3}{8} + 4\frac{2}{5}$ **[3 marks]** **(b)** $4\frac{4}{7} - 2\frac{2}{3}$ **[3 marks]** **(c)** $1\frac{1}{3} \times \frac{7}{10} \div \frac{2}{5}$ **[3 marks]**

..............................  ..............................  ..............................

## 10 Working with mixed numbers in context

Grade 5

**3.** A satellite makes 6 revolutions of the Earth in one day. How many revolutions does it make in $7\frac{1}{2}$ days? **[2 marks]**

..............................

**4.** A bolt has $5\frac{1}{3}$ turns per cm. It is $1\frac{7}{8}$ cm long. How many turns does it have? **[2 marks]**

..............................

**5.** A bookshelf is $49\frac{1}{2}$ cm long. How many $2\frac{3}{4}$ cm thick books will the bookshelf hold? **[3 marks]**

..............................

**6.** A restaurant has bags of rice that contain $3\frac{3}{4}$ kg each. The restaurant has $10\frac{3}{4}$ bags of rice left.
What is the total weight of rice the restaurant has left? **[3 marks]**

..............................kg

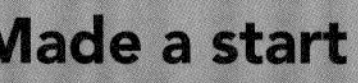

Made a start | Feeling confident | Exam ready

# Factors, multiples and prime numbers

## 2 Quick quiz

**1.** Fill in the missing number.

**(a)** 12 = 4 × .......... **(b)** 15 = 5 × .......... **(c)** 7 = 7 × ..........

**2.** Write down the next two numbers.

3, 6, 9, .........., ..........

## 5 Factors — Grade 1

**1.** Write down all the factors of

List the factor pairs.

**(a)** 15 **[1 mark]** **(b)** 24 **[1 mark]** **(c)** 75 **[1 mark]** **(d)** 100 **[1 mark]**

15 = 1 × 15, 3 × ..........

The factors of 15 are

1, 3, .............................. .............................. .............................. ..............................

## 5 Multiples — Grade 1

**2.** Write down the first five multiples of 3. **[1 mark]**

**3.** Write down the first five multiples of 6. **[1 mark]**

**4.** Write down the third multiple of 8. **[1 mark]**

**5.** Write down the fifth multiple of 12. **[1 mark]**

.............................. .............................. 8, 16, .......... ..............................

## 5 Primes — Grade 2

**6.** Write down all the prime numbers between 30 and 50. **[2 marks]**

..............................

**7.** Write down all the prime numbers between 60 and 80. **[2 marks]**

..............................

## 5 Factors, multiples and primes — Grades 1–2

**8.** Here is a list of eight numbers:

4 5 25 29 30 33 39 40

From the list, write down

**(a)** a factor of 20 **[1 mark]**

..............................

**(b)** a multiple of 10 **[1 mark]**

..............................

**(c)** a prime number greater than 15. **[1 mark]**

..............................

**9.** Here is a list of eight numbers:

4 5 30 31 39 49 72 100

From the list, write down

**(a)** a multiple of 8 **[1 mark]**

..............................

**(b)** a factor of 50 **[1 mark]**

..............................

**(c)** a prime number. **[1 mark]**

..............................

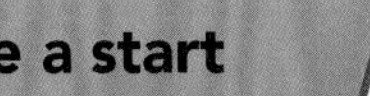

Made a start Feeling confident Exam ready

# Prime factors, HCF and LCM

## Quick quiz

Write in the missing powers.

**(a)** $2 \times 2 \times 2 \times 3 \times 3 \times 5 = 2^{\square} \times 3^{\square} \times 5$

**(b)** $5 \times 5 \times 7 \times 11 \times 11 \times 11 = 5^{\square} \times 7 \times 11^{\square}$

## Product of prime factors

Grade 5

**1.** Express each number as a product of its prime factors.

**(a)** 72 **[2 marks]**

..............................

**(b)** 180 **[2 marks]**

..............................

## Finding highest common factors and lowest common multiples

Grade 5

**2. (a)** Express 75 as a product of powers of its prime factors. **[2 marks]**

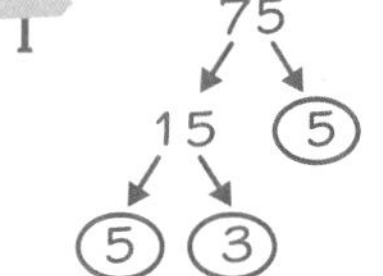


Use a factor tree to write 75 as a product of its prime numbers.

75 = 3 × ........... × ...........

..............................

**(b)** Find the highest common factor (HCF) of 75 and 90. **[2 marks]**

75 = ③ × ⑤ × 5

90 = 2 × ③ × 3 × ⑤

Circle the numbers that appear in **both** lists.

HCF = 3 × ...........................

..............................

**(c)** Find the lowest common multiple (LCM) of 75 and 90. **[1 mark]**

75 = 3 × 5 × 5

90 = 2 × 3 × 3 × 5

Look for the numbers that appear in **either** list.

LCM = 2 × 3 × ........... × 5 × ...........

..............................

**3.** $X = 2^2 \times 3 \times 5^2$ and $Y = 2^3 \times 5$.

**(a)** Find the highest common factor of $X$ and $Y$. **[1 mark]**

..............................

**(b)** Find the lowest common multiple of $X$ and $Y$. **[2 marks]**

..............................

**4.** The highest common factor of two numbers is 9. The lowest common multiple of the same two numbers is 90.

Write down **two** possible numbers that satisfy these conditions. **[2 marks]**

..............................

## Real-life problem

Grade 5

**5.** Aliya is planning a party. She wants to buy some naans and some kebabs. She is expecting more than 75 guests. A pack of 6 naans costs £1.75. A pack of 9 kebabs costs £3.40. Aliya wants to buy more than 75 naans and more than 75 kebabs. She wants to buy exactly the same number of naans as kebabs.

What is the smallest amount of money Aliya could spend? **[5 marks]**

£..............................

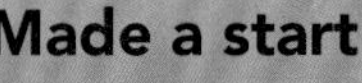

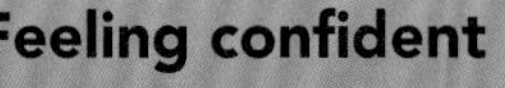

Exam ready

# Estimation and outcomes

## Quick quiz

Round each number to 1 significant figure.

**(a)** 82.6 .................... **(b)** 195.5 .................... **(c)** 0.198 .................... **(d)** 0.523 ....................

## Systematic listing strategies

**Grade 2**

**1.** Alan wants to buy a car. He can choose a saloon car (S) or an estate car (E) or a convertible car (C). He also has to choose the type of fuel needed for the car - petrol (P), diesel (D) or hybrid (H).

Work out the total number of possible combinations that Alan could choose. **[1 mark]**

SP, SD, SH, EP, ED, ...............................

...............................

**2.** Mischa has three tickets to go to the cinema. She chooses two friends to go with her. She chooses at random from Ravina (R), Alison (A), Molly (M), Pam (P) and Zoe (Z).

List all the possible combinations of friends that Nisha could choose. **[2 marks]**

Write down all the combinations and cross out any repeated pairs.

...............................

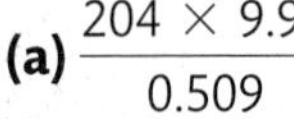

## Estimating an answer

**Grade 5**

**3.** Work out an estimate for

**(a)** $\frac{204 \times 9.95}{0.509}$ **[2 marks]**

$= \frac{200 \times \ldots\ldots}{0.5} = \frac{\square}{0.5}$ ..........................

**(b)** $\sqrt{4.99 \times 2.05 + 6.24}$ **[3 marks]**

$= \sqrt{5 \times \ldots\ldots + \ldots\ldots}$

..........................

**Exam focus**
Round each number correct to 1 significant figure. Make sure you write down your rounded numbers.

Remember BIDMAS.

**4.** The radius of a circle is 5.4 cm.

**(a)** Work out an estimate for the area of the circle. **[2 marks]**

............................... $cm^2$

**(b)** Without further calculation, explain whether your method gives you an overestimate or an underestimate for the area of the circle. **[1 mark]**

...............................

The area of a circle is $\pi r^2$.

The numerical value of $\pi$ is approximately 3.14 . You can approximate it as 3 when estimating.

When estimating, always round to 1 significant figure.

**5.** Kathy has some cows. The cows produce an average total of 22.3 litres of milk per day for 191 days. Kathy sells the milk in half-litre cartons.

Estimate the total number of cartons that Kathy will be able to fill with the milk produced over the 191 days. You must show clearly how you got your estimate. **[3 marks]**

...............................

 Made a start  Feeling confident 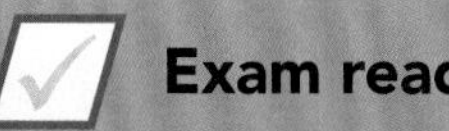

# Indices and roots

## Quick quiz

1. Work out the value of

(a) $3 \times 3$ ..................... (b) $2 \times 2 \times 2$ .....................

2. Complete the calculations, using only **one** number in each calculation.

(a) ..........×..........= 4 (b) ..........×..........×..........= 27

## Squares, cubes and roots

**Grade 1**

1. Find the square of 8 **[1 mark]**

$8 \times 8$

...............................

2. Find the value of $10^3$ **[1 mark]**

$10 \times 10 \times 10$

...............................

3. Find the value of $\sqrt[3]{125}$ **[1 mark]**

...............................

4. Here is a list of numbers: 10 15 30 58 61 85 100 125

From the numbers in the list, write down

(a) two different numbers that add up to a square number **[1 mark]**

...............................

(b) a square number **[1 mark]**

...............................

(c) two different numbers that have a difference that is a cube number **[1 mark]**

...............................

(d) a cube number. **[1 mark]**

...............................

## Using a calculator

**Grade 1**

5. Calculate the value of $\dfrac{\sqrt[3]{24.9 - 10.1}}{3.2^2 + 0.4}$

Write down all the figures on your calculator display. **[1 mark]**

$24.9 - 10.1 =$ ..........

$3.2^2 + 0.4 =$ ..........

$\sqrt[3]{\dots\dots}$ ÷ .......... = ..........

...............................

6. Use your calculator to work out the value of $120^2 + \dfrac{170}{\sqrt{80}}$

Write down all the figures on your calculator display. **[1 mark]**

...............................

7. Work out the value of $\dfrac{\sqrt{62} + \sqrt{98}}{3.1^2 - 1.2^3}$

Write down all the figures on your calculator display. **[1 mark]**

...............................

8. Joseph's age is a square number. Nina's age is a cube number. Nina is 28 years older than Joseph.

How old are Joseph and Nina? **[3 marks]**

...............................

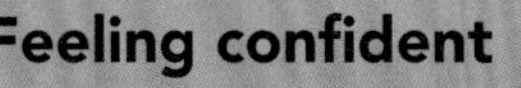

Made a start | Feeling confident | Exam ready

# Standard form

## Quick quiz

Write each number as a power of 10

**(a)** 1000 **(b)** 100 000 **(c)** 100 000 000 **(d)** 1 000 000 000

.................... .................... .................... ....................

## Standard form — Grade 5

**1. (a)** Write $7.8 \times 10^{-4}$ as an ordinary number. **[1 mark]**

$7.8 \times 0.0001 =$ ....................

..............................

**(b)** Write 95 600 000 as a number in standard form. **[1 mark]**

$9.56 \times 10\,000\,000 = 9.56 \times 10 \times$ ...... $\times$ ...... $\times$ ...... $\times$ ...... $\times$ ...... $\times$ ......

..............................

**(c)** Work out $(3 \times 10^8) \div (5 \times 10^6)$. Give your answer in standard form. **[2 marks]**

$(3 \div 5) \times (10^8 \div 10^6) =$ ......... $\times 10^{\square}$

$=$ ......... $\times 10^{\square}$

..............................

**Exam focus**

A number in standard form is written as $A \times 10^n$, where $1 \leq A < 10$ and $n$ is an integer.

Take out a factor that is a power of 10 to leave a number in the range $1 \leq A < 10$

Make sure the first number lies in the range $1 \leq A < 10$

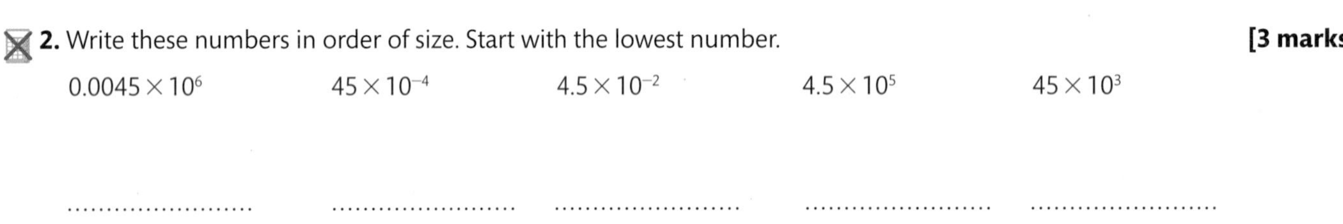

**2.** Write these numbers in order of size. Start with the lowest number. **[3 marks]**

$0.0045 \times 10^6$ $45 \times 10^{-4}$ $4.5 \times 10^{-2}$ $4.5 \times 10^5$ $45 \times 10^3$

........................ ........................ ........................ ........................ ........................

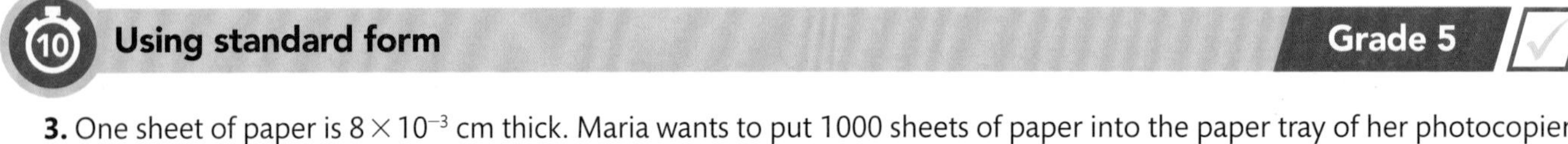

## Using standard form — Grade 5

**3.** One sheet of paper is $8 \times 10^{-3}$ cm thick. Maria wants to put 1000 sheets of paper into the paper tray of her photocopier. The paper tray is 7.5 cm deep.

Is the paper tray deep enough for 1000 sheets of this paper? You must explain your answer. **[3 marks]**

..............................

**4.** A satellite is travelling at a speed of 3460 metres per second.

How many seconds will the satellite take to travel a distance of $4.75 \times 10^{12}$ metres?
Give your answer in standard form, correct to 3 significant figures. **[3 marks]**

time = distance ÷ speed

d
s t

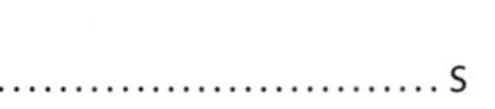
.............................. s

 Made a start  Feeling confident  Exam ready

# Error intervals

## Quick quiz

Work out

**(a)** $100 + 10$ ..........
**(b)** $100 - 10$ ..........
**(c)** $200 + 20$ ..........
**(d)** $200 - 20$ ..........
**(e)** $10 + 0.5$ ..........
**(f)** $10 - 0.5$ ..........
**(g)** $1 + 0.05$ ..........
**(h)** $1 - 0.05$ ..........

## Smallest and greatest numbers

**1.** Irie's car has a value of £8000 correct to 1 significant figure.

**(a)** Write down the lowest possible value of the car. **[1 mark]**

£..............................

**(b)** Write down the greatest possible value of the car. **[1 mark]**

Remember that 8500 would round up to 9000

£..............................

**2.** Seo-yun recorded the total attendance at a football match. The number of people who attended was 25 700 to the nearest hundred.

**(a)** Write down the lowest number of people who could have attended the match. **[1 mark]**

..............................

**(b)** Write down the greatest number of people who could have attended the match. **[1 mark]**

..............................

**3.** Rob's flat has a value of £120 000 correct to 2 significant figures.

**(a)** Write down the lowest possible value of the flat. **[1 mark]**

£..............................

**(b)** Write down the greatest possible value of the flat. **[1 mark]**

The given value is the average of the highest and lowest values.

£..............................

## Error intervals

**4.** The area, $A$ cm², of a plate is 79 cm² to the nearest integer.

Complete this error interval to show the range of possible values of $A$. **[2 marks]**

.................... $\leqslant A < 79.5$

**5.** The length, $L$ cm, of a stick is 42.7 cm to 1 decimal place.

Complete this error interval to show the range of possible values of $L$. **[2 marks]**

.............................. $\leqslant L <$ ..............................

**6.** Zalika rounds a number, $x$, to the nearest whole number. The result is 18

Write down the error interval for $x$. **[2 marks]**

..........................................................................

**7.** Jenny rounds a number, $y$, to 1 decimal place. The result is 16.7

Write down the error interval for $y$. **[2 marks]**

..........................................................................

**8.** A length of pipe, $p$ cm, is given as 42.45 cm correct to 2 decimal places.

Give the error interval for the range of possible values for $p$. **[2 marks]**

$42.445 \leqslant p <$ ....................

**9.** Mia is at a basketball game. Her team is losing and it is nearly the end of the match. The time is on the scoreboard but a flag keeps getting in the way.

Write down the range of possible values for the actual time shown on the scoreboard, $t$. **[2 marks]**

Think about what the value of the final digit could be.

.............................. $\leqslant t \leqslant$ ..............................

# Number

## Negative numbers

Grade 2 

**1.** Davina recorded the maximum temperature and the minimum temperature on five days in December.
The table shows her results.

| | Mon | Tues | Wed | Thurs | Fri |
|---|---|---|---|---|---|
| **Maximum temperature (°C)** | 2 | 4 | 6 | 8 | 5 |
| **Minimum temperature (°C)** | −5 | −3 | −7 | −2 | 0 |

**(a)** Write down the lowest temperature. **[1 mark]**

You could draw a number line to help check your answers.

...............................°C

**(b)** Work out the difference between the maximum temperature and the minimum temperature on Thursday. **[1 mark]**

............................... degrees

The minimum temperature on Saturday was 4 degrees higher than the minimum temperature on Wednesday.

**(c)** Work out the minimum temperature on Saturday. **[1 mark]**

Find the minimum temperature on Wednesday from the table. Then add 4 to that value.

...............................°C

## Money

Grade 2 

**2.** The diagram shows the costs of a bag of soil, a box of grass seeds and a bottle of weedkiller.

| Bag of soil £4.55 | Box of grass seed £3.50 | Bottle of weedkiller £6.30 |
|---|---|---|

Sue buys three bags of soil, four boxes of seeds and a bottle of weedkiller.
She gets $\frac{2}{5}$ off the total cost.
Sue pays with two £20 notes.

How much change should she get? **[3 marks]**

£...............................

## LCM problem

Grade 4 

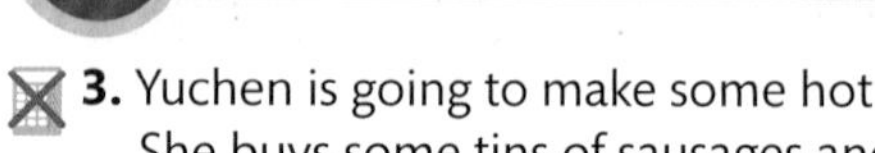

**3.** Yuchen is going to make some hot dogs for a party.
She buys some tins of sausages and some packets of bread rolls.
There are 15 sausages in each tin.
There are 12 bread rolls in each packet.

Yuchen buys exactly the same number of sausages and bread rolls.

**(a)** What is the lowest number of tins of sausages and packets of bread rolls that she could have bought? **[3 marks]**

...............................

Yuchen wants to put one sausage into each bread roll.
She wants to use all the sausages and all the bread rolls.

**(b)** How many hot dogs does Yuchen make? **[1 mark]**

...............................

# Function machines

## Quick quiz

Complete these calculations.

(a) Start with 3, add 6 and then multiply by 2 ..............................

(b) Start with 20, subtract 12 and then divide by 4 ..............................

## Using function machines

**Grades 2–3**

**1.**

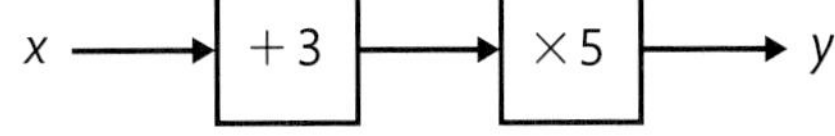

Use the function machine to find

**(a)** the value of $y$ when $x = 4$ **[1 mark]**

4 + 3 = .........

......... × 5 = ......... ..............................

**(b)** the value of $x$ when $y = 20$ **[1 mark]**

20 ÷ 5 = .........

......... − 3 = 1

To find the value of $x$ apply the inverse operations.

..............................

**2.**

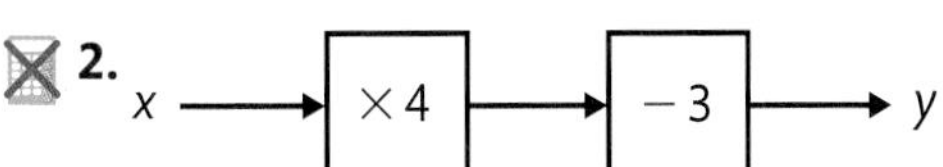

Use the function machine to find

**(a)** the value of $y$ when $x = 5$ **[1 mark]**

5 × 4 = .........

......... − 3 = ......... ..............................

**(b)** the value of $x$ when $y = 3$ **[1 mark]**

..............................

## Completing function machines

**Grades 2–3**

**3. (a)** Complete the function machine to show the formula $y = 4x + 2$ **[2 marks]**

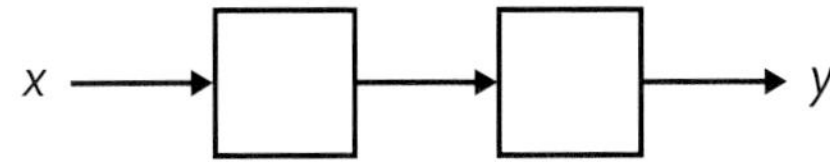

**(b)** Complete the boxes to show the formula $y = 4(x - 2)$ **[2 marks]**

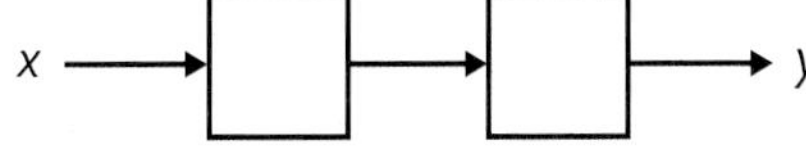

**4. (a)** Complete a two-step function machine for the given inputs and outputs. **[2 marks]**

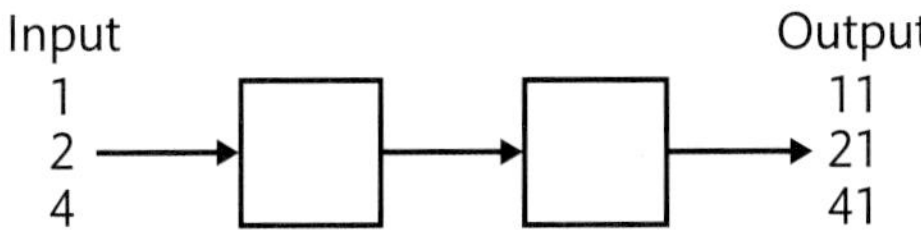



**(b)** Complete a two-step function machine for the given inputs and outputs. **[2 marks]**

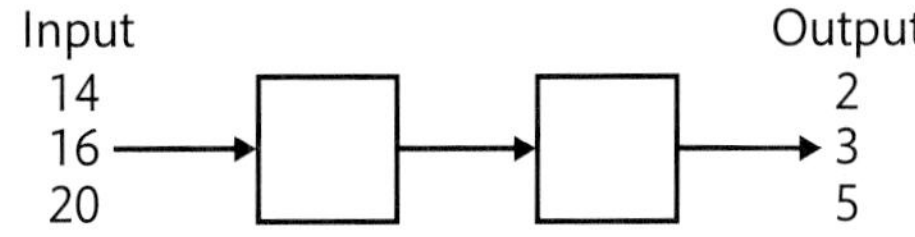



**5.** Explain why, for any value of $x$, both function machines give the same value of $y$. **[3 marks]**

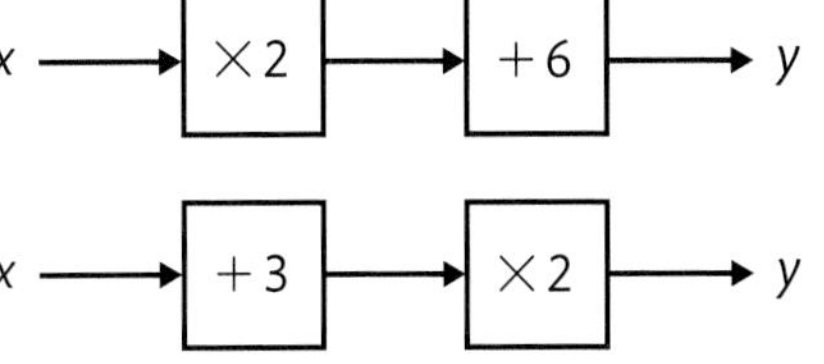



Output of first function machine is $2x + 6$

Output of second function machine is $(x + 3) \times 2$

..............................

..............................

**Problem solving**

You can use algebra to explain why the two function machines produce the same output. Write expressions for the outputs in terms of $x$ and show that they are equal to each other.

# Algebraic substitution

## Quick quiz

Work out the value of $a \times b$ when

**(a)** $a = 4$ and $b = 6$ **(b)** $a = 3$ and $b = -4$ **(c)** $a = -7$ and $b = 10$ **(d)** $a = -2$ and $b = -8$

.................. .................. .................. ..................

## Substituting numbers

Grades 2–3

**1. (a)** $p = 5$ and $q = 3$

Work out the value of $2p + 4q$. **[2 marks]**

$2 \times 5 + 4 \times 3$

$= 10 + \ldots\ldots = \ldots\ldots$

..................

**(b)** $T = 2x - 3y$, $x = 6$ and $y = 4$

Work out the value of $T$. **[2 marks]**

$T = 2 \times 6 - 3 \times 4$

$= \ldots\ldots - \ldots\ldots = \ldots\ldots$

..................

**(c)** $v = u + 5t$, $u = 4$ and $t = 3$

Work out the value of $v$. **[2 marks]**

$v = \ldots\ldots + 5 \times \ldots\ldots$

$= \ldots\ldots + \ldots\ldots = \ldots\ldots$

..................

Use BIDMAS.

**2. (a)** $p = -2$ and $q = 3$

Work out the value of $2p + 4q$. **[2 marks]**

..................

**(b)** $T = 2x - 3y$, $x = -3$ and $y = 2$

Work out the value of $T$. **[2 marks]**

..................

**(c)** $v = u + 5t$, $u = -3$ and $t = 4$

Work out the value of $v$. **[2 marks]**

..................

Check whether your answer should be negative or positive.

**3. (a)** Work out the value of $3x^2$ when $x = 4$ **[2 marks]**

$3 \times 4^2$

$= 3 \times 4 \times 4$

..................

**(b)** Work out the value of $2x^2 + 7$ when $x = 5$ **[2 marks]**

..................

**(c)** Work out the value of $3x^2 + 4y$ when $x = -3$ and $y = -2$ **[2 marks]**

..................

Multiplying two negative numbers will result in a positive answer.

## Substituting in formulae

Grade 3

**4.** $T = 10n + 15$

You can use this rule to work out the total cost of hiring a car, where $n$ is the number of hours for which the car is hired and $T$ is the total cost in £.

Jay hires a car for 7 hours.

**(a)** Work out the total amount that Jay pays. **[2 marks]**

£..................

**Problem solving**

Substitute the value for $n$ into the formula.

Billy hires a car. The total cost is £90

**(b)** For how many hours did Billy hire the car? **[2 marks]**

..................

**Problem solving**

For part **(b)** you need to rearrange the formula to make $n$ the subject. Practise this on page 30.

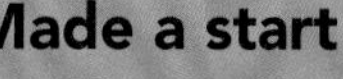

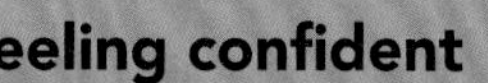

Made a start | Feeling confident | Exam ready

# Collecting like terms

## Quick quiz

Tick each expression that can be simplified.

$d + d$ ☐ $a + b$ ☐ $x^2 + x^2$ ☐ $x^2 + y^2$ ☐

## Collecting like terms

Grades 1–2

**1.** Simplify

**(a)** $d + d + d$ **[1 mark]**

$= 3$..........

..............................

**(b)** $t + 2t + t + t$ **[1 mark]**

$=$ .......... $t$

..............................

**(c)** $r + 2r + r + 3r$ **[1 mark]**

..............................

If the variables are the same, you can add the coefficients.

**2.** Simplify

**(a)** $2c + 3c + 4c$ **[1 mark]**

..............................

**(b)** $5e + e - 10e$ **[1 mark]**

..............................

**(c)** $7g - 4g - 8g$ **[1 mark]**

..............................

**3.** Simplify

**(a)** $3f + 4 - 2f + 6$ **[2 marks]**

..............................

**(b)** $3x + 8y + x - 2y$ **[2 marks]**

$= 3x + x + 8y - 2y$

..............................

**(c)** $3x - 5y + x + 4y$ **[2 marks]**

..............................

**(d)** $5f + 7 - 6f - 4$ **[2 marks]**

..............................

**4.** Jane simplifies $3ef + 5ef - ef$ to get $9ef$. Explain why Jane is wrong. **[2 marks]**

Think how you would have simplified the expression and then what Jane might have done differently.

..............................................................................................

## Collecting terms with powers

Grade 2

**5.** Simplify

**(a)** $m^2 + m^2 + m^2$ **[1 mark]**

There are three lots of $m^2$.

..............................

**(b)** $3a^2 + 2h + a^2 - 3h$ **[1 mark]**

**Exam focus**

Always give your answer in its simplest form.

..............................

**(c)** $5x^2 - 4y + 3x^2 - 3y$ **[2 marks]**

..............................

**(d)** $9p^2 + 2t - 2p^2 + 3t$ **[2 marks]**

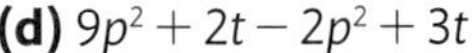

..............................

**(e)** $3x^2 - 5y + x^2 + 4y$ **[2 marks]**

..............................

**(f)** $3x^2 + 7y^2 + 2x^2 - y^2$ **[2 marks]**

..............................

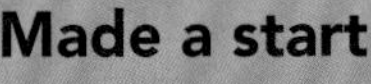

Made a start ☐ Feeling confident ☐ Exam ready

# Simplifying expressions

## Quick quiz

Fill in the gaps.

**(a)** $a \times a = a$ .........  **(b)** $ab = a$ ......... $b$  **(c)** $a \times c = a$ .........  **(d)** $a^3 = a \times$ ......... ......... .........

## Simplifying with single operations

Grade 1

**1.** Simplify

**(a)** $5 \times e \times f$ **[1 mark]**

$= 5 \times ef$

..............................

**(b)** $7 \times 2t$ **[1 mark]**

$= 7 \times 2 \times t$

..............................

**(c)** $5 \times 3g$ **[1 mark]**

$=$ ......... $\times$ ......... $\times g$

..............................

When multiplying, remember that letters in algebra are generally written next to each other in alphabetical order.

**2.** Simplify

**(a)** $2m \times 3n$ **[1 mark]**

$= 2 \times 3 \times m \times n$

$=$ ......... $\times mn$

..............................

**(b)** $2e \times 3f$ **[1 mark]**

..............................

**(c)** $3 \times c \times c$ **[1 mark]**

$=$ ......... $\times c$ .........

..............................

Multiply the coefficients and multiply the letters.

Remember the index laws: $c \times c = c^2$

**3.** Simplify

**(a)** $24x \div 3$ **[1 mark]**

$= \frac{24x}{3}$

$= 8$ .........

..............................

**(b)** $15a \div 5$ **[1 mark]**

..............................

**(c)** $36y \div 12$ **[1 mark]**

..............................

**Exam focus**

Simplifying with division:

Step 1: Write the expression as a fraction.

Step 2: Cancel the numbers, then the letters.

Step 3: Use the index laws.

**(d)** $48g^2 \div 4g$ **[1 mark]**

..............................

**(e)** $10a^4 \div 5a^2$ **[1 mark]**

..............................

**(f)** $42t^3 \div 7t^2$ **[1 mark]**

..............................

**(g)** $25x^2 \div 5x^2$ **[1 mark]**

..............................

## Mixed operations

Grade 2

**4.** Simplify

**(a)** $\frac{25x^3y^2}{xy}$ **[2 marks]**

..............................

**(b)** $\frac{24a^4b^3}{12ab}$ **[2 marks]**

$= \frac{24 \times a^4 \times b^3}{12 \times a \times b}$

$= 2 \times a^3 \times$ .........

$=$ .........

..............................

**(c)** $\frac{30c^4d^5}{10c^3d^2}$ **[2 marks]**

..............................

**(d)** $\frac{42g^5h}{g^3}$ **[2 marks]**

..............................

**(e)** $\frac{84t^7v^5}{12v^5}$ **[2 marks]**

..............................

**(f)** $\frac{15s^5t^4}{s^2t^3}$ **[2 marks]**

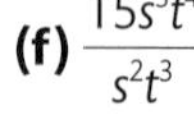

..............................

**5.** Ben simplifies $\frac{14m^5n^8}{2m^3n^6}$ to get $7m^8n^{14}$

Explain why Ben is wrong. **[2 marks]**

..............................................................................

Made a start  Feeling confident  Exam ready

# Writing expressions

## Quick quiz

Given that $x = 4$, $y = 3$ and $t = 5$, find the value of

**(a)** $10 \times x$ ..............................

**(b)** $5 + y$ ..............................

**(c)** $15 \div t$ ..............................

## Using information — Grade 3

**1.** Bruno has $x$ counters. Saira has three times as many counters as Bruno. Dylan has three more counters than Bruno.

Write an expression, in terms of $x$, for the total number of counters Bruno, Saira and Dylan have. **[2 marks]**

Number of counters:

Bruno has $x$ counters

Saira has 3.......... counters

Dylan has $x +$ .......... counters

So an expression for the total number of counters is

$x + 3x + x + 3 =$ ........................................

> The expression for Bruno's counters is $x$. Use that to write expressions for Saira and Dylan's counters.
>
> The expression for the total will be all of these added together.

**2.** There are 6 pens in a box of pens. There are 9 pencils in a box of pencils.

Nita buys $m$ boxes of pens and $n$ boxes of pencils.

Write an expression for the total number of pens and pencils that Nita buys. **[1 mark]**

..............................

**3.** Sweets are sold in packets and in boxes. There are 8 sweets in a packet. There are 12 sweets in a box.

Frank buys $x$ packets of sweets and $y$ boxes of sweets.

Write an expression for the total number of sweets that Frank buys. **[1 mark]**

..............................

**4.** Rachel uses this rule to work out the cost in £ of hiring a car for $n$ days:

Multiply the number of days by £45, then add £60

**(a)** Write an expression for the cost of hiring a car. **[1 mark]**

$45 \times$ number of days $+ 60$

45.......... + ..........

£..............................

**(b)** Imran hired a car for 12 days. Using your expression, work out the cost that Imran has to pay. **[1 mark]**

Input 12 as $n$

$45 \times 12 + 60 =$ ..........

£..............................

**5.** At the start of the week, the value in £ of a number of shares in a gas company can be worked out using this rule:

Multiply the number of shares by 3.5

**(a)** Write an expression for the value of $n$ shares. **[1 mark]**

£..............................

**(b)** Use your expression to work out the value of 250 shares. **[1 mark]**

£..............................

By Thursday, the value of each share has dropped by 50p.

**(c)** Write an expression for the new value of the shares. **[2 marks]**

Value of each share = $(3.5 - 0.5)$

Value of 250 shares = $250 \times$ ..........

£..............................

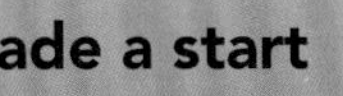

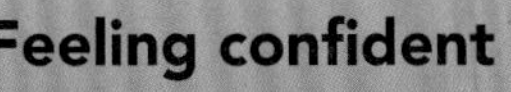

Made a start | Feeling confident | Exam ready

# Algebraic formulae

## 2 Quick quiz

Simplify each expression.

**(a)** $x + 5 - x$ ..............................

**(b)** $3 \times x$ ..............................

**(c)** $2x + x + 6$ ..............................

**(d)** $x + 2 + x - 3$ ..............................

## 5 Finding perimeter

Grade 3

**1.** The diagram shows a shape made from rectangles. All the measurements are in centimetres.

Find an expression, in terms of $x$, for the perimeter of the shape. **[3 marks]**

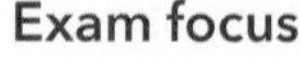



Use the lengths you are given to work out the missing lengths.

Add all the lengths together.

List them in order, so you won't miss any.

**Exam focus**

Give your answer in its simplest form.

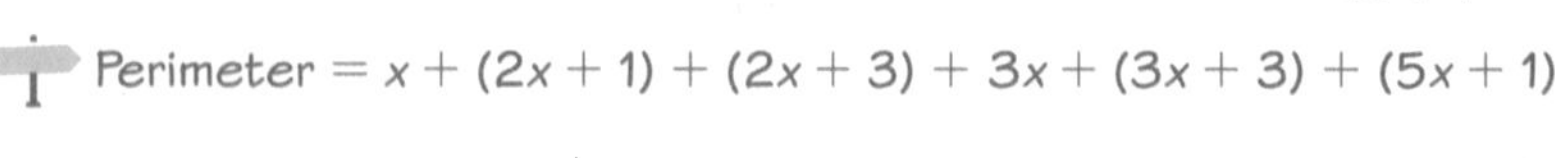

Perimeter $= x + (2x + 1) + (2x + 3) + 3x + (3x + 3) + (5x + 1)$

$= .........x + .........$

..............................cm

**2.** Simon sent $x$ parcels on Monday.
On Tuesday, he sent twice as many parcels as on Monday. On Wednesday, he sent 6 fewer parcels than on Monday.
It cost £8 to send each parcel. The total cost of sending all the parcels is £$T$.

Write down a formula for $T$ in terms of $x$. **[3 marks]**

..............................

**3.** The diagram shows a trapezium.
$AD = x$ cm. $BC$ is the same length as $AD$.
$AB$ is twice the length of $AD$. $DC$ is 5 cm longer than $AB$.
The perimeter of the trapezium is $P$ cm.

Find a formula for $P$ in terms of $x$. **[3 marks]**

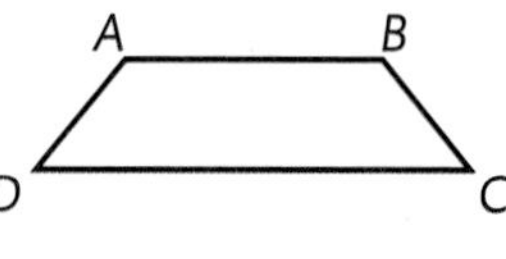



..............................

**Problem solving**

Write the length of each side on the diagram in the order you read them.

$AB = 2 \times x$

$DC = 5 + (2 \times x)$

Then add them together to equal $P$.

## 5 Deriving expressions

Grade 5

**4.** The diagram shows a shape made from rectangles.
All the measurements are in centimetres. All the corners are right angles.
The area of the shape is $A$ cm$^2$.

Find a formula for $A$ in terms of $x$. Give your answer in its simplest form. **[4 marks]**

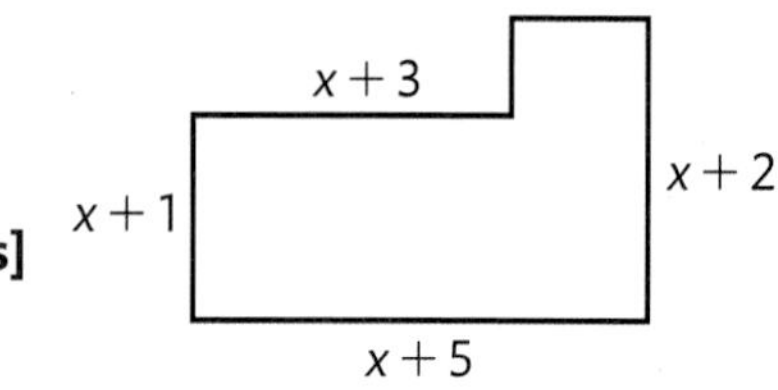



To find the area you will need to know how to expand two brackets. Practise expanding brackets on page 26.

..............................



Made a start  Feeling confident Exam ready

# Algebraic indices

## Quick quiz

Simply each expression fully.

**(a)** $a \times a \times a \times a$ **(b)** $\frac{a \times a \times a \times a \times a \times a}{a \times a}$ **(c)** $6 \times a \times 3 \times a \times b$ **(d)** $3 \times a \times a \times b \times b \times b$

.............................. .............................. .............................. ..............................

## Applying laws of indices

Grades 4–5

**1.** Simplify these expressions.

**(a)** $p^2 \times p^7$ **[1 mark]**

$= p^{2+7}$

$= p^{\square}$

..............................

**(b)** $x^8 \div x^3$ **[1 mark]**

$= x^{8-3}$

$= x^{\square}$

..............................

**(c)** $\frac{y^5 \times y^3}{y^4}$ **[1 mark]**

$= y^{\square} \div y^4$

$= y^{\square} = y^{\square}$

..............................

You can combine powers when the bases are the same. When you multiply, add the powers.

When you divide, subtract the powers.

When you raise a power to a power, multiply the powers.

**2.** Simplify these expressions.

**(a)** $\frac{q^3 \times q^4 \times q}{q^2}$ **[2 marks]** **(b)** $(y^4)^3$ **[2 marks]** **(c)** $(3x^2)^3$ **[2 marks]**

.............................. .............................. ..............................

In part **(c)** you need to raise a number **and** a power of $x$ to a power.

**(d)** $3x^2y \times 5xy^3$ **[2 marks]** **(e)** $\frac{20x^5y^3}{12xy}$ **[2 marks]**

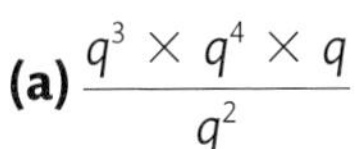

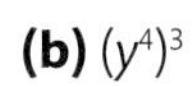

.............................. ..............................

## Finding indices

Grade 5

**3.** $p^5 \times p^x = p^{12}$

Find the value of $x$. **[2 marks]**

..............................

**4.** $(5^3)^y = 5^{15}$

Find the value of $y$. **[2 marks]**

..............................

**5.** Given that $x = 5^p$ and $y = 5^q$, express the following in terms of $x$ and $y$.

**(a)** $5^{p+q}$ **[1 mark]** **(b)** $5^{3q}$ **[1 mark]** **(c)** $5^{2p+1}$ **[1 mark]**

.............................. .............................. ..............................

**Problem solving**

The bases in $x$ and $y$ are the same. For **(a)** find the index law in which you would add the indices together.

**6.** Write these numbers in order of size. Start with the lowest number. **[2 marks]**

$2^{-1}$ $0.2$ $-2$ $2^0$

......... ......... ......... .........

Made a start

Feeling confident

Exam ready

# Expanding brackets

## Quick quiz

Simplify each expression.

**(a)** $x \times 4$ ..............................

**(b)** $5 \times y$ ..............................

**(c)** $v \times v$ ..............................

**(d)** $a \times 4a$ ..............................

## Expanding brackets

Grades 2–3

Multiply the terms inside the bracket by the term outside the bracket.

**1.** Expand

**(a)** $3(a + 5)$ **[1 mark]**

$= 3 \times a + 3 \times 5$

$= 3$.......... + ..........

..............................

**(b)** $5(b - 4)$ **[1 mark]**

..............................

**(c)** $-4(c + 1)$ **[1 mark]**

$= -4 \times$ .......... $+ -4 \times$ ..........

= ..........

..............................

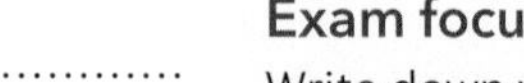

**Exam focus**
Write down your method step by step.

**2.** Expand these expressions.

**(a)** $e(e + 2)$ **[1 mark]**

..............................

**(b)** $2f(f - 3)$ **[1 mark]**

$= 2f \times f + 2f \times -3$

= .......... − ..........

**(c)** $-4g(g + 2)$ **[1 mark]**

..............................

**(d)** $-3h(h - p)$ **[1 mark]**

..............................

## Expanding brackets and simplifying expressions

Grade 4

**3.** Expand and simplify

**(a)** $8a + 3(a - 2b)$ **[2 marks]**

..............................

**(b)** $5(x + 7) + 3(x - 2)$ **[2 marks]**

$= 5 \times x + 5 \times 7 + 3 \times x + 3 \times -2$

$= 5x +$ .......... $+ 3x +$ ..........

= .......... + ..........

**(b)** has two sets of brackets separated by an addition. Expand them separately and simplify by collecting like terms.

**(c)** $5(y - 2) + 2(y - 3)$ **[2 marks]**

..............................

**(d)** $3m(m + 4) - 2m(4m + 1)$ **[2 marks]**

..............................

**(e)** $5x(2x + 1) - 3x(3x - 1)$ **[2 marks]**

..............................

**4.** Taylor expands and simplifies $3x(2x - 5) - 4x(x + 3)$. Her working is shown here:

$3x(2x - 5) - 4x(x + 3) = 6x^2 - 5 - 4x^2 - 7x = 2x^2 - 7x - 5$

Identify two mistakes in Taylor's working. **[2 marks]**

..............................................................................................................................

Made a start
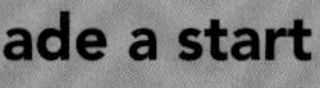

Feeling confident

Exam ready

# Expanding double brackets

## Quick quiz

**(a)** Simplify $6t - 3 - 8t + 7$

........................................

**(b)** Expand $x(x + 2)$

........................................

**(c)** Expand and simplify

$4(2d + 3) - 2(3d - 5)$

........................................

## Double brackets

**Grade 4**

**1.** Expand and simplify

**(a)** $(x - 3)^2$ **[2 marks]**

$= (x - 3)(x - 3)$

$=$ .......... $-$ .......... $-$ .......... $+$ ..........

$=$ .......... $-$ .......... $+$ ..........

Box method:

| $\times$ | $x$ | $-3$ |
|---|---|---|
| $x$ | $x^2$ | $-3x$ |
| $-3$ | $-3x$ | 9 |

**(b)** $(y + 4)^2$ **[2 marks]**

$= (y + 4)(y + 4)$

$y \times y =$

$y \times 4 =$

$4 \times y =$

$4 \times 4 =$

F – First
O – Outer
I – Inner
L – Last

$(y + 4)(y + 4) =$ ......................

$=$ ......................

**(c)** $(5 - t)^2$ **[2 marks]**

**Exam focus**
Give your answer in its simplest form.

................................

**2.** Expand and simplify

**(a)** $(x - 9)(x + 2)$ **[2 marks]**

$= x(x + 2) - 9(x + 2)$

$= x^2 + 2x -$ ................

$= x^2$................

**(b)** $(x + 2)(x + 5)$ **[2 marks]**

................................

**(c)** $(10 + y)(y - 2)$ **[2 marks]**

................................

## Using double brackets

**Grade 4**

**3.** The diagram shows a rectangle.

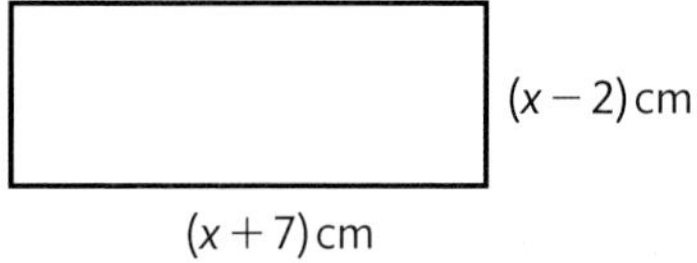


Write down an expression for the area of the rectangle in terms of $x$. Simplify your answer as much as possible. **[3 marks]**

................................ $cm^2$

**4.** The diagram shows a right-angled triangle.

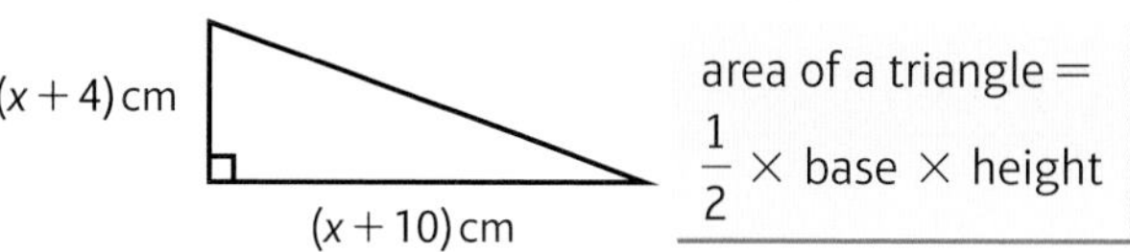


Write down an expression for the area of the triangle in terms of $x$. Simplify your answer as much as possible. **[3 marks]**

................................ $cm^2$

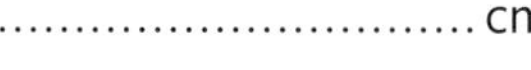

# Factorising

## Quick quiz

Write down the highest common factor of

**(a)** 3 and 12 ..............................

**(b)** 12 and 16 ..............................

**(c)** $x$ and $x^2$ ..............................

**(d)** $y^2$ and $y^3$ ..............................

## Factorising

**1.** Factorise

**(a)** $3x + 9$ **[1 mark]**

$= 3 \times x + 3 \times 3$

$= 3(\ldots\ldots + \ldots\ldots)$

**(b)** $4x - 12$ **[1 mark]**

The highest common factor of 4 and 12 is 4.

..............................

**(c)** $4x + 8y$ **[1 mark]**

$= 4 \times x + 4 \times 2y$

$= 4(\ldots\ldots\ldots\ldots$

**(d)** $12x - 20y$ **[1 mark]**

..............................

**(e)** $x^2 + 3x$ **[2 marks]**

..............................

**(f)** $5x^2 + 10x$ **[2 marks]**

..............................

**2.** Simon factorises $7x^2 - 28x$ and gets $7(x^2 - 4x)$. Explain why the expression is not fully factorised. **[2 marks]**

..............................

**3.** Factorise fully

**(a)** $6xy^2 - 12xy$ **[2 marks]**

..............................

**(b)** $4x^2y + 3xy$ **[2 marks]**

..............................

**(c)** $xy^3 + 3xy$ **[2 marks]**

..............................

## Factorisation in problems

Grade 5

**4.** The diagram shows a rectangle.

Sides: $(x - 3)$ cm and $(x + 10)$ cm

Show that the perimeter can be written as $2(2x + 7)$ cm. **[3 marks]**



Made a start  Feeling confident  Exam ready

# Linear equations

## Quick quiz

Solve

**(a)** $x + 8 = 13$ **(b)** $x - 6 = -3$ **(c)** $3x = 12$ **(d)** $\frac{x}{5} = -6$

$x =$ ...................... $x =$ ...................... $x =$ ...................... $x =$ ......................

## Solving equations

Grades 4–5

**1.** Solve these equations.

**(a)** $6x + 7 = 18$ **[2 marks]**

$6x = 18 -$ ..............

$6x =$ ..............

Apply inverse operations to each step to collect $x$ terms on one side and numbers on the other.

$x =$ ..............

**(b)** $9x + 6 = 2x - 19$ **[3 marks]**

$9x -$ .......... $= -19 -$ .........

**Exam focus**
Every line of working should include an equals sign.

$x =$ ..............

**(c)** $7(x + 2) = 21$ **[2 marks]**

$7x +$ .............. $= 21$

$x =$ ..............

**(d)** $4(y - 7) = 2(4 - y)$ **[3 marks]**

$4y -$ .............. $=$ .............. $-$ ..............

$y =$ ..............

**(e)** $4 - 3x = 11$ **[2 marks]**

$x =$ ..............

**(f)** $5x - 14 = 2(3 + 2x)$ **[3 marks]**

$x =$ ..............

**2. (a)** Solve $3(5 - 2x) - 2(2x + 3) = 2$ **[3 marks]**

$x =$ ..............

**(b)** Solve $2(3x + 2) - 5(x - 2) = 4(x - 1)$ **[3 marks]**

$x =$ ..............

## Applying algebra to problems

Grade 5

**3.** Arianne and Betty are selling plates in a shop. They sell boxes of plates and single plates. Arianne sells 6 boxes of plates and 32 single plates. Betty sells 5 boxes of plates and 4 single plates. Altogether, Arianne sells twice as many plates as Betty.

Let $x$ represent the number of plates in a box.

Work out how many plates there are in a box. You must show your working. **[4 marks]**

..............................

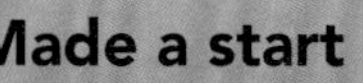

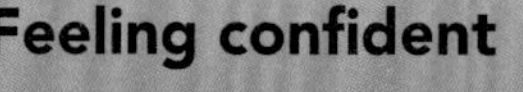

# Rearranging formulae

## Quick quiz

Write down the inverse operation of:

**(a)** addition ..............................

**(b)** subtraction ..............................

**(c)** multiplication ..............................

**(d)** division. ..............................

## One inverse operation

Grade 2

**1.** Rearrange each formula to make $x$ the subject.

**(a)** $y = x + 2$ **[1 mark]**

$y - 2 = x + 2 - 2$

$x =$ ..............................

**(b)** $y = x - 5$ **[1 mark]**

$y +$ ......... $= x - 5 +$ .........

Add 5 to both sides of the equation.

$x =$ ..............................

**(c)** $y = 10 - x$ **[1 mark]**

$x =$ ..............................

**Exam focus**

The subject of a formula is the letter on its own.

**2.** Rearrange each formula to make $d$ the subject.

**(a)** $n = 4d$ **[1 mark]**

$d =$ ..............................

**(b)** $P = \frac{d}{10}$ **[1 mark]**

$d =$ ..............................

**(c)** $c = \frac{d}{2}$ **[1 mark]**

$d =$ ..............................

**3.** Make the letter in brackets the subject of the formula.

**(a)** $y = a + t$ $(a)$ **[1 mark]**

..............................

**(b)** $c = b + w$ $(b)$ **[1 mark]**

..............................

**(c)** $k = t + c$ $(c)$ **[1 mark]**

..............................

**(d)** $n = 5g$ $(g)$ **[1 mark]**

..............................

**(e)** $h = \frac{e}{f}$ $(e)$ **[1 mark]**

..............................

**(f)** $y = \frac{t}{r}$ $(t)$ **[1 mark]**

..............................

## Two or more inverse operations

Grade 4

**4.** Mateo rearranges the formula $x = 6h + 9$ to make $h$ the subject and gets $h = x - \frac{9}{6}$

Is Mateo correct? Show all your working. **[2 marks]**

**5.** Make $a$ the subject of the formula $v = u + at$ **[2 marks]**

$a =$ ..............................

**6.** Make $a$ the subject of the formula $s = \frac{1}{2}at^2$ **[2 marks]**

$a =$ ..............................

**7.** Make $s$ the subject of the formula $v^2 = u^2 + 2as$ **[2 marks]**

$s =$ ..............................

 Made a start  Feeling confident  Exam ready

# Inequalities

## 2 Quick quiz

Write down the meaning of each inequality sign in words.

(a) $<$ ..............................

(b) $\leqslant$ ..............................

(c) $>$ ..............................

(d) $\geqslant$ ..............................

## 5 Representing inequalities on number lines — Grade 4

**1.** Show the inequality $x < 4$ on the number line. **[2 marks]**

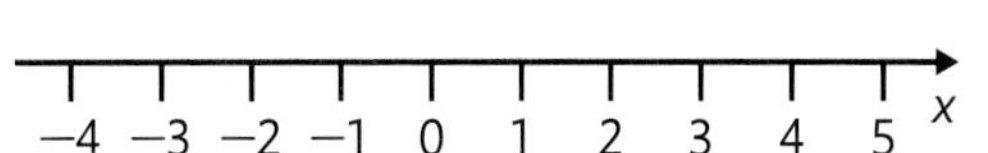

You must use an open circle on the number line as 4 is not included.

**2.** Show the inequality $x \geqslant -1$ on the number line. **[2 marks]**

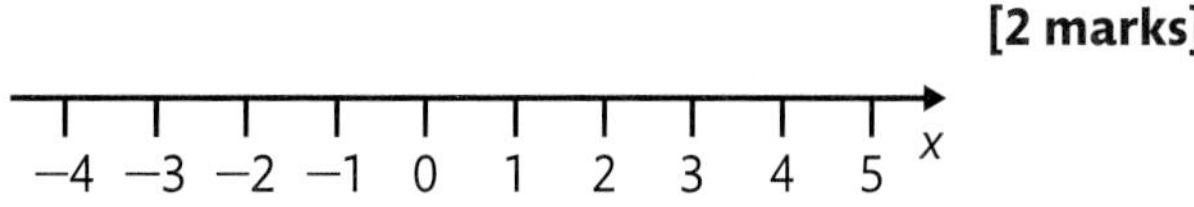

Here, $-1$ is included therefore you must use a shaded-in circle on the number line.

**3.** Show the inequality $-3 \leqslant x < 4$ on the number line. **[2 marks]**

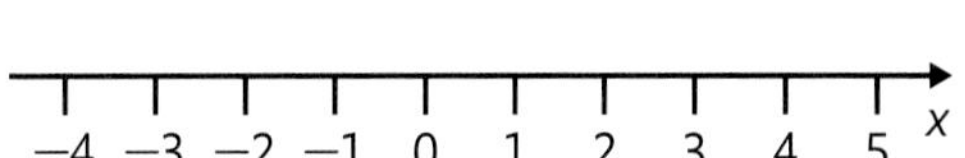

**4.** Show the inequality $-2 < x < 5$ on the number line. **[2 marks]**

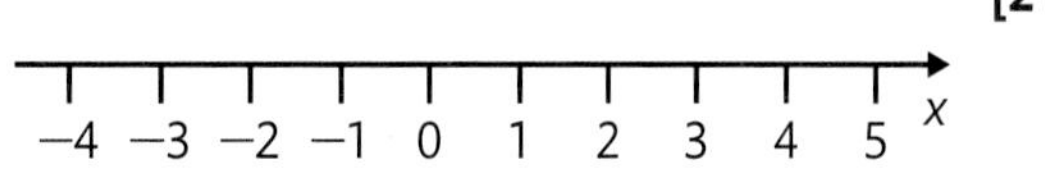

## 5 Interpreting number lines — Grade 4

**5.**

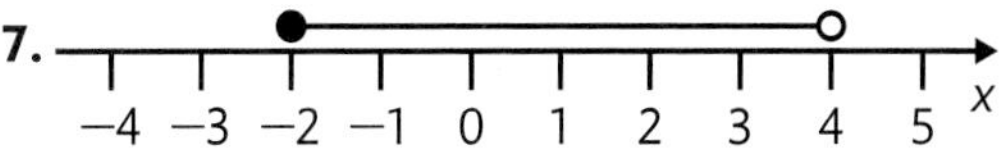

Write down the inequality represented on the number line. **[2 marks]**

..............................

**6.**

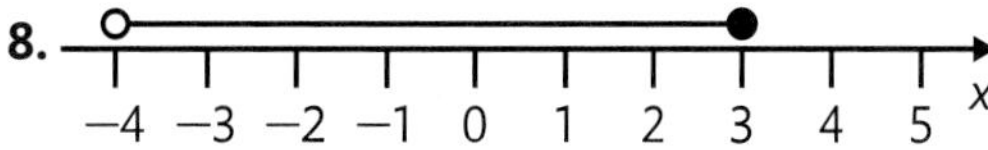

Write down the inequality represented on the number line. **[2 marks]**

For an open circle use $<$ or $>$ and for a closed circle use $\leqslant$ or $\geqslant$.

..............................

**7.**

Write down the inequalities represented on the number line. **[2 marks]**

......... $\leqslant x <$ .........

**8.**

Write down the inequalities represented on the number line. **[2 marks]**

..............................

## 5 Integers and inequalities — Grade 3

**9.** $-2 < x \leqslant 3$

$x$ is an integer.

Write down all the possible values of $x$. **[2 marks]**

..............................

**10.** $-1 \leqslant x < 4$

$x$ is an integer.

Write down all the possible values of $x$. **[2 marks]**

..............................

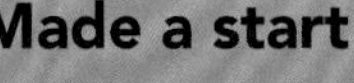

Made a start | Feeling confident | Exam ready

# Solving inequalities

## 2 Quick quiz

Solve these equations.

**(a)** $x + 5 = 12$ ..............................

**(b)** $2y - 10 = 25$ ..............................

**(c)** $6t + 9 = 21$ ..............................

## 5 Solving inequalities — Grade 4

**1.** Solve these inequalities.

**(a)** $3x + 8 < 35$ **[2 marks]**

$3x + 8 < 35$

$3x + 8 - 8 < 35 - 8$

$3x <$ .........

$x <$ ......... $\div$ .........

$x <$ .........

**(b)** $4x + 13 \geqslant 27$ **[2 marks]**

Leave your answer as a fraction.

..............................

**(c)** $4(x + 3) > 8$ **[2 marks]**

You can add or subtract the same number from both sides of an inequality, or divide both sides by a positive number.

..............................

## 10 Two inequalities — Grade 5

**2. (a)** Solve the inequality $p - 3 < 0$ **[1 mark]**

Make $p$ the subject of the inequality.

..............................

**(b)** Solve the inequality $1 - 4p < 3$ **[2 marks]**

..............................

**(c)** Write down the integer values of $p$ that satisfy both of these inequalities.

$p - 3 < 0$ and $1 - 4p < 3$ **[1 mark]**

Use your answers from parts **(a)** and **(b)**.

..............................

**3. (a)** Solve the inequality $4 \leqslant n + 5 < 8$ **[3 marks]**

$4 \leqslant n + 5$ $\qquad$ $n + 5 < 8$

$4 - 5 \leqslant n + 5 - 5$ $\qquad$ $n + 5 - 5 < 8 - 5$

......... $\leqslant n$ $\qquad$ $n <$ .........

......... $\leqslant n <$ .........

**(b)** $n$ is an integer. Write down all the values of $n$ that satisfy $4 \leqslant n + 5 < 8$ **[1 mark]**

..............................

## 5 Greatest and least values — Grade 5

**4. (a)** Solve the inequality $2(y - 3) \geqslant 1$ **[3 marks]**

..............................

**(b)** Write down the lowest integer that satisfies this inequality. **[1 mark]**

..............................

**5. (a)** Solve the inequality $3x + 5 > 16$ **[2 marks]**

..............................

$x$ is an integer.

**(b)** Find the lowest possible value of $x$. **[1 mark]**

..............................



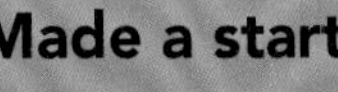 Made a start  Feeling confident  Exam ready

# Solving sequence problems

## 5 Quick quiz

Write down the next three terms in each sequence.

**(a)** 1, 3, 6, 10 .......... .......... .......... **(b)** 1, 4, 9, 16 .......... .......... .......... **(c)** 1, 1, 2, 3, 5 .......... .......... ..........

## 5 Fibonacci sequence — Grade 5

**1.** Here are the first three terms of a Fibonacci sequence: $p$ $q$ $p+q$

Find an expression for

**(a)** the fourth term **[2 marks]**

...............................

**(b)** the fifth term. **[2 marks]**

...............................

## 5 Arithmetic sequences — Grade 5

**2.** The second term of an arithmetic sequence is 7 and the fourth term is 12.

Find the first term of the sequence. **[3 marks]**

+? +? +?

.......... 7 .......... 12

...............................

**3.** Here is part of a number chart.

| Column 1 | Column 2 | Column 3 | Column 4 | Column 5 |
|---|---|---|---|---|
| 4 | 10 | 16 | 22 | 28 |
| 6 | 12 | 18 | 24 | 30 |
| 8 | 14 | 20 | 26 | 32 |

**(a)** What number will be in the first row of column 20? **[1 mark]**

...............................

**(b)** What is the number of the column that starts with 238? **[2 marks]**

...............................

**(c)** What is the number of the column that contains the number 482? **[2 marks]**

...............................

## 5 The *n*th term — Grade 5

**4.** The $n$th term of a sequence is $4n^2$. Mike says that the 5th term of this sequence is 110.

Is Mike right? Show how you get your answer.

**Problem solving**

Using BIDMAS, work out the indices first.

**[1 mark]**

...............................

 Made a start  Feeling confident  Exam ready

# Arithmetic sequences

## Quick quiz

Write down the next three terms in each sequence.

**(a)** 2, 5, 8 ......... ......... .........  **(b)** 100, 97, 94 ......... ......... .........  **(c)** 16, 21, 26 ......... ......... .........

## The *n*th term

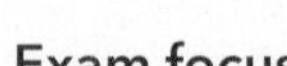

**1.** Here are the first four terms of an arithmetic sequence: 8 13 18 23

**(a)** Write an expression, in terms of *n*, for the *n*th term of this sequence. **[2 marks]**

Common difference = + .......

Zero term = + .......

*n*th term = ....... *n* + .......

**(b)** The *n*th term of another sequence is $4n + 7$. Is 206 a term of this sequence? You must show your working. **[2 marks]**

$4n + 7 =$ .......

...............................

Work out the common difference and use this as the coefficient of *n*.

In part **(b)**, equate 206 with $4n + 7$ and then solve for *n*. If 206 is a term in the sequence then *n* will be a whole number.

**Exam focus**

Once you have worked out the value of *n*, you can answer the question with 'yes' or 'no'.

**2.** Here are the first four terms of an arithmetic sequence: 5 12 19 26

Write an expression, in terms of *n*, for the *n*th term of this sequence. **[2 marks]**

...............................

**3.** The *n*th term of an arithmetic sequence is $3n + 4$

**(a)** Determine whether 110 is a term in this arithmetic sequence. **[2 marks]**

...............................

**(b)** Find an expression for the sum of the *n*th term and the $(n - 1)$th terms of this sequence. Give your answer in terms of *n* in its simplest form. **[2 marks]**

...............................

## The *n*th term for proofs

**4.** The *n*th term of sequence X is $4n - 3$. The *n*th term of sequence Y is $14 - 3n$.

Show that there is only one number that appears in both sequences. You must explain your answer. **[3 marks]**

...............................................................................................................................

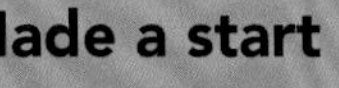

Made a start

Feeling confident

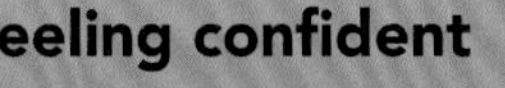

Exam ready

# Factorising quadratics

## Quick quiz

Work out the values of *a* and *b*.

**(a)** $a \times b = 8$ and $a + b = -6$ ..............................

**(b)** $a \times b = 4$ and $a + b = 4$ ..............................

**(c)** $a \times b = -24$ and $a + b = 2$ ..............................

## Factorising when c = 0

Grade 3

**1.** Factorise fully

Find the common factor of the two terms.

**(a)** $x^2 + 2x$ **[1 mark]** ..............................

**(b)** $x^2 - 6x$ **[1 mark]** ..............................

**(c)** $x^2 - 9x$ **[1 mark]** ..............................

## Difference of two squares

Grades 4–5

**2.** Factorise fully

**(a)** $x^2 - 25$ **[2 marks]** ..............................

**(b)** $x^2 - 49$ **[2 marks]** ..............................

**(c)** $x^2 - 121$ **[2 marks]** ..............................

Exam focus

$a^2 - b^2 = (a + b)(a - b)$

**3.** Supraj has attempted to factorise $x^2 + 6x + 5$. His working is shown below:

$$x^2 + 6x + 5 = x(x + 6) + 5$$
$$= (x + 5)(x + 6)$$

Evaluate Supraj's method. **[2 marks]**

..............................................................................................................................................................

## Factorising three-term quadratics

Grade 4

**4.** Factorise fully

**(a)** $x^2 + 7x + 10$ **[2 marks]**

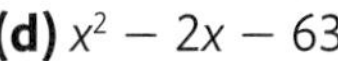

5 × .......... = 10

5 + .......... = 7

$x^2 + 7x + 10 = (x + \ldots\ldots)(x + \ldots\ldots)$

**(b)** $x^2 + 3x + 2$ **[2 marks]** ..............................

**(c)** $x^2 - 9x + 20$ **[2 marks]** ..............................

**(d)** $x^2 - 2x - 63$ **[2 marks]** ..............................

**(e)** $x^2 + 3x - 18$ **[2 marks]** ..............................

**(f)** $x^2 - x - 72$ **[2 marks]** ..............................

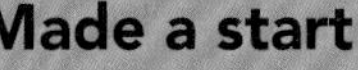

Made a start

Feeling confident

Exam ready

# Solving quadratic equations

## 5 Quick quiz

Fill in both pairs of brackets with the same two numbers to make two correct calculations.

**(a)** (.......) × (.......) = 20
(.......) + (.......) = 12

**(b)** (.......) × (.......) = −15
(.......) + (.......) = 2

**(c)** (.......) × (.......) = 4
(.......) + (.......) = −5

**(d)** (.......) × (.......) = −20
(.......) + (.......) = −1

## 15 Solving quadratic equations — Grades 4–5

**1.** Solve

**(a)** $x^2 = 4$ **[1 mark]**

...............................

**(b)** $2x^2 = 32$ **[2 marks]**

...............................

**(c)** $5x^2 = 500$ **[2 marks]**

...............................

**2.** Solve

**(a)** $2x^2 - 8x = 0$ **[2 marks]**

$2x(x - \ldots\ldots) = 0$

$x =$ ....... or $x =$ .......

**(b)** $x^2 - 11x + 10 = 0$ **[2 marks]**

(.......) × (.......) = 10
(.......) + (.......) = −11
$(x\ldots\ldots\ldots)(x\ldots\ldots\ldots) = 0$

$x =$ ....... or $x =$ .......

**(c)** $x^2 - x - 12 = 0$ **[2 marks]**

(.......) × (.......) = −12
(.......) + (.......) = −1

$x =$ ....... or $x =$ .......

**3.** Solve

**(a)** $x^2 - 5x - 36 = 0$ **[2 marks]**

$x =$ ....... or $x =$ .......

**(b)** $x^2 - 8x + 15 = 0$ **[2 marks]**

$x =$ ....... or $x =$ .......

Factorise the left-hand side, then find the values of $x$ that make each factor equal to 0.

## 5 Using quadratic equations — Grade 5

**4.** *EFG* is a right-angled triangle. All measurements are in centimetres.

The area of the triangle *EFG* is 54 cm².

**(a)** Show that $x^2 + 7x - 44 = 0$ **[3 marks]**

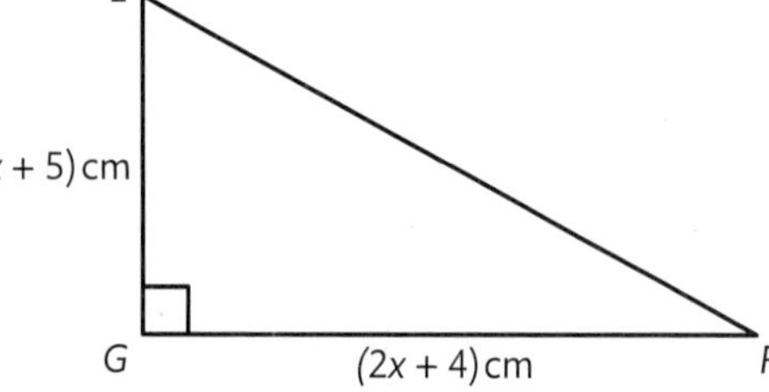


**(b)** Solve this equation to find the value of $x$. **[2 marks]**

$x =$ ...............................

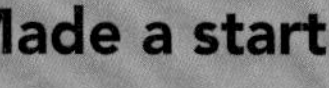

Made a start | Feeling confident | Exam ready

# Simultaneous equations

## 2 Quick quiz

Solve

**(a)** $x = 6$ and $2x - 3y = 0$ ........................................

**(b)** $x = -1$ and $4x + 10y = 5$ ........................................

## 10 Algebraic method — Grade 5

**1.** Solve these simultaneous equations: **[3 marks]**

$8x + 3y = 35$ (1)

$2x - 5y = 3$ (2)

$8x + 3y = 35$ (1)

........$x$ − ........$y$ = ........ (2) × 4

........................ Subtract (2) from (1)

........$y$ = ........

$y$ = ........

Substitute $y$ = ........ into (1)

$8x + 3(........) = 35$

Rearrange for $x$

..............................................

$x$ = ........, $y$ = ........

Number each equation, then multiply one of the equations so that the coefficients of one unknown are the same.

Substitute the value for this unknown into one of the original equations to find the other unknown.

**Exam focus**
Check the answer by substituting both unknowns into the unused original equation.

**2.** Solve the simultaneous equations $x - 15 = 5y$ and $3x + 8y = -1$ **[4 marks]**

$x$ = ........, $y$ = ........

## 5 Graphical method — Grade 5

**3.** The graph shows a straight line with the equation $y = 6 - x$.

**(a)** On the same axes, draw the graph of $y = 4 - \frac{1}{2}x$. **[2 marks]**

**(b)** Use the graph to solve the simultaneous equations $y = 6 - x$ and $y = 4 - \frac{1}{2}x$. **[1 mark]**

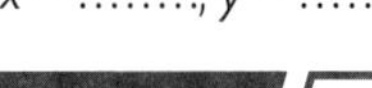

When drawing a straight line, always choose three values of $x$ and work out the corresponding $y$ values.

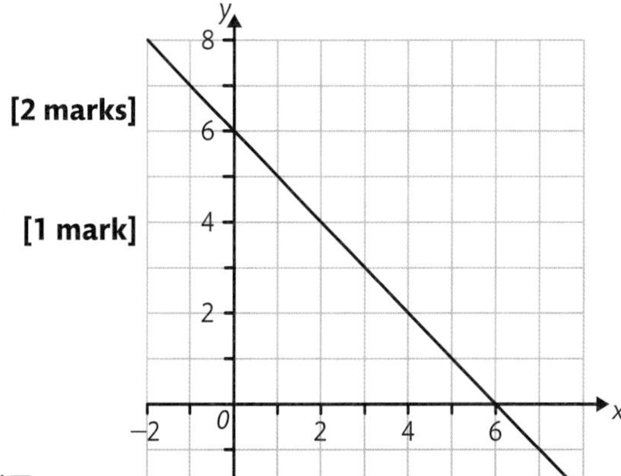



$x$ = ........, $y$ = ........

## 5 Setting up equations — Grade 5

**4.** The total cost of 5 shirts and 4 pairs of trousers is £134.50
The total cost of 4 shirts and 2 pairs of trousers is £86

Find the cost of each shirt and each pair of trousers. **[4 marks]**

Set up two equations.

shirt = £........................, trousers = £........................

 Made a start 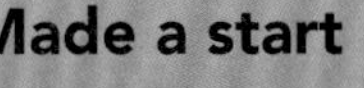  Feeling confident  Exam ready

# Gradients of lines

## Quick quiz

Is the gradient of each graph positive or negative? Circle the correct answer.

(a)

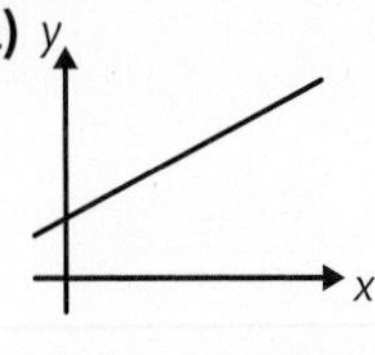

positive / negative

(b)

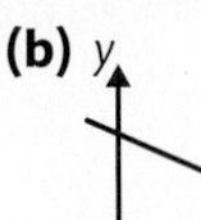

positive / negative

## Finding the gradient

Grade 5

**1.** Work out the gradient of the straight line. **[2 marks]**

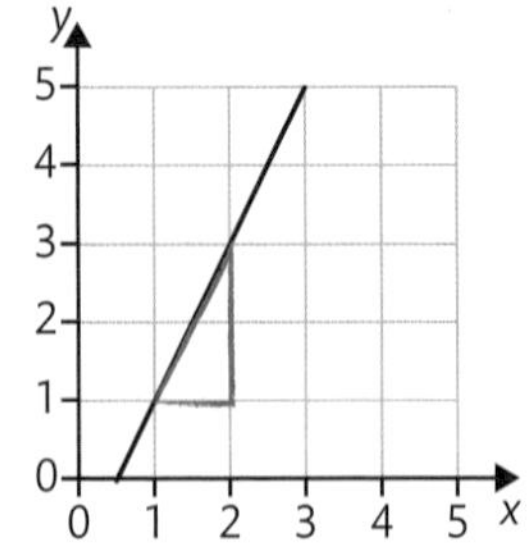

Draw a right-angled triangle to help you.

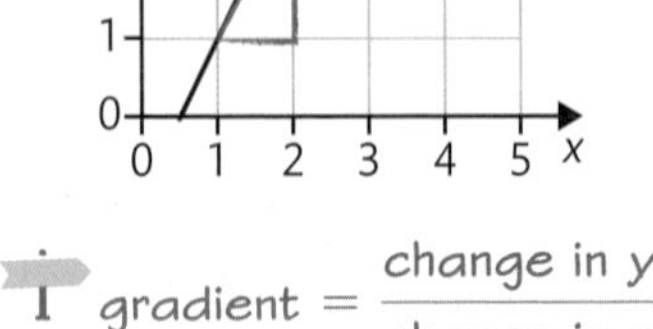

gradient $= \frac{\text{change in } y}{\text{change in } x}$

From the triangle, gradient $= \frac{3-1}{2-1} = \frac{\square}{\square}$

..............................

**2.** Show that the gradient of the straight line is $-\frac{1}{2}$
You must show all of your working.

**[2 marks]**

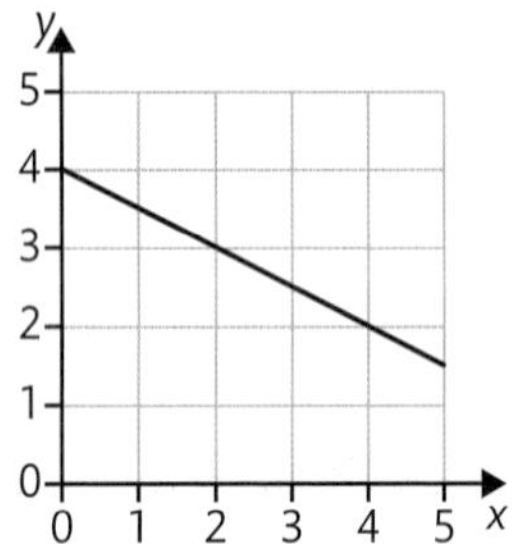

**3.** Work out the gradient of the straight line. **[2 marks]**

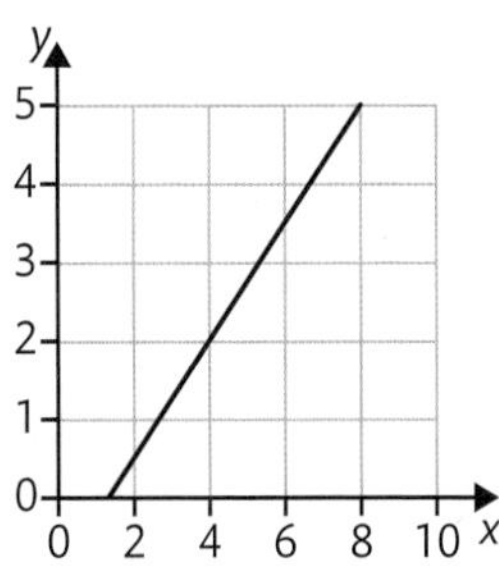

Read the axis scales carefully – don't just count grid squares.

..............................

**4.** Work out the gradient of the straight line. **[2 marks]**

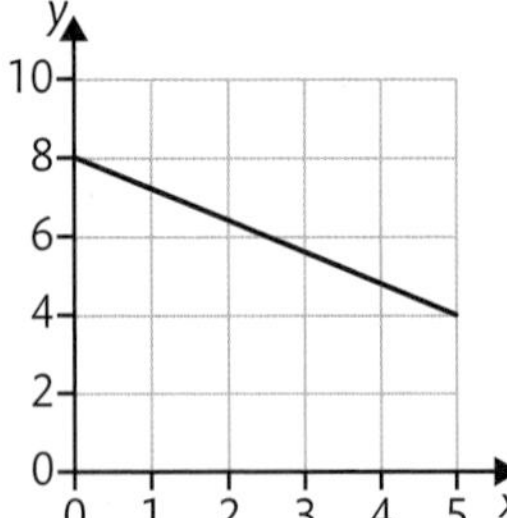

**Exam focus**
Is this gradient positive or negative?

..............................

 Made a start  Feeling confident Exam ready

# Drawing straight-line graphs

## Quick quiz

1. The equation of a straight line is $y = mx + c$. Write down the letter that represents the gradient of the line.

..............................

2. Given that $y = 3x + 1$, work out the value of $y$ when

**(a)** $x = 4$ ..............................

**(b)** $x = -5$ ..............................

## Drawing straight-line graphs

**Grade 4**

1. On the grid, draw the graph of $y = 3x + 2$ for values of $x$ from $-2$ to 2 **[4 marks]**

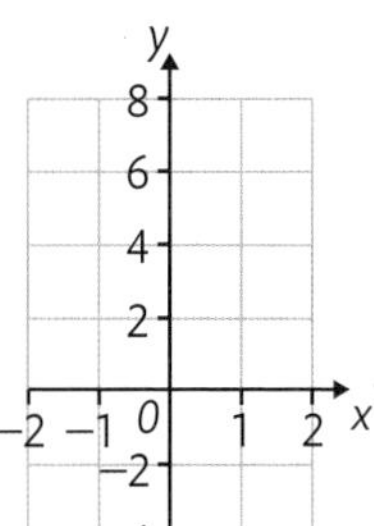


2. On the grid, draw the graph of $y = 3 - 2x$ for values of $x$ from $-2$ to 3 **[4 marks]**

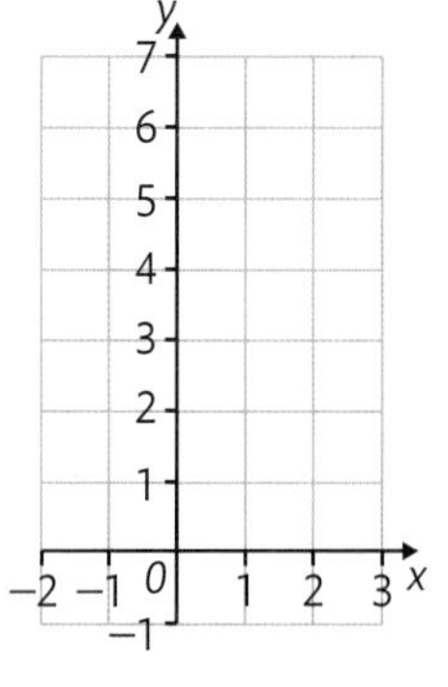


## Interpreting straight-line graphs

**Grade 4**

3. The graph gives information about the temperature of water and the length of time it has been heated.

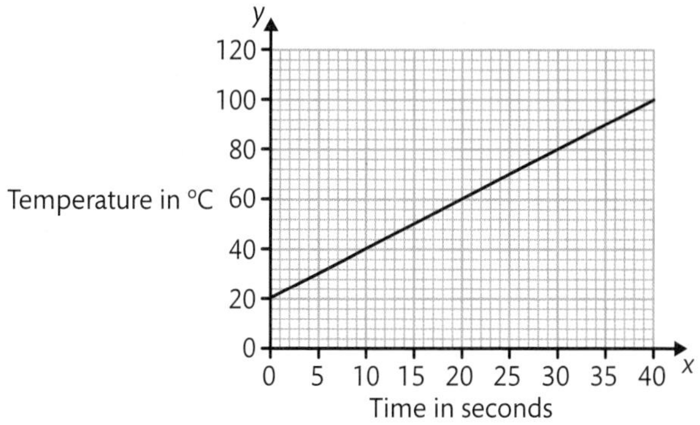

Temperature in °C (y: 0, 20, 40, 60, 80, 100, 120); Time in seconds (x: 0, 5, 10, 15, 20, 25, 30, 35, 40)

**(a)** Find the gradient of the line and interpret this value. **[3 marks]**

..............................

**(b)** Find the equation of the straight line. **[1 mark]**

..............................

## Finding the equation from graphs

**Grade 5**

4. Find the equation of the straight line **L**.  **[3 marks]**

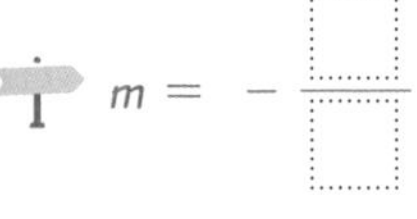


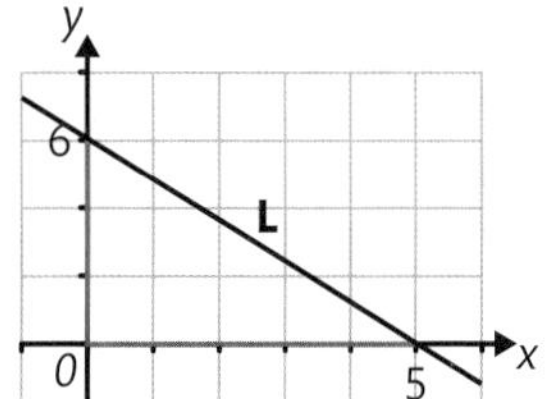


Work out the gradient of the line by drawing a right-angled triangle with the line as the hypotenuse.

A line sloping down from left to right has a negative gradient.

**Exam focus**

Write the equation of the straight line as $y = mx + c$.

..............................

 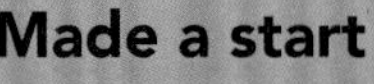  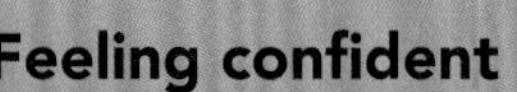 

Made a start | Feeling confident | Exam ready

# Equations of straight lines

## Quick quiz

Given that $y = mx + c$, work out the value of $c$ when

**(a)** $x = 3$, $y = 4$ and $m = 2$

...............................

**(b)** $x = -4$, $y = -5$ and $m = -3$

...............................

## Finding the equation

Grade 5

1. Find an equation of the line with gradient −5 that passes through the point (3, 7). **[2 marks]**

$7 = -5 \times 3 + c$

...............................

$m$ is the gradient and $c$ is the $y$-intercept. Substitute the gradient and the coordinates into $y = mx + c$ to find $c$.

**Exam focus**

Write the equation of the straight line as $y = mx + c$.

2. The line **L** passes through the points (6, 17) and (2, 9).
   Find an equation for the line **L**. **[3 marks]**

...............................

3. $AB$ is a line segment. The midpoint of line segment $AB$ has coordinates (4, 5). Point $A$ has coordinates (7, 3).

   **(a)** Work out the coordinates of point $B$. **[2 marks]**

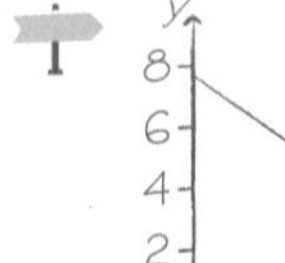


...............................

   **(b)** Work out an equation of the straight line that passes through $A$ and $B$. **[3 marks]**

...............................

4. $\mathbf{L}_1$ is a straight line. The gradient of $\mathbf{L}_1$ is 4. $\mathbf{L}_1$ passes through the point (0, 8).

   **(a)** Write down an equation of the straight line $\mathbf{L}_1$. **[2 marks]**

...............................

   $\mathbf{L}_2$ is a straight line. $\mathbf{L}_2$ passes through the points with coordinates (1, −5) and (4, −3).

   **(b)** Find an equation of $\mathbf{L}_2$.
   Give your answer in the form $ay + bx = c$, where $a$, $b$ and $c$ are integers. **[4 marks]**

...............................

Made a start

Feeling confident

Exam ready

# Parallel lines

## Quick quiz

1. Rearrange the following to make $y$ the subject:

**(a)** $2y = 4x + 10$ ……………………………

**(b)** $3y + 9x = 5$ ……………………………

2. Work out the gradient of the line between (4, 5) and (12, 9). ……………………………

## Finding equations of parallel lines

Grade 5

1. The straight line **L** has equation $y = 2x - 5$

Find an equation of the straight line that passes through (3, 4) and is parallel to **L**. **[2 marks]**

For $y = 2x - 5$, the gradient is 2 and the $y$-intercept is $-5$.

For the new line, $y = mx + c$, $m = 2$

$y = 2x + c$

Substitute in the values for the point (3, 4).

$4 = 2(3) + c$

$c =$ ……………

In $y = mx + c$, $m$ is the gradient and $c$ is the $y$-intercept.

**Exam focus**

Two straight lines are parallel if their gradients are the same.

……………………………

2. The straight line $\mathbf{L}_2$ is parallel to $\mathbf{L}_1$. $\mathbf{L}_2$ passes through (0, 3).

Find the equation of the straight line $\mathbf{L}_2$. **[2 marks]**

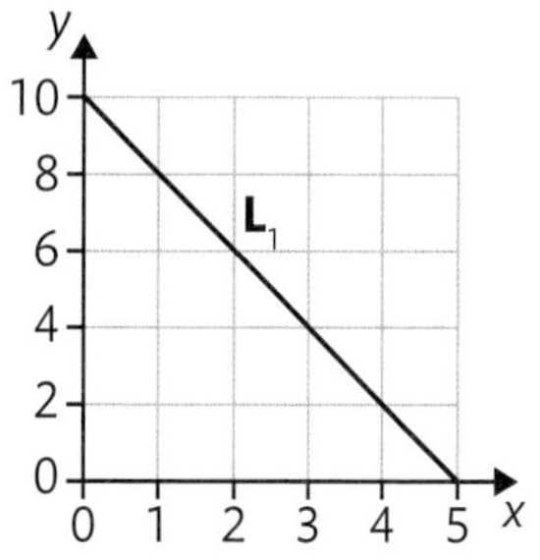


……………………………

## Are they parallel?

Grade 5

3. The equation of the line $\mathbf{L}_1$ is $y = 2x - 1$. The equation of the line $\mathbf{L}_2$ is $3y - 6x + 4 = 0$. Show that these two lines are parallel. **[2 marks]**

**Problem solving**

Rearrange the equations so they are both in the form $y = mx + c$.

4. $A$ is the point with coordinates (6, −4). $B$ is the point with coordinates (9, 8). The straight line **L** goes through both $A$ and $B$.

Is the line with equation $y = 4x + 1$ parallel to line **L**? You must show how you got your answer. **[3 marks]**

……………………………

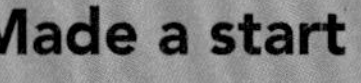

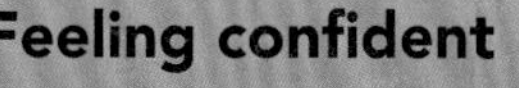

Made a start | Feeling confident | Exam ready

# Real-life graphs

## Quick quiz

Tick (✓) the correct answer.

**(a)** What does the gradient on a distance–time graph represent? ☐ acceleration ☐ speed

**(b)** How do you represent an object that is stationary on a distance–time graph? ☐ horizontal line ☐ vertical line

## Distance–time graphs

Grade 5

**1.** Here is part of the travel graph of Aziz's journey from his house to the airport and back.

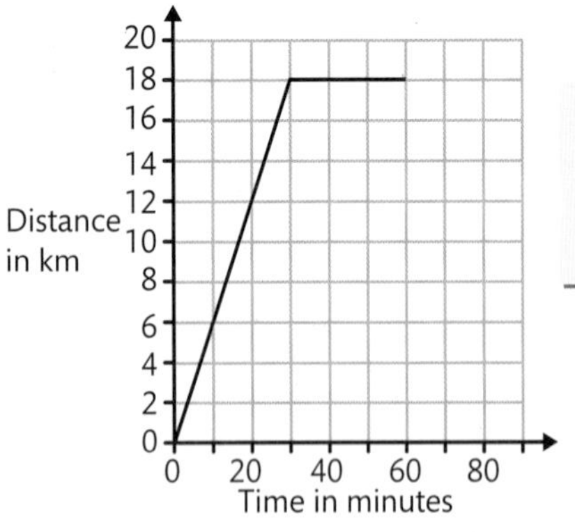



The gradient on a distance–time graph represents speed.

**(a)** Work out Aziz's speed for the first 30 minutes of his journey. Give your answer in km/h. **[2 marks]**

.............................. km/h

**(b)** At $t = 60$ minutes, Aziz travels back to his house at 54 km/h. Complete the travel graph. **[2 marks]**

**(c)** How long does he spend at the airport? **[1 mark]**

.............................. minutes

**2.** Farat walks along a path from her home to the town centre. Here is the distance–time graph for her journey from her home to the town centre.

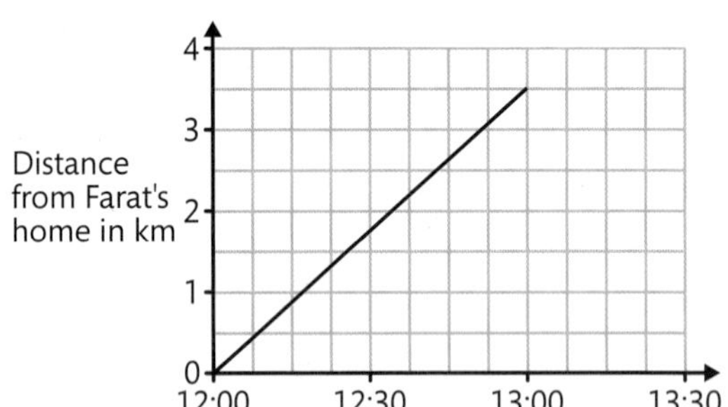



Mala leaves the town centre at 12:30 and walks at a constant speed along the same path to Farat's home. She arrives at Farat's home at 13:15.

**(a)** Show the information about Mala's journey on the graph. **[2 marks]**

**(b)** How far from Farat's home were Farat and Mala when they passed each other? **[1 mark]**

.............................. km

## Real-life graphs

Grade 5

**3.** This graph can be used to convert between degrees Celsius, $C$, and degrees Fahrenheit, $F$.

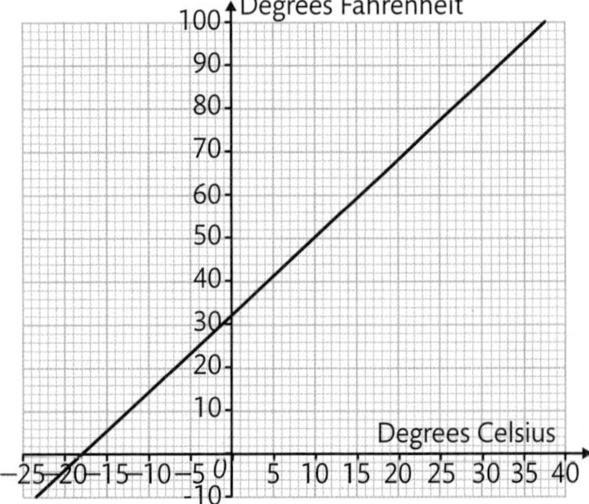



**(a)** Convert

**(i)** 0 °C into degrees Fahrenheit. **[1 mark]**

..............................°F

**(ii)** 70 °F into degrees Celsius. **[2 marks]**

..............................°C

**(b)** The temperature in Manchester is −4 °C.
The temperature in New York is 40 °F.

Where is it colder? **[1 mark]**

..............................

# Quadratic graphs

## Quick quiz

1. Sketch the graph of $y = x^2$

2. Sketch the graph of $y = -x^2$

3. Delete one word in the brackets to make the statement below true.

   A quadratic graph has a (horizontal / vertical) line of symmetry.

## Drawing quadratic graphs

**Grade 5**

**1. (a)** Complete the table of values for $y = x^2 - 4x + 2$ **[2 marks]**

| **x** | −1 | 0 | 1 | 2 | 3 | 4 | 5 |
|---|---|---|---|---|---|---|---|
| **y** | 7 | | | −2 | | | |

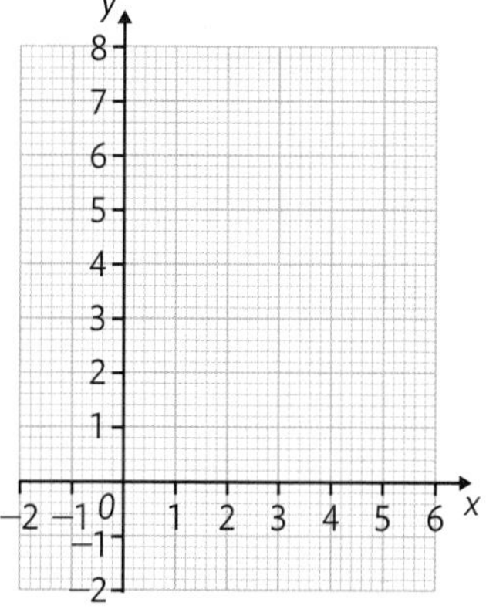

Substitute the $x$-values into the equation to find the corresponding $y$-values.

**(b)** On the grid, draw the graph of $y = x^2 - 4x + 2$ for values of $x$ from −1 to 5. **[3 marks]**

Always draw a smooth curve. Never join the points with straight lines.

**(c)** Write down the coordinates of the turning point. **[2 marks]**

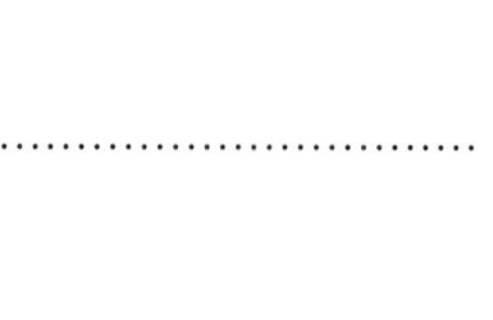

..............................

**2.** This is the graph of $y = x^2 - 4x + 7$

Write down the coordinates of the turning point. **[2 marks]**

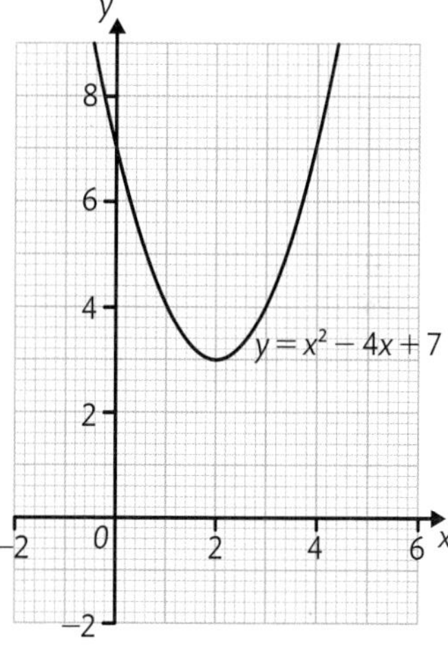


..............................

**3. (a)** Complete the table of values for $y = 5 - x - x^2$ **[2 marks]**

| **x** | −4 | −3 | −2 | −1 | 0 | 1 | 2 | 3 |
|---|---|---|---|---|---|---|---|---|
| **y** | −7 | | | | 5 | | | −7 |

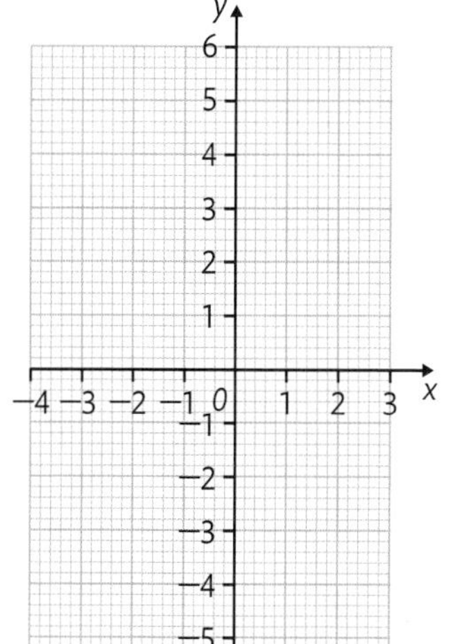

**(b)** On the grid, draw the graph of $y = 5 - x - x^2$ for values of $x$ from −4 to 3 **[3 marks]**

**(c)** Write down an estimate for the coordinates of the turning point. **[2 marks]**

..............................

# Using quadratic graphs

## 5 Quick quiz

Match each equation on the left with one equation on the right.

| |
|---|
| **(a)** $x^2 + 7x + 1 = 0$ |
| **(b)** $x^2 + 2x - 14 = 0$ |
| **(c)** $x^2 - 5x + 9 = 0$ |

| |
|---|
| **(i)** $x^2 - 3x + 4 = 2x - 5$ |
| **(ii)** $x^2 + 6x + 5 = 4 - x$ |
| **(iii)** $x^2 + 5x - 11 = 3x + 3$ |

## 10 Simultaneous equations — Grade 5

**1. (a)** Complete the table of values for $y = x^2 - 2x - 1$ **[2 marks]**

| $x$ | −2 | −1 | 0 | 1 | 2 | 3 | 4 |
|---|---|---|---|---|---|---|---|
| $y$ | | 2 | | | −1 | | |

$y = (-2)^2 - 2(-2) - 1 = ........$

$y = (0)^2 - 2(0) - 1 = ........$

$y = (1)^2 - 2(1) - 1 = ........$

$y = (........)^2 - 2(........) - 1$

Substitute the $x$-values into $y = x^2 - 2x - 1$ to find the corresponding $y$-values.

**(b)** On the grid, draw the graph of $y = x^2 - 2x - 1$ for values of $x$ from −2 to 4 **[3 marks]**

**(c)** On the same grid, draw the graph of $y = 2$ **[1 mark]**

**(d)** Write down the points of intersection of $y = x^2 - 2x - 1$ and $y = 2$ **[2 marks]**

..............................

Always draw a smooth curve and never join up the points with straight lines.

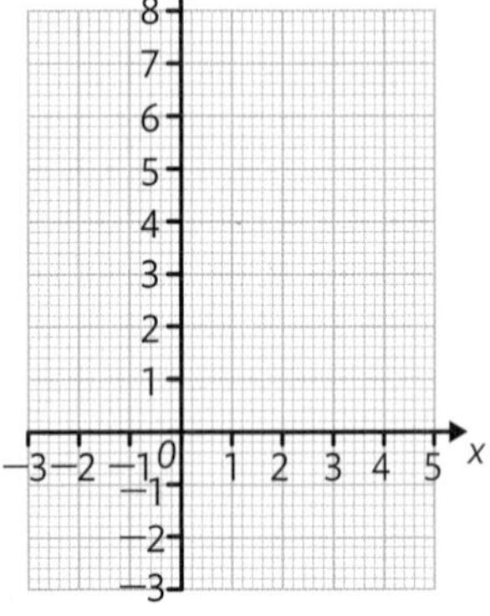


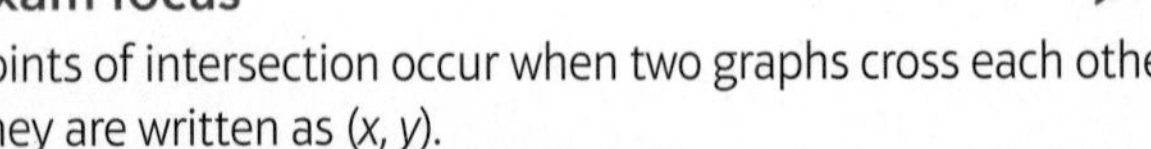

**Exam focus**

Points of intersection occur when two graphs cross each other. They are written as $(x, y)$.

## 10 Hidden linear equations — Grade 5

**2. (a)** Complete the table of values for $y = x^2 - 3x + 2$ **[2 marks]**

| $x$ | −1 | 0 | 1 | 2 | 3 | 4 |
|---|---|---|---|---|---|---|
| $y$ | | 2 | | | | |

**(b)** On the grid, draw the graph of $y = x^2 - 3x + 2$ for values of $x$ from −1 to 4 **[3 marks]**

**(c)** By drawing a suitable straight line on your graph, estimate the solutions of the equation $x^2 - 3x + 2 = 3$ **[2 marks]**

..............................

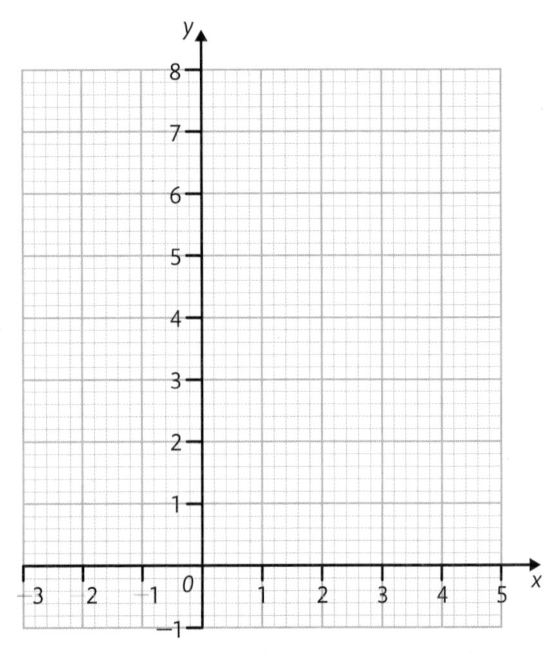

 Made a start  Feeling confident Exam ready

# Cubic and reciprocal graphs

## Quick quiz

Match each equation with the correct graph.

| $y = \frac{1}{x}$ | $y = x^3$ | $y = -\frac{1}{x}$ | $y = -x^3$ |
|---|---|---|---|

| 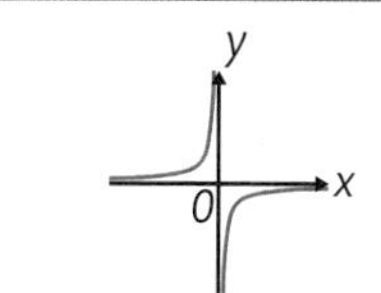 | 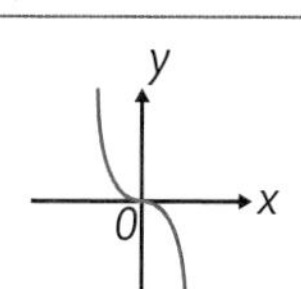 | 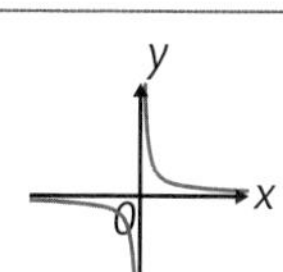 | 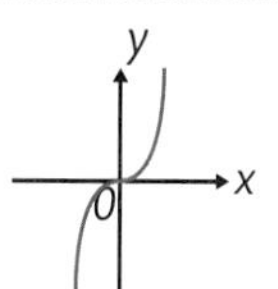 |
|---|---|---|---|

## Drawing cubic and reciprocal graphs

Grade 5

**1. (a)** Complete the table of values for $y = x^3 + 2$ **[2 marks]**

| **x** | −1.5 | −1 | −0.5 | 0 | 0.5 | 1 | 1.5 |
|---|---|---|---|---|---|---|---|
| **y** | −1.375 | | | 2 | | | |

**(b)** On the grid, draw the graph of $y = x^3 + 2$ for values of $x$ from −1.5 to 1.5 **[3 marks]**

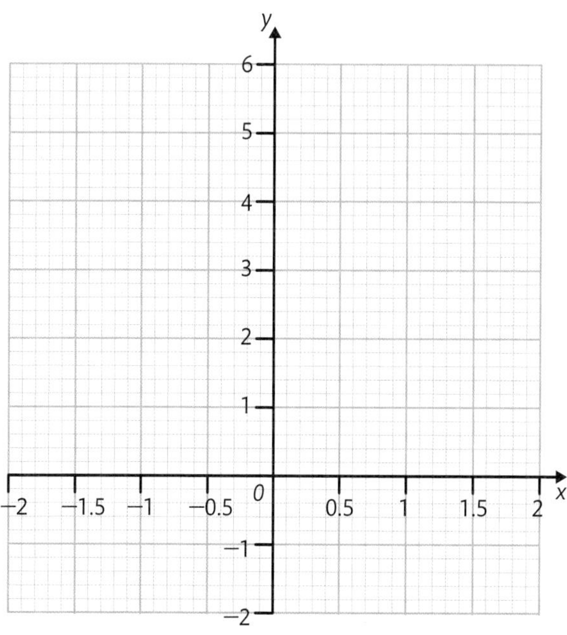

**(c)** Find an estimate for the solution to the equation $x^3 + 2 = 0$ **[2 marks]**

..............................

Substitute the $x$-values into the equation to find the corresponding $y$-values.

Always draw a smooth curve. Do not join up the points with straight lines.

**2. (a)** Complete the table of values for $y = \frac{4}{x}$ **[2 marks]**

| **x** | 0.5 | 1 | 2 | 4 | 5 | 8 |
|---|---|---|---|---|---|---|
| **y** | | 4 | | | 0.8 | |

**(b)** On the grid, draw the graph of $y = \frac{4}{x}$ for $0.5 \leqslant x \leqslant 8$ **[3 marks]**

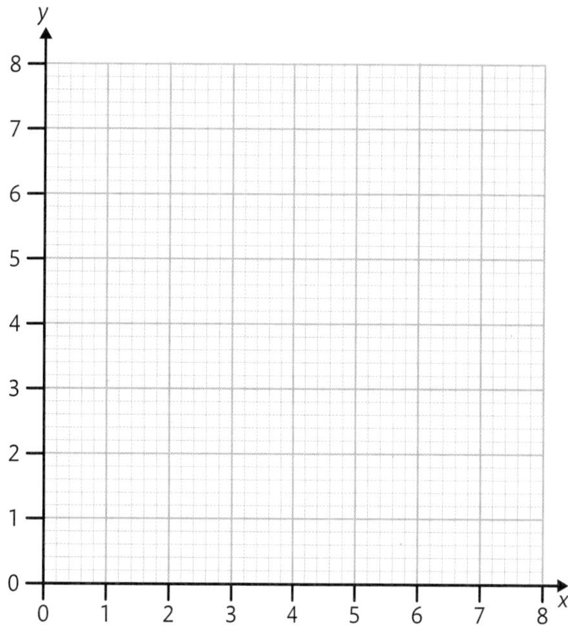

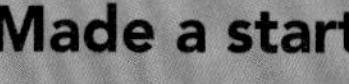 Made a start  Feeling confident Exam ready

# Recognising graphs

## Quick quiz

In the space below, sketch the shape of the following graphs.

**(a)** $y = x^2$ **(b)** $y = -x^3$ **(c)** $y = \frac{1}{x}$

You will need to recognise graphs for the exams, so make sure you memorise the shapes of these three graphs.

## Recognising graphs

Grade 5

**1.** Write down the letter of the graph that could match each equation.

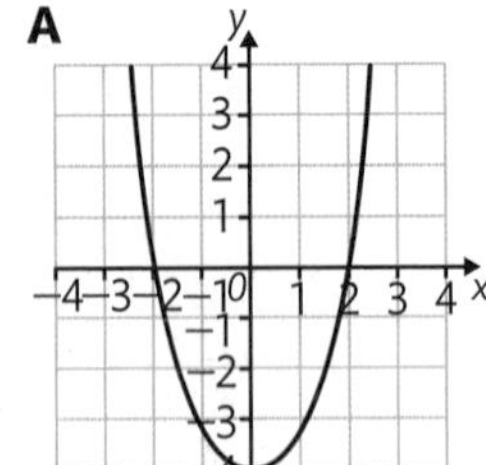
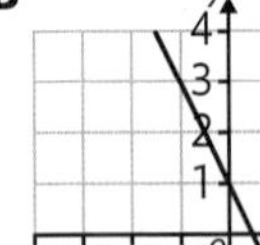
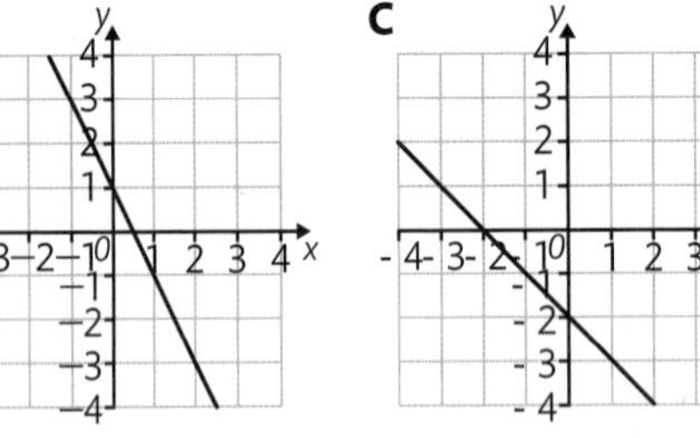

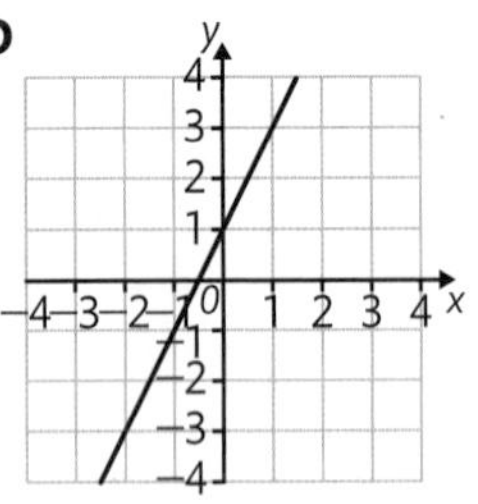
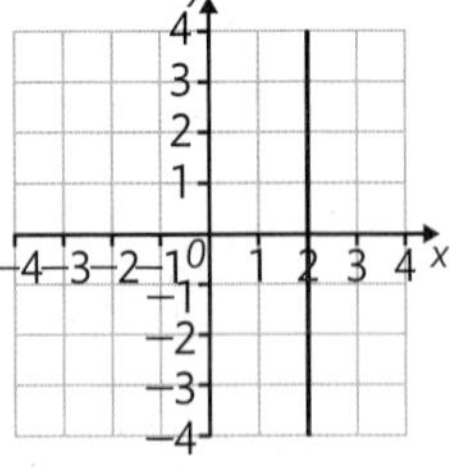

**(a)** $y = -2x + 1$ ...........B...........

**(b)** $y = -x - 2$ ..........................

**(c)** $x = 2$ ..........................

Use what you know about $y = mx + c$ and $y = x^2$ to match the graphs.

**2.** Write down the letter of the graph that could match each equation.

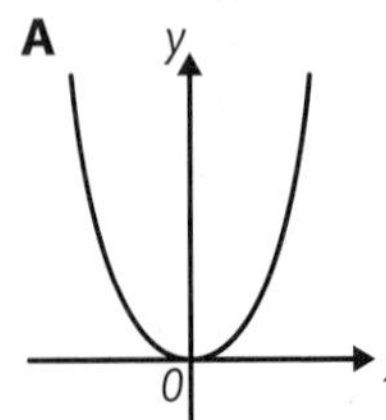

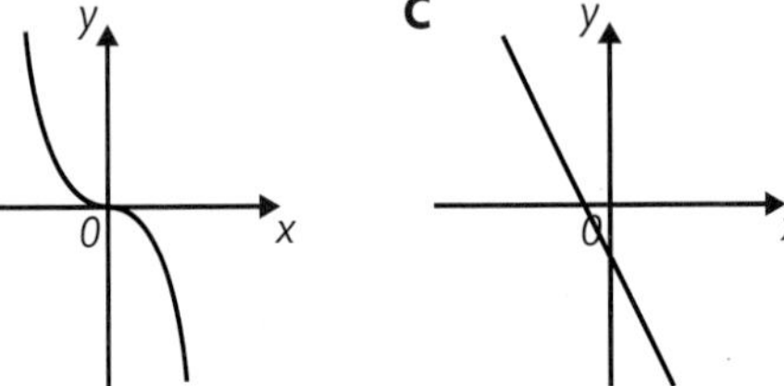
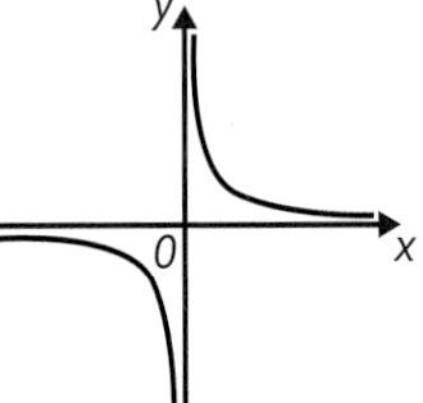
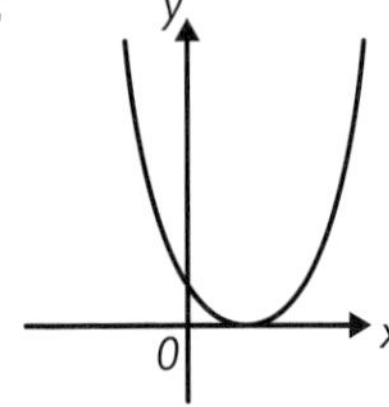

**(a)** $y = \frac{1}{x}$ ..........................

**(b)** $y = (x - 1)^2$ ..........................

**(c)** $y = -3x - 1$ ..........................

**(d)** $y = -x^3$ ..........................

**(e)** $y = x^2$ ..........................

**3.** Write down the letter of the graph that could match each equation.

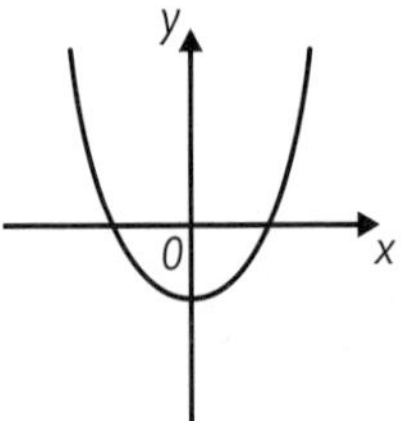
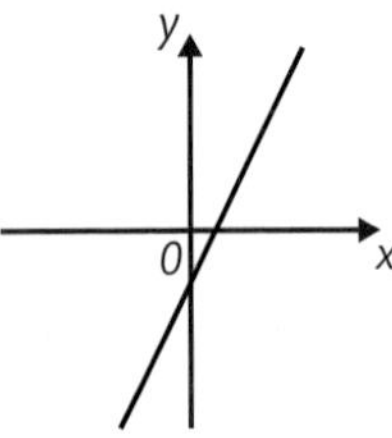
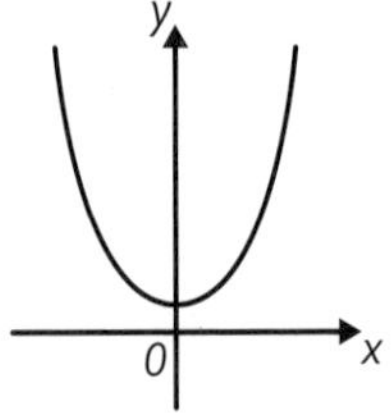
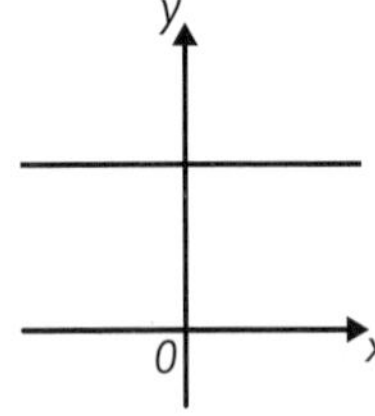

**(a)** $y = x^2 - 3$ ..........................

**(b)** $y = 4x - 3$ ..........................

**(c)** $y = 5$ ..........................

**(d)** $y = x^3$ ..........................

**(e)** $y = x^2 + 2$ ..........................



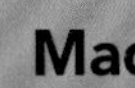 Made a start  Feeling confident  Exam ready

# Algebraic reasoning

## 2 Quick quiz

Expand and simplify these expressions.

**(a)** $x(x+2)$ ..............................

**(b)** $(y-3)(y-3)$ ..............................

**(c)** $(t-4)^2$ ..............................

## 5 Language of algebra

Grade 2

**1.** Tick (✓) the appropriate column of the table to show whether each of these is an equation, an expression, a formula or an identity. **[4 marks]**

| | Expression | Formula | Equation | Identity |
|---|---|---|---|---|
| $9x - 3x \equiv 6x$ | | | | |
| $V = L \times W \times H$ | | ✓ | | |
| $4x + 9 = 15$ | | | | |
| $2xy + 5x$ | | | | |

**Exam focus**
Equations and formulae always contain an = sign.

## 15 Reasoning with algebra

Grades 4–5

**2.** Show that

$3(x+5) + 4(x+2) \equiv 7x + 23$ **[2 marks]**

LHS ≡ 3x + ........ + ........ + 8

≡ ........ + ........

≡ RHS

Expand and simplify the left hand side so it is the same as the right hand side.

**3.** Show that

$2(y^2 - 3y) - 10(y-1) \equiv 2y^2 - 16y + 10$ **[2 marks]**

**4.** $n$ is a positive integer. State, with a reason, whether each of the following is odd or even.

**(a)** $2n+1$ **[1 mark]**

..............................................................................

**(b)** $n(n+1)$ **[1 mark]**

..............................................................................

**(c)** $n+n$ **[1 mark]**

..............................................................................

**5.** $n$ is a positive whole number.

Jonah adds together $n$, the number 1 above it, and the number 2 above it.

**(a)** Write an expression for Jonah's total in terms of $n$. Simplify your answer as much as possible. **[2 marks]**

..............................

**(b)** Explain why Jonah's total must be a multiple of 3 **[1 mark]**

..............................

**6.** Give an example to show that each statement is **not** true:

**(a)** All multiples of 4 end in the digits 2, 4, 6 or 8 **[1 mark]**

..............................

**(b)** The product of two different prime numbers is always an odd number. **[1 mark]**

..............................

**7.** Show that $(n+1)^2 - (n-1)^2$ is always even for all positive values of $n$. **[3 marks]**

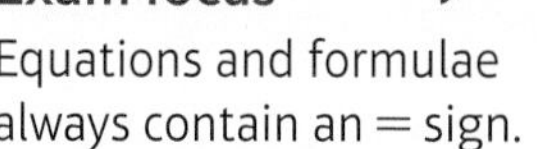

 Made a start  Feeling confident Exam ready

# Algebra

## Quadratic graphs — Grade 5

**1. (a)** Complete the table of values for $y = x^2 - 5x + 3$ **[2 marks]**

| $x$ | −1 | 0 | 1 | 2 | 3 | 4 | 5 | 6 |
|---|---|---|---|---|---|---|---|---|
| $y$ | 9 | | −1 | | −3 | | | |

For $x = -1$, $y = (-1)^2 - 5(-1) + 3 = 1 + 5 + 3 = 9$

Substitute each value of $x$ into the equation to find the corresponding value of $y$.

**(b)** On the grid below, draw the graph of $y = x^2 - 5x + 3$ for values of $x$ from $x = -1$ to $x = 6$ **[2 marks]**

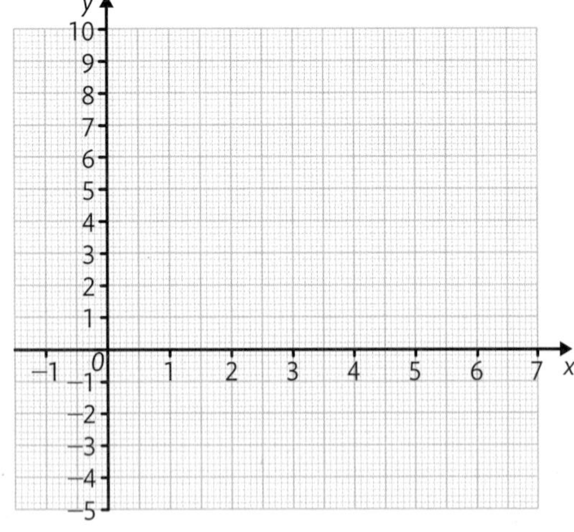

Is this a linear graph or a quadratic graph?

**(c)** Find estimates of the solutions of the equation $x^2 - 5x + 3 = 0$ **[2 marks]**

..............................

**(d)** Write down the coordinates of the turning point. **[2 marks]**

**Exam focus**

Read off graphs to the nearest small square.

..............................

## Factorisation — Grade 5

**2.** The diagram shows an isosceles triangle.

Show that the perimeter can be written in the form $a(x + b)$ cm where $a$ and $b$ are integers. **[3 marks]**

$(x + 7)$ cm

$(x + 1)$ cm

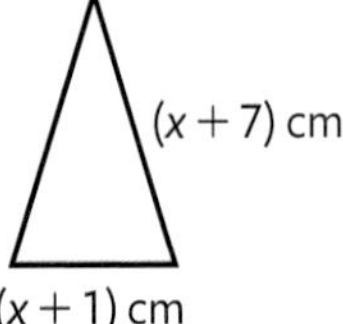

**Problem solving**

This is an isosceles triangle, so the two long sides are the same length. Add all the sides together and then factorise the result.

## Simultaneous equations — Grade 5

**3.** Solve the simultaneous equations.

$3x + 2y = 9$ (1)

$2x - y = 13$ (2) **[3 marks]**

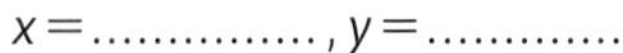

$x =$ ..............., $y =$ ...............

 Made a start  Feeling confident Exam ready

# Ratio

## 2 Quick quiz

Simplify each ratio as much as possible.

**(a)** 2:8 ..................... **(b)** 16:24 ..................... **(c)** $4:\frac{3}{2}$ ..................... **(d)** $\frac{5}{2}:\frac{4}{3}$ .....................

## 10 Ratios in context

Grades 2–4

**1.** Kobe and Anton share some money in the ratio 2:3

**(a)** What fraction of the money does Kobe get? **[1 mark]**

...............................

Anton gets £7.50

**(b)** How much does Kobe get? **[1 mark]**

£...............................

Polly and Samir share some chocolate coins. Polly gets $\frac{1}{3}$ of the chocolate coins.

**(c)** Write the ratio of the number of chocolate coins Polly gets to the number Samir gets. **[1 mark]**

...............................

**2.** Jim is building a house. He is putting some bricks and some blocks on a pallet.
The ratio of the number of bricks to the number of blocks is 5:1
The total number of bricks and blocks is 48. Each brick weighs 1.65 kg.
The total weight of the bricks and blocks is 76 kg. The blocks all weigh the same.

Work out the weight of one block. **[4 marks]**

Number of bricks : number of blocks = 5 : ........
Total number of parts = 5 + ........
= ........ parts
So ........ parts = 48
Number of bricks = 48 × ........ ÷ ........ = ........
Number of blocks = 48 × ........ ÷ ........ = ........
Total weight of bricks = ........ × 1.65 = ........ kg
Total weight of blocks = ........................ = ........ kg

........................ kg

Write down the ratio of the number of bricks to the number of blocks.

Work out the number of bricks and the number of blocks.

**Exam focus**
Make sure the units for bricks and blocks are the same.

## 15 Using different types of ratio

Grades 2–4

**3.** The perimeter of a triangle is 255 cm. The lengths of the sides of the triangle are in the ratio 2:7:8

Work out the length of the longest side of the triangle. **[3 marks]**

............................ cm

**4.** At a hospital, the ratio of the number of male patients to the number of female patients is 2:3
30% of the male patients and 40% of the female patients are over the age of 60

What percentage of all the patients in the hospital are over the age of 60? **[4 marks]**

............................ %

 Made a start 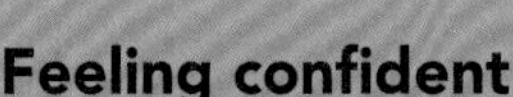 Feeling confident  Exam ready

# Direct proportion

## Quick quiz

**(a)** 1 sweet costs 5p. How much do 12 sweets cost?

.............................. p

**(b)** 3 marbles cost 90p. How much does 1 marble cost?

.............................. p

## Direct proportion

Grade 4

**1.** These are the ingredients to make 15 pancakes.

| **Pancakes (makes 15)** |
|---|
| 450 ml milk, 180 g flour, 3 eggs |

Bill makes 45 pancakes.

**(a)** Work out how much flour he uses. **[2 marks]**

45 ÷ 15 = 3

15 pancakes need 180 g of flour.

So 45 pancakes need 180 × 3

= ........g of flour

.............................. g

Lola makes some pancakes. She uses 750 ml of milk.

**(b)** Work out how many pancakes she makes. **[2 marks]**

15 pancakes need 450 ml of milk.

So 1 pancake needs 450 ÷........

= ........ml of milk.

So 750 ml of milk makes ........ ÷........ = ........ pancakes.

..............................

**2.** $y$ is directly proportional to $x$.
$y = 18$ when $x = 4$
Work out

**(a)** $y$ when $x = 7$ **[2 marks]**

18 ÷ 4 = ........

........ × ........ = ........

Divide the numbers to find the constant of proportionality. Multiply the result by the value of $x$ to find the value of $y$.

..............................

**(b)** $x$ when $y = 72$ **[2 marks]**

..............................

**Exam focus**
Write your method clearly and check back through your working.

## Currency

Grade 4

**3.** Identical necklaces are sold in London, in New York and in Paris.
These necklaces cost £242 in London, \$289 in New York and €295 in Paris.
Take the exchange rates as £1 = \$1.43 and £1 = €1.19.

Are the necklaces cheapest in London or in New York or in Paris? You must show how you get your answer. **[3 marks]**

..............................

## Proportional reasoning

Grade 3

**4.** The weight of a copper wire is directly proportional to its length.
A piece of copper wire is 30 cm long and has a weight of 60 grams.

Work out the weight of a piece of the same copper wire that is 25 cm long. **[2 marks]**

.............................. g

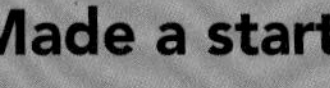

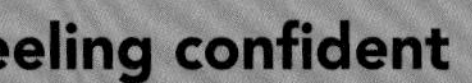

Made a start Feeling confident Exam ready

# Inverse proportion

## Quick quiz

Circle the correct answer.

**(a)** In inverse proportion, as one quantity increases the other quantity **increases** / **decreases**.

**(b)** In direct proportion, as one quantity decreases the other quantity **increases** / **decreases**.

## Using inverse proportion

Grade 5

**1.** $y$ is inversely proportional to $x$.

$y = 8$ when $x = 3$

Calculate the value of $y$ when $x = 10$ **[2 marks]**

$8 \times 3 =$ ..........

.......... ÷ .......... = ..........

Multiply the numbers to find the constant of proportionality.

Divide by the value of $x$ to find the value of $y$.

$y =$ ..............................

**2.** It takes 2 builders 6 days to build a wall.

How long would it take 5 builders to build the same wall?

**[2 marks]**

..............................

## Inverse proportion

Grade 5

**3.** It takes 5 people 12 days to pitch the tents for an exhibition.

How long would it take 6 people to pitch the same tents?

**[2 marks]**

One person takes $5 \times 12 = 60$ days

60 ÷ .......... = ..........

Work out how long it will take one person to pitch the tents. Then divide that by the new number of people.

..............................

**4.** $p$ is inversely proportional to $q$.

$p = 36$ when $q = 8$

Calculate the value of $p$ when $q = 16$. **[2 marks]**

$p =$ ..............................

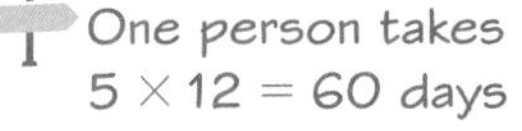

**5.** $f$ is inversely proportional to $d$.

When $d = 75$, $f = 256$

Find the value of $f$ when $d = 20$. **[2 marks]**

$f =$ ..............................

**6.** The current through an electrical circuit, $I$ amps, is inversely proportional to the resistance of the circuit, $R$ ohms.

When the resistance is 24 ohms, the current in the circuit is 16 amps.

Find the current when the resistance in the circuit is reduced to 5.2 ohms. **[2 marks]**

.............................. amps

**7.** Hui Yin has 8 identical taps that all have the same rate of flow.
When all the taps are turned on full, it takes 27 minutes to fill a tank. **[3 marks]**

If only 6 of the taps are turned on full, how long would it take to fill the same tank?

.............................. minutes

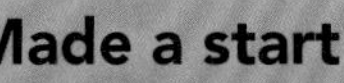

Made a start

Feeling confident

Exam ready

# Percentages

## 2 Quick quiz

Work out

(a) 50% of 200 ..............................

(b) 10% of 80 ..............................

(c) 25% of 160 ..............................

(d) 1% of 1000 ..............................

## 5 Finding a percentage of a quantity without a calculator — Grade 2

**1. (a)** Find 15% of 300 **[2 marks]**

10% of 300 = 300 ÷ 10 = .........

5% of 300 = ......... ÷ 2 = .........

So 15% of 300 = ......... + ......... = .........

Divide 10% by 2 to get 5%.

..............................

**(b)** Find 45% of 360 **[2 marks]**

Multiply 10% by 4 to get 40%.

..............................

## 5 Finding a percentage of a quantity with a calculator — Grade 3

**2. (a)** Find 18% of 125 kg **[2 marks]**

Remember 18% means 18 out of 100.

..............................

**(b)** Find 64% of 256 m **[2 marks]**

..............................

**(c)** Find 17.5% of £94 **[2 marks]**

**Exam focus**
If no degree of accuracy is stated, give money answers correct to the nearest penny.

£..............................

## 15 Interpreting percentage problems — Grade 3

**3.** There are 850 counters in a box.
24% of these counters are yellow.

Work out the number of yellow counters in the box. **[2 marks]**

..............................

**4.** Amana invests £600 in a savings account. Each year she is paid 4% simple interest, which she withdraws.

Find the total amount of interest earned by Amana in 2 years. **[2 marks]**

£..............................

**5.** There are 250 members in an athletic club.
110 of the members are female.

**(a)** Work out the percentage of the members who are female. **[2 marks]**

.............................. %

100 new female members join the club.

**(b)** Work out the percentage of the members who are male. **[3 marks]**

.............................. %

**6.** A television has a price of £360.
In a sale its price is reduced by £54.

Write the reduction as a percentage of the original price. **[3 marks]**

.............................. %

 Made a start  Feeling confident  Exam ready

# Fractions, decimals and percentages

## Quick quiz

Fill in the missing equivalent values for each row.

| Fraction | Decimal | Percentage |
|---|---|---|
| $\frac{1}{2}$ | | |
| | 0.25 | |
| | | 75% |

## Converting between fractions, decimals and percentages

Grade 2 

**1.** Write

**(a)** 0.7 as a fraction **[1 mark]**

$0.7 = \frac{\square}{10}$

..............................

**(b)** 0.6 as a percentage **[1 mark]**

$0.6 = \frac{6}{10} = \frac{60}{100}$

.............................. %

**(c)** $\frac{3}{8}$ as a decimal **[2 marks]**

..............................

**(d)** 90% as a fraction. **[2 marks]**

Write 90 over 100 and then cancel.

..............................

## Ordering fractions, decimals and percentages

Grade 3 

**2.** Write these numbers in order of size. Start with the lowest number. **[2 marks]**

35% $\frac{3}{10}$ 0.32 $\frac{2}{5}$ 0.25

.......... .......... .......... .......... ..........

Convert all the numbers into decimals or percentages.

**3.** Write these numbers in order of size. Start with the lowest number. **[2 marks]**

$\frac{3}{7}$ 41% 0.45 $\frac{2}{3}$ 0.401

.......... .......... .......... .......... ..........

**Exam focus**

Always write the numbers in the answers in the same form as they are given in the question.

## Interpreting fractions, decimals and percentages

Grade 3 

**4.** In a safe there are 240 bank notes.
45% of them are £5 notes.
$\frac{1}{3}$ of them are £10 notes.
The rest are £20 notes.

Work out the value of all the £20 notes. **[4 marks]**

£..............................

**5.** Alison wins £500 in a raffle.
She gives 15% of the £500 to Jenny.
She saves $\frac{2}{5}$ of the £500
She spends the rest of the money on a holiday.

Convert $\frac{2}{5}$ into a percentage.

Work out how much of the money Alison spends on her holiday. **[3 marks]**

£..............................

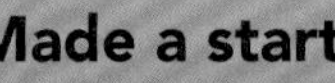
Made a start

Feeling confident

Exam ready

# Percentage change

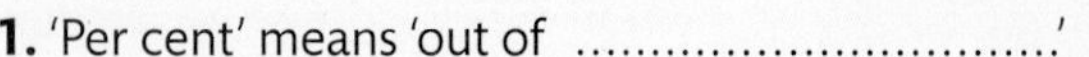

## Quick quiz

**1.** 'Per cent' means 'out of ...............................'

**2.** 10% of 60 = ...............................

**3.** 25% of 80 = ...............................

**4.** 50% of 90 = ...............................

## Percentage change

Grade 4

**1.** Find the percentage increase or decrease.

Divide by the original amount and then multiply by 100

**(a)** 36.4 g to 41.3 g **[2 marks]**

$41.3 - 36.4 = 4.9$

$\frac{4.9}{36.4} \times 100 =$ ........................ %

**(b)** 83.4 m to 69.5 m **[2 marks]**

........................ %

**(c)** 16.38 kg to 24.56 kg **[2 marks]**

........................ %

**2. (a)** Increase 840 by 28% **[2 marks]**

$\frac{28}{100} \times 840 =$ ..........

840 + .......... = ..........

........................

**(b)** Decrease 238 by 18% **[2 marks]**

$238 \times 0.82 =$ ..........

........................

**(c)** Increase £63.50 by 45% **[2 marks]**

........................

To increase or decrease an amount by a percentage, find the percentage of the original amount, then add or subtract it to or from the original amount. Alternatively, use the multiplier method.

## Everyday percentages

Grade 4

**3.** Gary buys and sells antique clocks. He wants to reach a target of at least 30% profit on each antique clock he sells. In January, Gary buys an antique clock for £2500. In February, Gary sells the antique clock for £3250.

Does Gary reach his target for this antique clock? **[3 marks]**

...............................

**4.** The table shows the costs, per person, of a holiday at two different hotels. It shows the cost for 5 nights per adult and the cost for each extra night. It also shows the discount for each child.

| | Hotel 1 | | Hotel 2 | |
|---|---|---|---|---|
| | **Cost for 5 nights** | **Cost for each extra night** | **Cost for 5 nights** | **Cost for each extra night** |
| **1 Apr–31 May** | £1269 | £160 | £949 | £95 |
| **1 Jun–16 Jul** | £1329 | £160 | £1319 | £105 |
| **17 Jul–31 Aug** | £1720 | £170 | £1950 | £300 |
| **Discount for each child** | 10% off adult price | | 25% off adult price | |

There are 2 adults and 2 children in the Granta family. The family want a holiday for 7 nights, starting on 1 August. One hotel will be cheaper than the other hotel for them.

Work out which hotel offers the cheaper stay. You must show your working. **[5 marks]**

...............................

 Made a start  Feeling confident  Exam ready

# Reverse percentages

## Quick quiz

Match each multiplier with the correct percentage change.

| Multiplier |
|---|
| 0.972 |
| 1.12 |
| 1.105 |
| 0.85 |

| Percentage change |
|---|
| an increase of 12% |
| a decrease of 15% |
| an increase of 10.5% |
| a decrease of 2.8% |

## Working out the normal price

Grade 5

**1.** The normal price of a television is reduced by 35% in a sale.
The sale price of the television is £780.

Work out the normal price of the television. **[3 marks]**

The normal price is always 100%.

Method 1

Subtract the percentage reduction from 100% and equate this value with the sale price.

Sale price = £780 = 100% − 35%

= ........................ %

1% = $\frac{780}{\square}$ = ...........

100% = ........... × 100

£..............................

Method 2

Divide the sale price by the multiplier for a 35% decrease.

100% − 35% = ........................ %

........................ ÷ 100 = ..........................

Normal price = £780 ÷ ........................

£..............................

**Exam focus**
Choose the method that you find easiest.

**2.** In a sale, normal prices are reduced by 12.5%.
The normal price of a tablet is reduced by £18.

Work out the normal price of the tablet. **[3 marks]**

The amount of the decrease is given, so £18 = 12.5%

£..............................

**3.** Each year, Sol records how long it takes him, on average, to get to work each day. In 2017, he took 8% more time than in 2016. In 2017, the average time he took to get to work was 34 minutes.

Work out the average time he took to get to work in 2016.
Give your answer to the nearest minute. **[3 marks]**

.............................. minutes

**4.** Ravina has two investments: a fixed bond and an ISA. During a 5-year period, the value of the fixed bond increased by 5% to £40 530. In the same period, the value of the ISA increased by 7.5% to £27 004.

In this 5-year period, which investment has grown more in terms of monetary value? **[4 marks]**

..............................

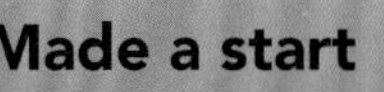

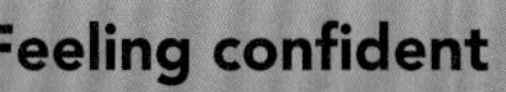

Made a start | Feeling confident | Exam ready

# Growth and decay

## 5 Quick quiz

Write down the multiplier for each percentage change.

**(a)** an increase of 15% ..............................

**(b)** a decrease of 18% ..............................

**(c)** an increase of 2.35% ..............................

**(d)** a decrease of 6.9% ..............................

## 5 Growth — Grade 5

**1.** Jarrah invests £1800 at 2.75% per annum compound interest.

Work out the value of Jarrah's investment after 3 years. **[3 marks]**

As it is an increase, add the percentage.

100% + .............% = .............%

Multiplier = ............. ÷ 100 = .............

Value of investment = 1800 × (.............)$^3$

£.......................

**Exam focus**
Give your answer to 2 decimal places.

## 5 Decay — Grade 5

**2.** John buys a new car for £32 400. The value of the car depreciates at the rate of 15% per year. After $n$ years, the value of the car is £19 897.65.

Find the value of $n$. **[2 marks]**

As it is a decrease, subtract the percentage.

100% − .............% = .............%

Multiplier = ............. ÷ 100 = .............

Value = 32 400 × (.............)$^n$ = £19 897.65

Try different values of $n$ using your calculator.

$n$ = .......................

## 10 Money — Grade 5

**3.** Anna invests £6000 in a savings account for 2 years.
The account pays compound interest at an annual rate of 5% for the first year and 4% for the second year.

Work out the value of the investment after 2 years. **[3 marks]**

£..............................

**4.** A ball is dropped from a height of 4 m and bounces on the ground.
Each time the ball bounces, it loses 20% of its height.

Find the height of the ball after

**(a)** the first bounce **[2 marks]**

.............................. m

**(b)** the fourth bounce. Give your answer to the nearest cm. **[2 marks]**

.............................. cm

## 5 Populations — Grade 5

**5.** A scientist studies a rabbit population. She finds that the population has been decreasing due to disease. The scientist assumes that the population is decreasing at a rate of 12% each year. At the beginning of 2012, the rabbit population was 4800.

Using the scientist's assumption, work out the size of this rabbit population at the start of 2017. **[2 marks]**

..............................

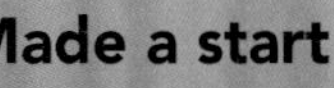

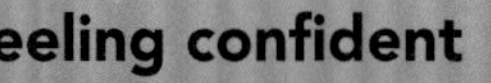

Exam ready

# Compound measures

## Quick quiz

1. Complete the sentence.

A compound measure is a mathematical measurement made up of ...................... or more other measures.

2. Tick (✓) the measures that are compound measures.

☐ speed ☐ length ☐ density ☐ area ☐ volume

## Using the formula for pressure

Grade 5

1. A parcel exerts a force of 150 N on a table.
The pressure on the table is 40 N/m².

Calculate the area of the box that is in contact with the table. **[3 marks]**

$40 = \frac{150}{A}$

.............. $A =$ ..............

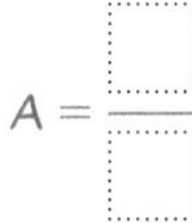

$A = \frac{\square}{\square}$

$p = \frac{F}{A}$ where $p$ = pressure, $F$ = force, $A$ = area

Rearrange the formula to find $A$.

**Exam focus**

You can leave your answer as a fraction or a decimal.

............................... m²

## Rates of change

2. The diagram shows a water container in the shape of a cuboid.
Ravi fills the container completely. Water leaks out from the bottom of the container at a rate of 100 ml per minute.
1 ml = 1 cm³

Work out how long it takes the container to empty completely.
Give your answer in hours and minutes.

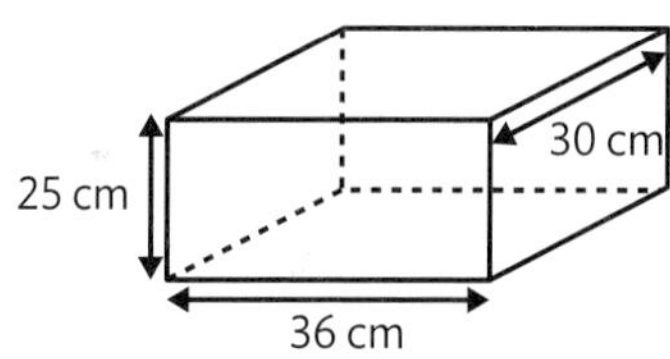


**[4 marks]**

.......................... hours and .......................... minutes

## Comparing rates of pay

Grade 5

3. Alan, Beth and Carina work for the same company. They receive their January payslips as shown below.

| **Alan** | **Beth** | **Carina** |
|---|---|---|
| Net pay £1260 | Net pay £1540 | Net pay £950 |
| 160 hours worked | 185 hours worked | 110 hours worked |

Whose hourly rate of pay is the greatest? You must show your working. **[3 marks]**

...............................

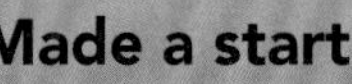

Made a start | Feeling confident | Exam ready

# Speed

## Quick quiz

This is the formula triangle for speed. Use this to complete these formulae in words.

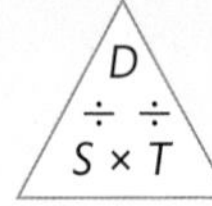


speed = ............................ distance = ............................ time = ............................

## Speed in context

**Grade 5**

**1.** Antony drives 210 km in 5 hours.

**(a)** What is his average speed? **[2 marks]**

............................... km/h

Pippa drives at an average speed of 36 mph for 3 hours.

**(b)** How many miles does Pippa drive? **[2 marks]**

............................... miles

**2.** Ian travels from Penn to Malvern at an average speed of 40 mph.
He takes a total time of 1.5 hours to travel from Penn to Malvern.
Ian then travels from Malvern to Rye at an average speed of 60 mph.
The distance from Malvern to Rye is 180 miles.

Calculate Ian's average speed for the total distance travelled from Penn to Rye. **[4 marks]**

Penn to Malvern: $d = s \times t$

$d = 1.5 \times 40 =$ ............. miles

Malvern to Rye:

$s = \frac{d}{t}$ so $60 = \frac{180}{t}$

$t = \frac{180}{60} =$ ............. hours

Total distance = ............. + .............

= ............. miles

Total time = ............. + .............

= ............. hours

............................... mph

Use the formula triangle for speed to write the formula for *d*.

Work out the distance from Penn to Malvern.

Work out the time taken from Malvern to Rye.

**Exam focus**

To work out the average speed, you will need the total time taken and the total distance travelled.

**3.** Amina drives from Wolverhampton to Edinburgh. She drives at an average speed of 60 mph for the first 2 hours of her journey. She drives the remaining 160 miles at an average speed of 40 mph.

Amina thinks her average speed from Wolverhampton to Edinburgh is 50 mph.

Is Amina right? You must show how you get your answer. **[4 marks]**

...............................

# Density

## Quick quiz

This is the formula triangle for density. Use this to complete these formulae in words.

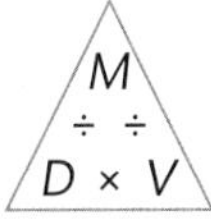

density = ..................... mass = ..................... volume = .....................

## Using density

Grade 5 

**1.** Given that mass = 156 kg and volume = 30 m$^3$, work out the density in kilograms per m$^3$. **[2 marks]**

Write down the formula and then substitute the numbers.

$d = \frac{m}{v} = \frac{156}{\square}$

............ kg/m$^3$

**2.** Given that mass = 16 kg and density = 2.8 kg/m$^3$, work out the volume in cubic metres. **[2 marks]**

$v = \frac{m}{d}$

............... m$^3$

**3.** Given that volume = 56 cm$^3$ and density = 2.8 g/cm$^3$, work out the mass in grams. **[2 marks]**

.................. g

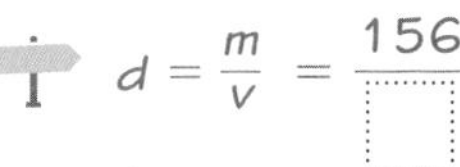

## Combining densities

Grade 5 

**4.** Asha mixes 190 g of metal A and 140 g of metal B to make an alloy. Metal A has a density of 18.2 g/cm$^3$. Metal B has a density of 7.8 g/cm$^3$.

Work out the density of the alloy. **[4 marks]**

**Exam focus**

To work out the density, you need the total mass and the total volume.

.................. g/cm$^3$

## Application of the density formula

Grade 5 

**5.** A cone is made from gold, as shown in the diagram. The mass of the cone is 909 g.

Work out the density, in g/cm$^3$, of the gold cone. Give your answer correct to 3 significant figures.

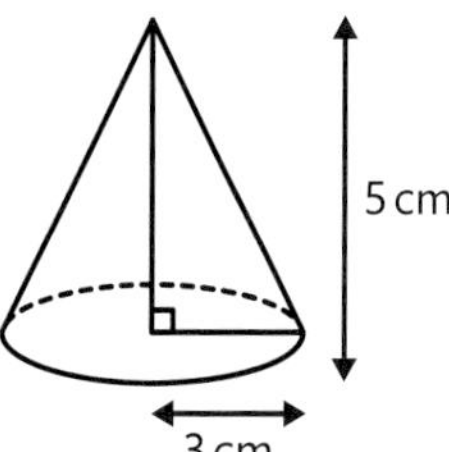


Volume of a cone = $\frac{1}{3}\pi r^2 h$

**[5 marks]**

.................. g/cm$^3$

**6.** Tom is transporting oak planks. The density of oak is 720 kg/m$^3$. Each plank of oak measures 140 cm by 90 cm by 20 cm. The maximum weight a pallet can hold is 2000 kg.

Work out the volume of the cuboid.

Work out the maximum number of oak planks the pallet can hold. You must show how you get your answer. **[4 marks]**

..............................

# Proportion and graphs

## Quick quiz

Choose one of these graphs to complete each sentence below.

**A** 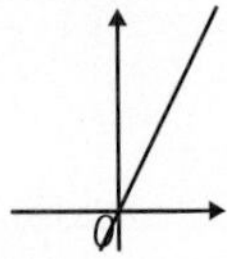

**B** 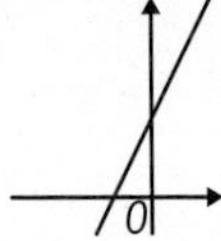

**C** 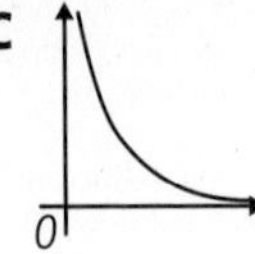

**D** 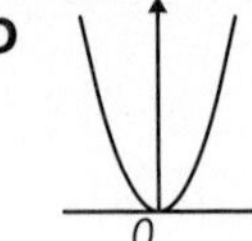

**(a)** Graph ........ represents direct proportion.

**(b)** Graph ........ represents inverse proportion.

## Setting up proportionality equations

**Grade 5**

**1.** *Y* is directly proportional to *X*.
$Y = 48$ when $X = 5$
Work out the value of *Y* when $X = 7$ **[2 marks]**

Express the information as a ratio or an equation.

$Y : 7 = 48 : 5$

$\frac{Y}{7} = \frac{48}{5}$

Solve the equation for *Y*.

$Y =$ ...............................

## Using graphs

**Grade 5**

**2.** You can use this conversion graph to change between miles and kilometres.
Troy drove 210 kilometres in one week. Adam drove 138 miles in one week.
Troy claims that he drove further than Adam.

Is Troy correct? You must show your working. **[3 marks]**

When you are comparing distances, they must both be in the same units, for example, miles or kilometres.

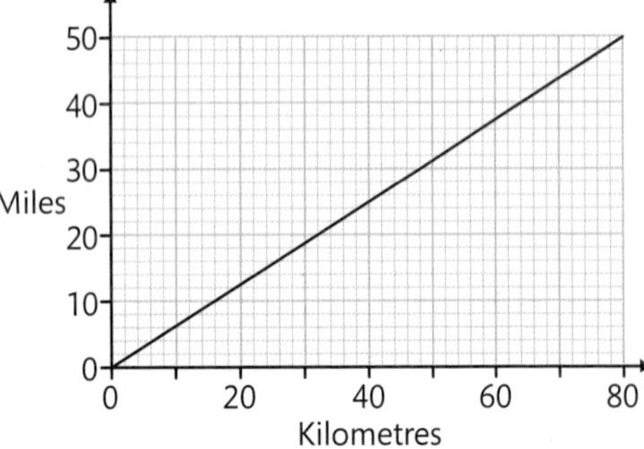


...............................

**3.** You can use this conversion graph to change between pounds (£) and euros.

**(a)** Change £65 into euros. **[1 mark]**

€ ...............................

**(b)** Change €250 into pounds (£). **[2 marks]**

£ ...............................

Euros (€): 0, 10, 20, 30, 40, 50, 60, 70, 80, 90, 100, 110
Pounds (£): 0, 20, 40, 60, 80



Made a start  Feeling confident  Exam ready

# Ratio and proportion

## 5 Percentages

Grade 2

1. Sanaa buys five tickets for a concert. Each ticket costs £68.
Sanaa also has to pay a booking fee. The booking fee is 8% of the total price of the tickets.

Work out the total amount Sanaa has to pay. **[3 marks]**

Cost of 5 tickets = .......... × .......... = ..........

1% of the cost of the tickets = .......... ÷ .......... = ..........

8% of the cost of the tickets = .......... × .......... = ..........

Total amount = .......... + ..........

First calculate how much it costs Sanaa to buy 5 tickets.

To find 8% of the total ticket cost, find 1% and then multiply by 8 to get 8%.

Sum the cost of the 5 tickets and the 8% booking fee.

£..............................

## 10 Ratio

Grade 4

2. There are 210 beads in a box. Each bead is either red or yellow.
There are five times as many red beads as yellow beads in the box.
Hakan takes 60% of the red beads from the box.

Work out the ratio of the number of red beads to the number of yellow beads now left in the box.
Give your ratio in its simplest form. **[4 marks]**

**Exam focus**
Write down each stage of your working.

..............................

## 10 Proportion

Grade 3

3. Here are the ingredients needed to make 8 chocolate biscuits.

| **Super simple chocolate biscuits** | | | |
|---|---|---|---|
| **Ingredients for 8 biscuits** | | | |
| 50 g margarine | 25 g sugar | 60 g flour | 10 g cocoa |

Anjali has the following ingredients in her kitchen.

125 g margarine    225 g sugar    300 g flour    70 g cocoa

Work out the greatest number of chocolate biscuits Anjali can make using this recipe.
You must show your working. **[4 marks]**

..............................

 Made a start 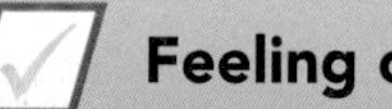 Feeling confident  Exam ready

# Angle properties

## Quick quiz

Complete the sentences below by circling the correct word or phrase.

**(a)** Alternate angles are **equal** / **not equal**.

**(b)** Corresponding angles are **equal** / **not equal**.

**(c)** Vertically opposite angles are **equal** / **not equal**.

**(d)** Allied angles add up to **180°** / **360°**.

**(e)** Angles on a straight line add up to **180°** / **360°**.

**(f)** Angles around a point add up to **180°** / **360°**.

## Recognising and finding angles

**Grades 2–3**

**1.** Study this scale diagram.

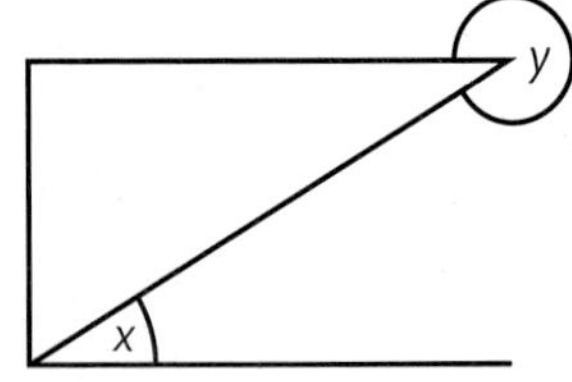


**(a)** Mark, with the letter *R*, a right angle. **[1 mark]**

**(b)** What type of angle is shown by the letter

**(i)** *x*? **[1 mark]**

This angle is less than 90°.

..............................

**(ii)** *y*? **[1 mark]**

This angle is between 180° and 360°.

..............................

**2.** In this diagram, the base line is a straight line.

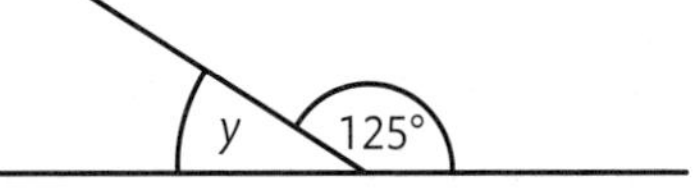


**(a)** Work out the size of the angle marked *y*.
Give a reason for your answer. **[2 marks]**

*y* = ..........° − 125° = ..........°

Angles on a straight line add up to ..........°

**(b)** Work out the size of the angle marked *x*.
Give a reason for your answer. **[2 marks]**

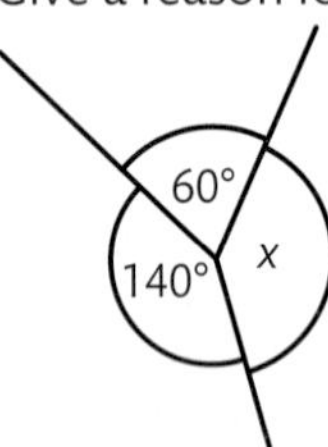


Angle *x* = .............................. °

Reason: ..............................................................

## Using angle properties

**Grade 4**

**3.** *ABC* is a straight line. *DEFG* is a straight line.
*AC* is parallel to *DG*. *EF* = *BF*. Angle *BEF* = 55°

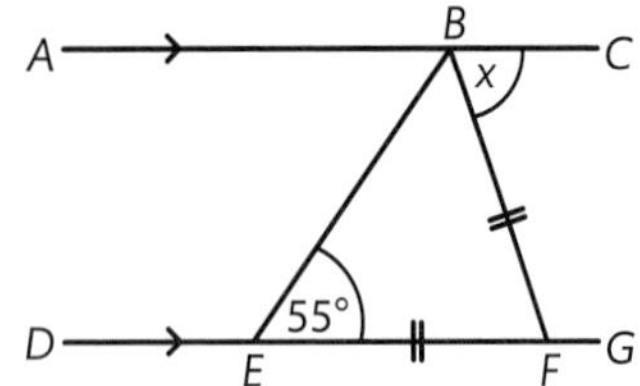


Work out the size of the angle marked *x*.
Give a reason for each stage of your working. **[4 marks]**

..............................°

**4.** *ABC* is a straight line. Angle *BCD* = 48°
The reflex angle *BDC* = 235°

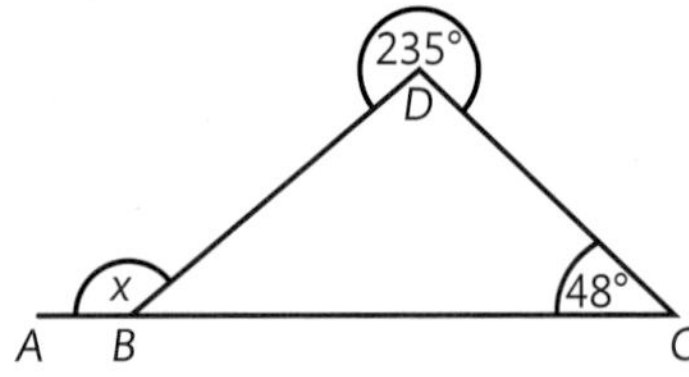


Work out the size of the angle marked *x*.
Give a reason for each stage of your working. **[4 marks]**

..............................°



Made a start  Feeling confident  Exam ready

# Solving angle problems

## Quick quiz

Use 'vertically opposite', 'alternate' or 'corresponding' to complete these three sentences.

**(a)** Angle *d* and angle *f* are .............................. angles.

**(b)** Angle *c* and angle *g* are .............................. angles.

**(c)** Angle *e* and angle *g* are .............................. angles.

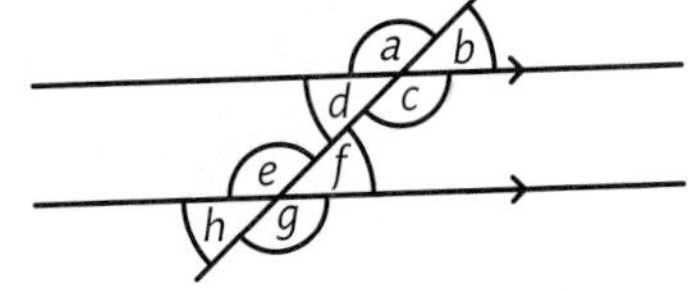

## Solving problems involving angles

**Grade 4**

**1.** In the diagram, *ABC* is parallel to *EFGH*.

*GB* = *GF*. Angle *ABF* = 70°

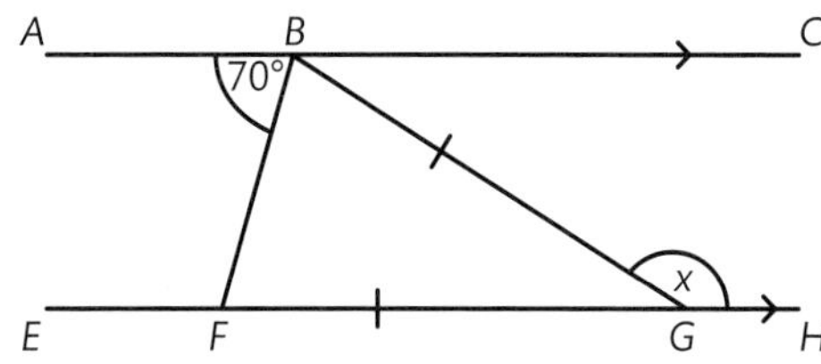


Work out the size of the angle marked *x*.
Give a reason for each stage of your working. **[4 marks]**

Angle *BFG* = .......... (alternate angles are equal)

Angle *FBG* = .......... (base angles of an isosceles triangle are equal)

Angle *ABG* = .......... + .......... = ..........

But angle *ABG* = ..........
(alternate angles)

So *x* = ..........

**Exam focus**

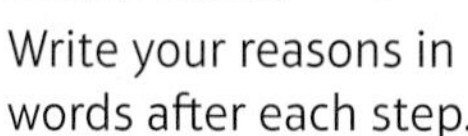

Write your reasons in words after each step.

.............................. °

**2.** In the diagram, *ABC* is a straight line.

*BD* = *CD*. Angle *BDC* = 50°
Angle *ADB* = 20°

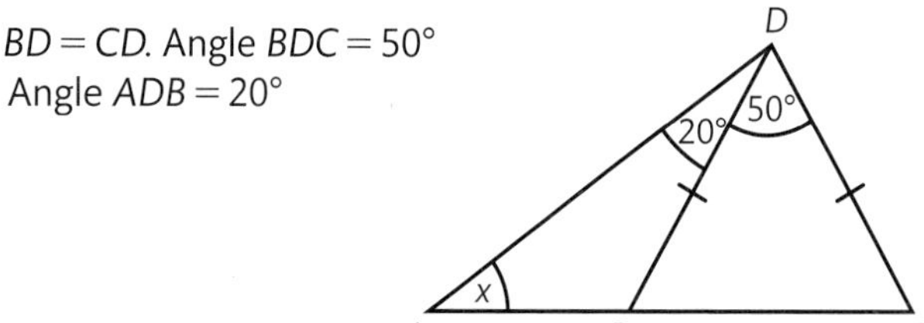


Work out the size of the angle marked *x*.
Give a reason for each stage of your working. **[4 marks]**

**Problem solving**

*BD* and *CD* are the same length, so you can work out the angle *DBC* as your first step.

.............................. °

## Applying angle properties to problems

**Grade 4**

**3.** In the diagram, *ABC* and *DE* are parallel lines. *AEG* and *BEF* are straight lines.

Angle *AED* = 55° and angle *FEG* = 65°

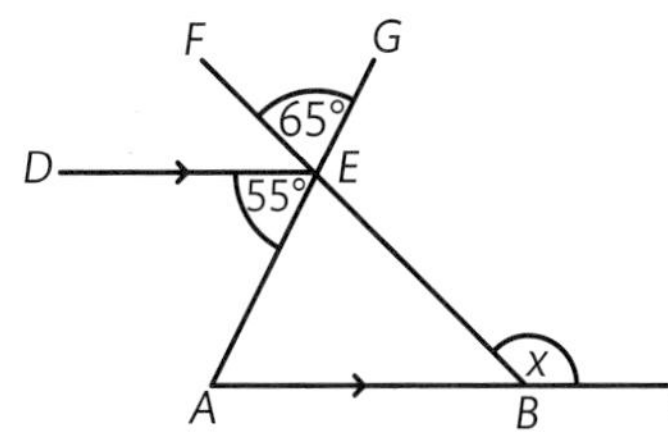


**Problem solving**

You need to find the angle adjacent to *x*.

Work out the size of the angle marked *x*.
Give a reason for each stage of your working. **[4 marks]**

.............................. °

**4.** In the diagram, *ABC* is a straight line. *AB* = *BD*.
Angle *BAD* = 25° and angle *BCD* = 70°

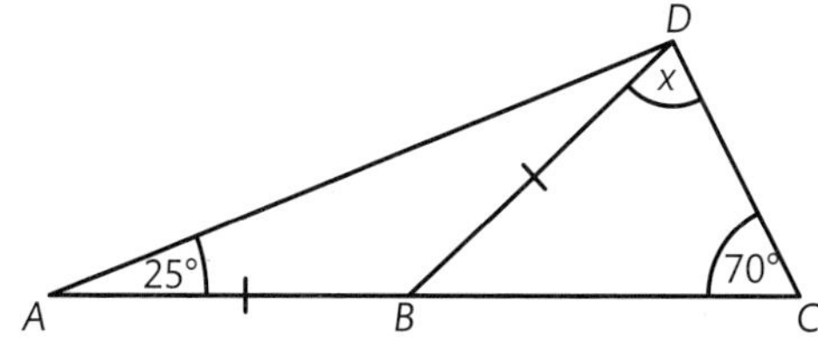


Work out the size of the angle marked *x*.
Give a reason for each stage of your working. **[4 marks]**

.............................. °

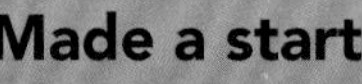

Made a start | Feeling confident | Exam ready

# Angles in polygons

## Quick quiz

Write the correct angle to complete each sentence:

**(a)** The sum of the exterior angles of any polygon is ..............................°

**(b)** Interior angle + exterior angle = ..............................°

## Regular polygons

Grade 5

**1.** The diagram shows part of a regular 12-sided polygon.

Work out the size of the angle marked $x$. **[3 marks]**

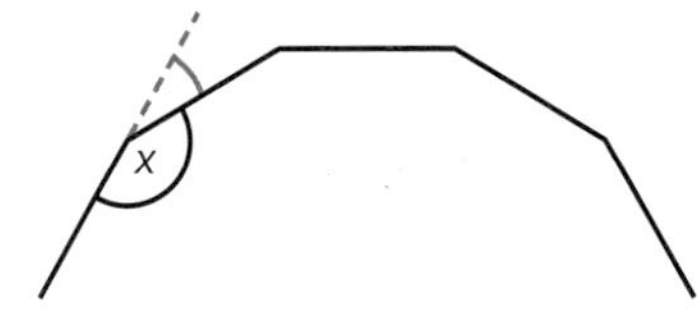


Exterior angle = ....................

$x$ = .........° − exterior angle

= .........° − .........°

= .........°

**Problem solving**

It is often easier to solve problems involving angles in regular polygons by working out the size of one exterior angle.

..............................°

## Multiple polygons

Grade 5

**2.** The diagram shows a regular hexagon and a regular octagon.

Calculate the size of the angle marked $x$.
You must show all your working. **[4 marks]**

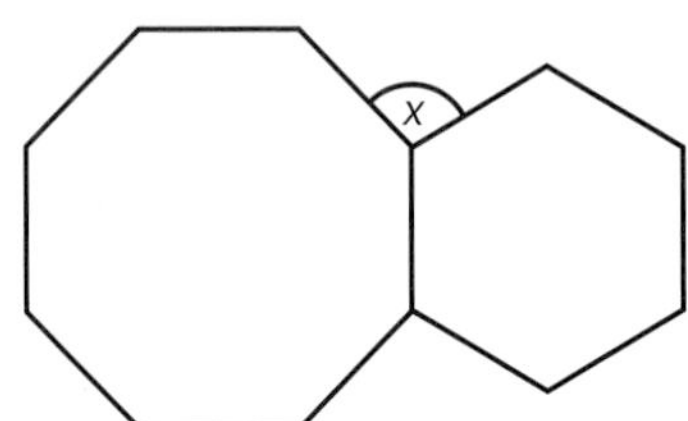


**Problem solving**

Work out the exterior angle of both shapes.

..............................°

**3.** $ABCDEF$ is a regular hexagon and $ABQP$ is a square.
Angle $CBQ = x°$.

Work out the value of $x$. **[4 marks]**

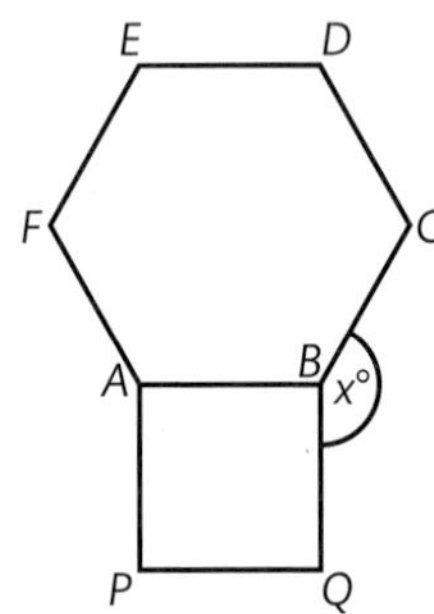


..............................

**4.** $ABCDE$ and $EHJKL$ are regular pentagons.
$AEL$ is an equilateral triangle.

Work out the size of angle $DEH$. **[4 marks]**

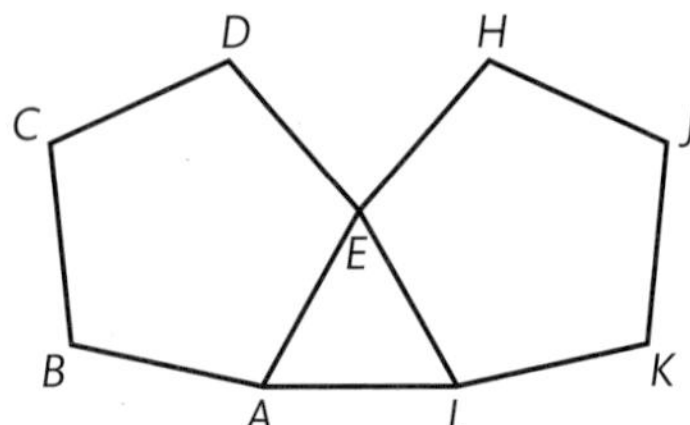


..............................°

**5.** The diagram shows a regular octagon.

Work out the size of the angle marked $x$. **[4 marks]**

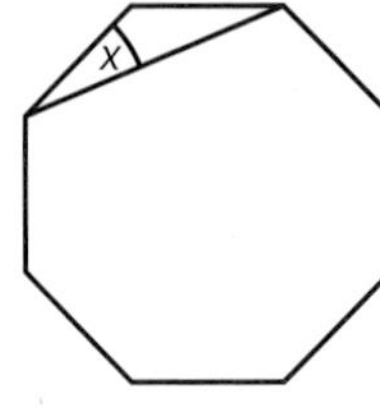


..............................°

 Made a start  Feeling confident  Exam ready

# Constructing perpendiculars

## Quick quiz

Complete the sentences below by circling the correct word.

**(a)** A bisector is a line that cuts another line in **half** / **thirds** / **quarters**.

**(b)** A perpendicular is a line that is at an angle of **180°** / **90°** to another line.

## Perpendicular bisector

Grade 5 

**1.** Use a ruler and a pair of compasses to construct the perpendicular bisector of the line *AB*.
You must show all your construction lines. **[2 marks]**

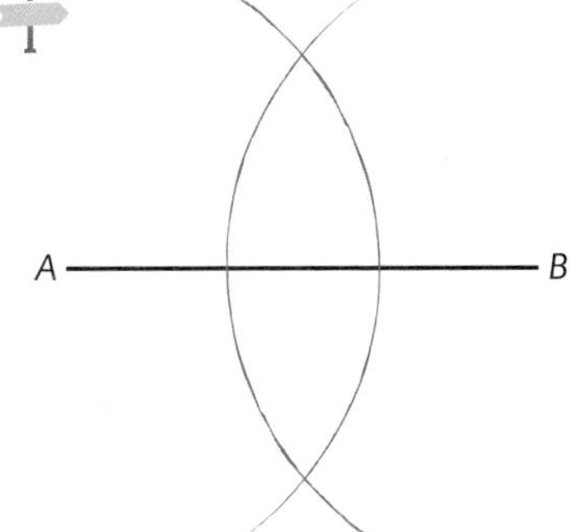


Make sure your compasses are set to a radius more than half of the length of the given line.

Place your compass point at *A* and draw an arc that crosses the given line. Do the same with the compass point at *B*.

Join the two points where the arcs cross. This is the perpendicular bisector of *AB*.

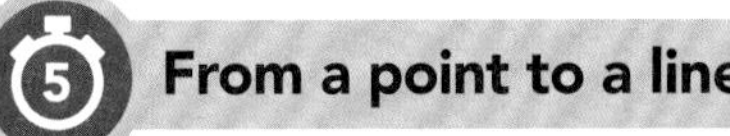

## From a point to a line

Grade 5 

**2.** Use a ruler and a pair of compasses to construct the perpendicular from *P* to the line segment *AB*.
You must show all construction lines. **[2 marks]**

**Exam focus**
Do not rub out your construction lines.

A ———————— B

## At a point on a straight line

Grade 5 

**3.** Use a ruler and a pair of compasses to construct the perpendicular to the line segment *AB* at the point *P*.
You must show all construction lines. **[2 marks]**

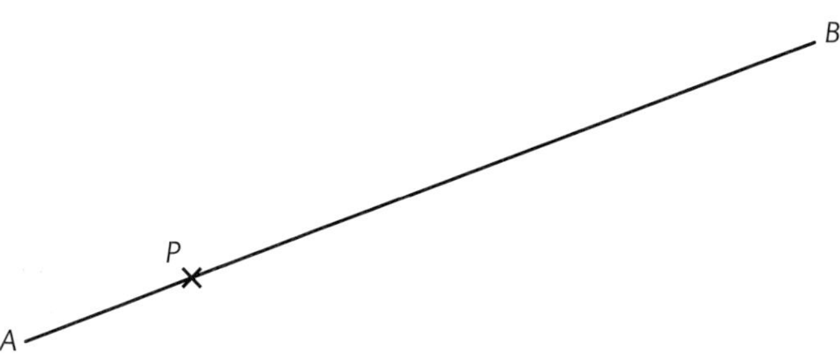

# Constructions with angles

## Quick quiz

Complete the sentences below by circling the correct words.

**(a)** To construct a 60° angle, construct an **isosceles** / **equilateral** triangle.

**(b)** To construct a 45° angle, **dissect** / **bisect** a **60°** / **90°** angle.

**(c)** To construct a 30° angle, **dissect** / **bisect** a **60°** / **90°** angle.

## Constructing a 60° angle

Grade 5

**1.** In the space below, use a ruler and a pair of compasses to construct an angle of 60°.
You must show all construction lines. **[2 marks]**

Make sure the compasses are set to the length of the given line. Keep the compasses at this setting throughout the construction.

Place your compass point at one end of the given line and draw an arc above the middle of the line. Do the same at the other end of the line.

## Bisecting an angle

Grade 5

**2.** Use ruler and compasses to construct the bisector of angle $RPQ$.
You must show all your construction lines. **[2 marks]**

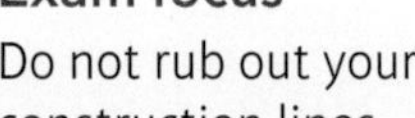

**Exam focus**
Do not rub out your construction lines.

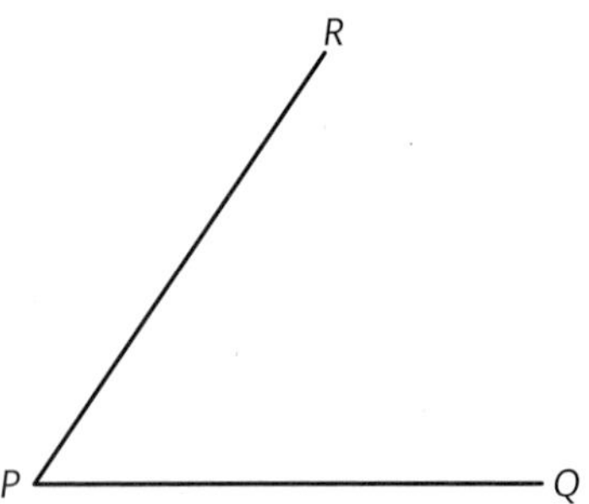




Made a start  Feeling confident Exam ready

# Loci

## 5 Quick quiz

(a) Given that 1 cm represents 5 km, 6 cm represents

............. km.

(b) Given that 1 cm represents 50 m, 8 cm represents

............. m.

(c) Given that 1 cm represents 20 km, 50 km is represented

by ............. cm.

## 5 Using scales — Grade 5

**1.** This is a scale drawing showing two points, *X* and *Y*, in Neil's garden.

The locus of points less than 20 m from *X* will be the inside of a circle with radius 2 cm and centre *X*.

*X* ×  *Y* ×

Scale: 1 cm represents 10 m.

Neil wants to plant a tree. The tree must be less than 20 m from *X* **and** less than 30 m from *Y*.

Shade the region on the scale drawing in which Neil can plant the tree. **[3 marks]**

## 5 Drawing loci — Grade 5

**2. (a)** Draw the locus of all points that are equidistant from the points *A* and *B*. **[2 marks]**

*A* ×  *B* ×

**(b)** Draw the locus of all points that are exactly 2 cm from the line *PQ*. **[2 marks]**

*P* ———— *Q*

## 5 Using loci to solve problems — Grade 5

**3.** The diagram is a scale drawing of a rectangular garden *ABCD*.

Scale: 1 cm represents 1 metre.

Lisa wants to put a water fountain in her garden. It must be at least 3 m from point *C*, nearer to *AB* than to *AD* and less than 1.5 m from *DC*.

On the diagram, shade the region where Lisa can put the water fountain. **[4 marks]**

*A* *B*

*D* *C*

# Perimeter and area

## Quick quiz

Circle the correct calculation to find the perimeter of this rectangle.

3 + 8 | 3 × 8

3 + 8 + 3 + 8 | 3 × 8 + 3 × 8

3 cm

8 cm

## Perimeter and area

Grade 1

**1.** This shaded shape is drawn on a grid of centimetre squares.

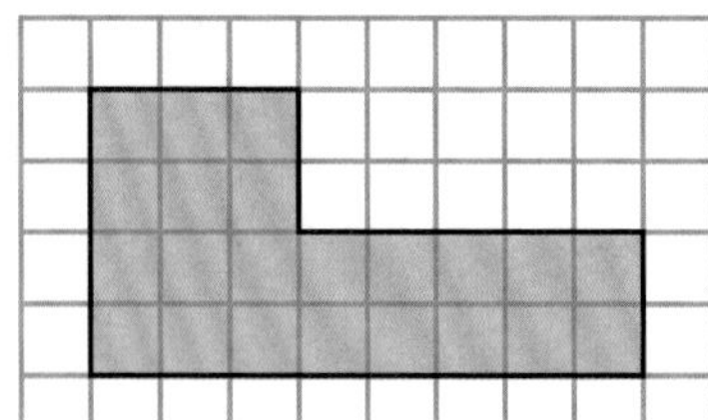

To find the area, split the shape into simpler shapes, such as two rectangles, or count squares.

**(a)** Find the perimeter of the shaded shape. **[1 mark]**

4 + .......... + .......... + .......... + .......... + 8 cm

............................... cm

**(b)** Find the area of the shaded shape. **[1 mark]**

............................... $cm^2$

**2. (a)** Work out the perimeter of this rectangle. **[2 marks]**

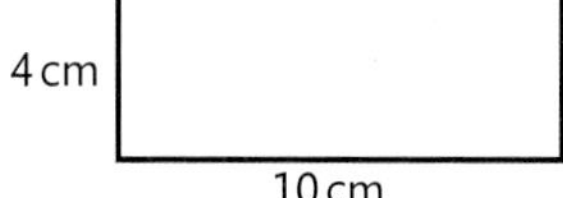


Add up the lengths of all the sides.

............................... cm

**(b)** Work out the perimeter of this compound shape.

**[2 marks]**

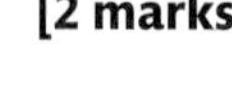

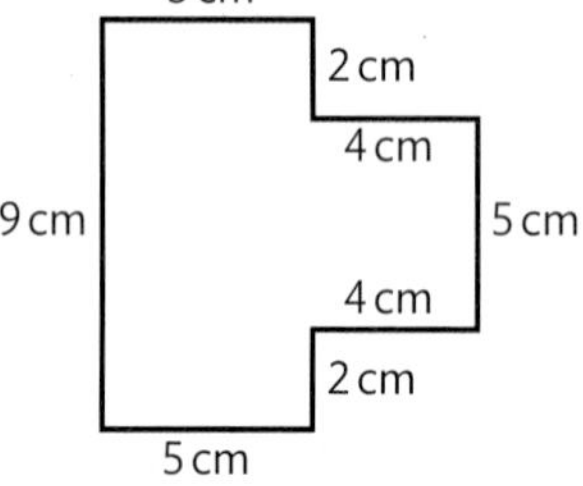


............................... cm

## Estimating and drawing areas

Grade 1

**3.** Here is a shaded shape on a grid of centimetre squares.

Estimate the area of the shaded shape. **[2 marks]**

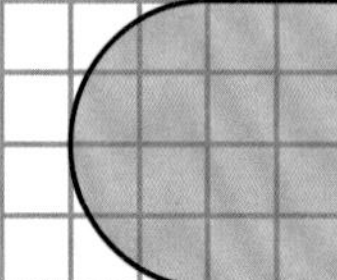

............................... $cm^2$

**4.** The grid is made of centimetre squares.

On the grid, draw a rectangle with an area of 12 $cm^2$. **[2 marks]**

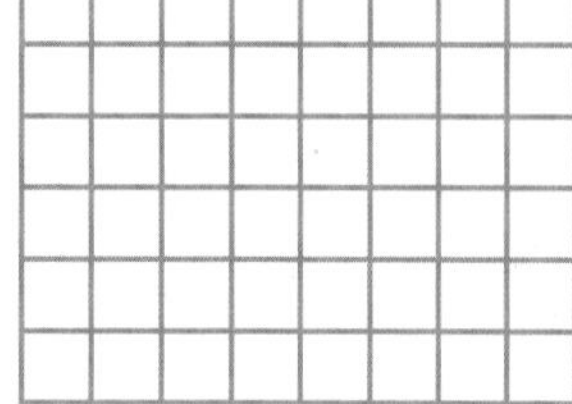

## Perimeter problems

Grade 2

**5.** The diagram shows a rectangle and a square.

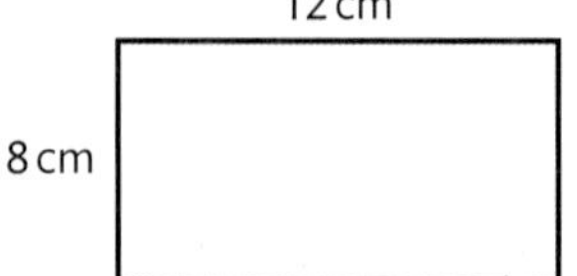

**Problem solving**

Work out the perimeter of the rectangle. As the sides of a square are all the same length, you can divide the perimeter by 4.

The perimeter of the rectangle is the same as the perimeter of the square.

Work out the length of one side of the square. **[3 marks]**

............................... cm

 Made a start 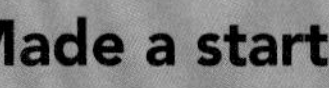  Feeling confident  Exam ready

# Areas of 2D shapes

## Quick quiz

Match each shape with the correct formula for area.

| Shape |
|---|
| rectangle |
| triangle |
| parallelogram |
| trapezium |

| Formula |
|---|
| $A = \frac{1}{2}(a + b)h$ |
| $A = bh$ |
| $A = l \times w$ |
| $A = \frac{1}{2}bh$ |

## Finding the area

Grades 2–3

**1.** Work out the area of this rectangle. **[2 marks]**

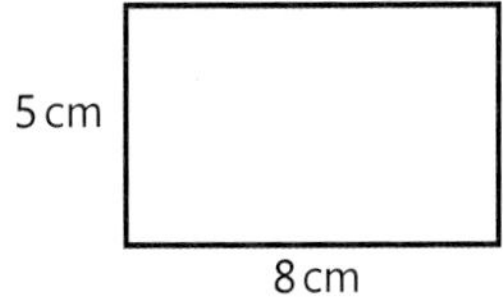


Area $= l \times w$

Area = .......... × ..........

= .......... cm²

................................cm²

**2.** Work out the area of this triangle. **[2 marks]**

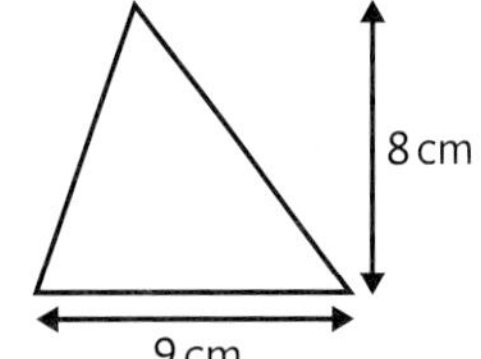


Area $= \frac{1}{2} \times \text{base} \times \text{height}$

................................cm²

**3.** Work out the area of the parallelogram. **[2 marks]**

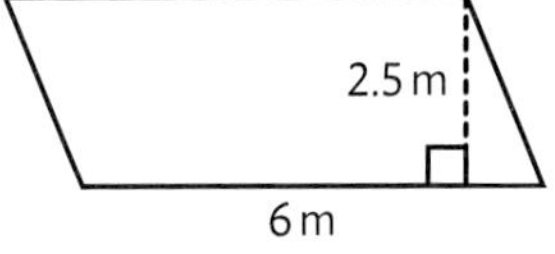


................................m²

**4.** Work out the area of the trapezium. **[2 marks]**

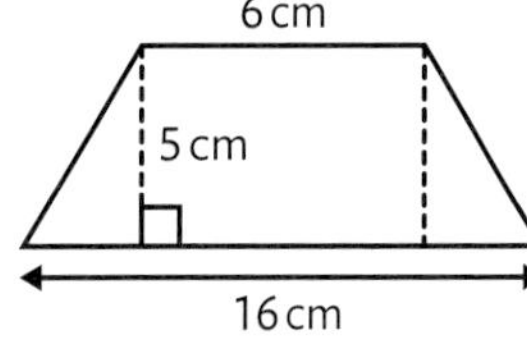


**Exam focus**
You need to remember the formula for the area of a trapezium.

................................cm²

## Area problems

Grades 2–3

**5.** Work out the area of this shape made from rectangles. **[3 marks]**

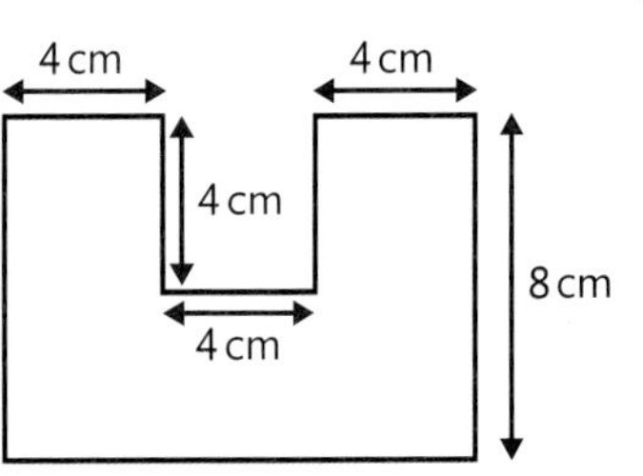


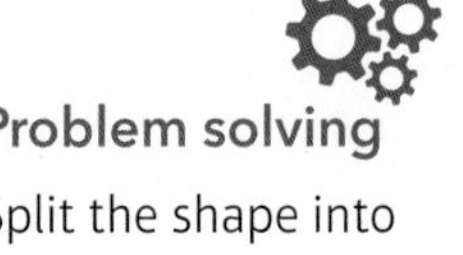

**Problem solving**
Split the shape into rectangles.

................................cm²

**6.** Work out the area of this shape. **[3 marks]**

2 m, 5 m, 9 m, 4 m

................................m²

# 3D shapes

## 2 Quick quiz

Circle the 3D shapes.

square cube rectangle circle sphere pyramid triangle

## 5 Naming 3D shapes — Grade 1

**1.** The diagram shows some solid shapes with some mathematical names.

Draw an arrow from each of the solid shapes to its mathematical name. **[3 marks]**

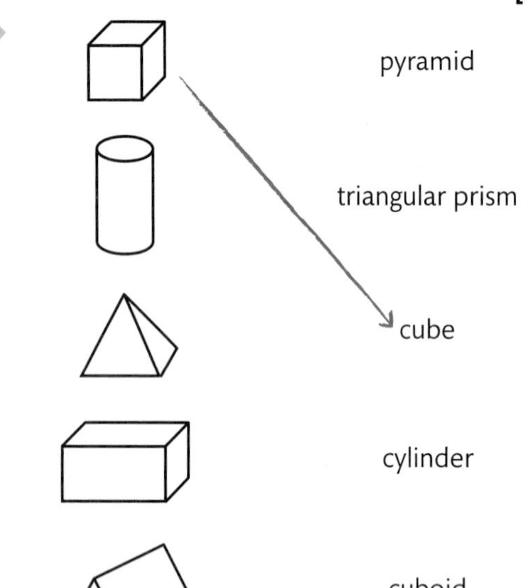


**2.** Write down the mathematical name of each of these 3D shapes.

You will need to recall the correct mathematical name for each 3D shape.

**(a)** **[1 mark]**

..............................

**(b)** **[1 mark]**

..............................

**(c)** **[1 mark]**

..............................

## 5 Edges, faces and vertices — Grade 1

**3.** The diagram shows a prism.

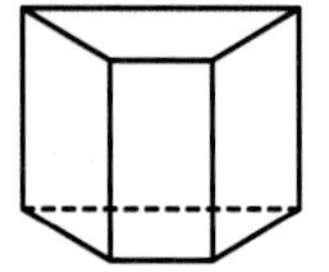

Write down the number of

**(a)** faces **[1 mark]**

.............6..............

**(b)** edges **[1 mark]**

..............................

**(c)** vertices. **[1 mark]**

..............................

**4.** The diagram shows a prism.

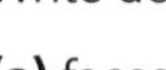

Write down the number of

**(a)** faces **[1 mark]**

..............................

**(b)** edges **[1 mark]**

..............................

**(c)** vertices. **[1 mark]**

..............................

Made a start

Feeling confident
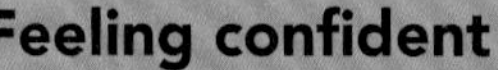

Exam ready

# Volumes of 3D shapes

## Quick quiz

Write down formula for the volume of

**(a)** a cube with sides of length $l$

$V =$ ..............................

**(b)** a cuboid with length $l$, width $w$ and height $h$.

$V =$ ..............................

## Finding volumes of 3D shapes

**Grades 2–3**

**1.** This is a diagram of a cuboid.

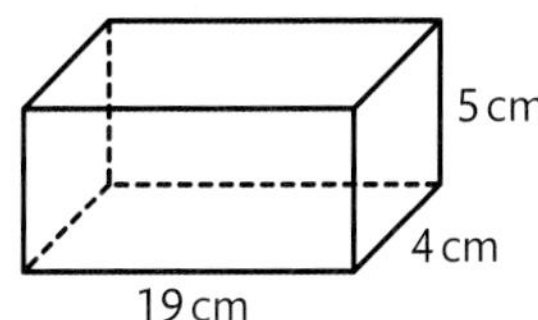


Work out the volume of the cuboid. **[2 marks]**

Volume = 19 × .......... × ..........

.............................. $cm^3$

**2.** This is a diagram of a cylinder.

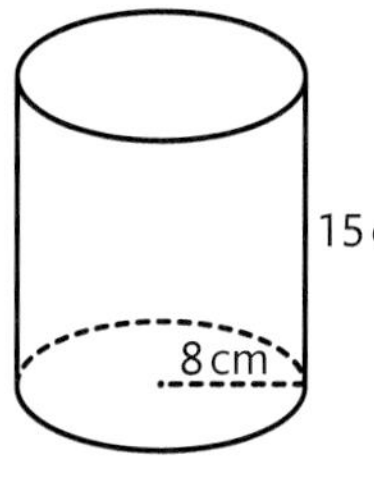


Work out the volume of the cylinder. **[3 marks]**

The area of a circle is $A = \pi r^2$. To work out the volume, multiply the area of the circle by the height.

Area of base = $\pi$ × .......... $^2$

Volume = 15 × ..........

.............................. $cm^3$

**3.** This is a diagram of a triangular prism.

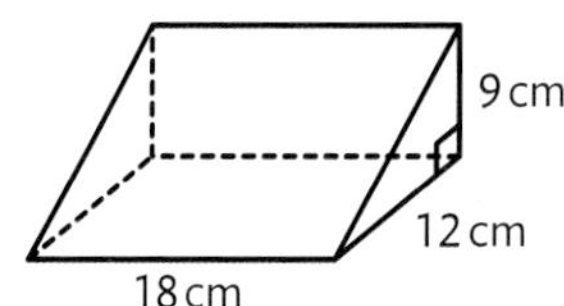


Work out the volume of the triangular prism. **[3 marks]**

Find the area of the triangular cross-section and then multiply by 18 cm.

.............................. $cm^3$

## Finding volumes of other 3D shapes

**Grades 4–5**

**4.** Volume of a cone $= \frac{1}{3}\pi r^2 h$

Use the formula to work out the volume of this cone. **[3 marks]**

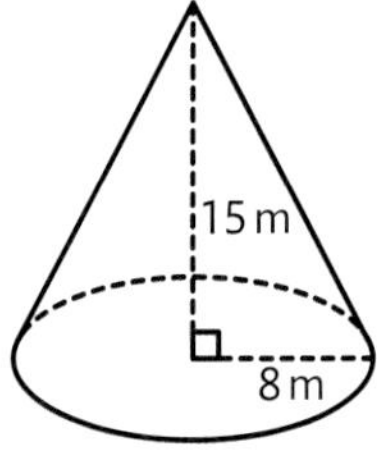


.............................. $m^3$

**5.** Volume of a pyramid $= \frac{1}{3} \times$ height × area of base

Use the formula to work out the volume of this pyramid. **[3 marks]**

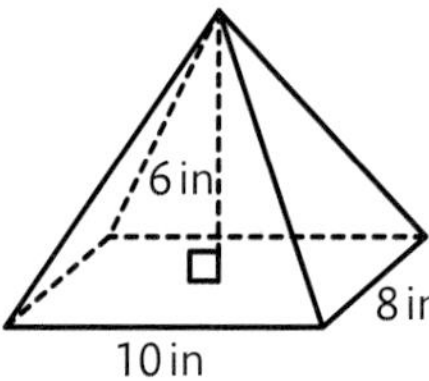


.............................. $inches^3$

**6.** Volume of a sphere $= \frac{4}{3}\pi r^3$

Use the formula to work out the volume of this sphere. **[3 marks]**

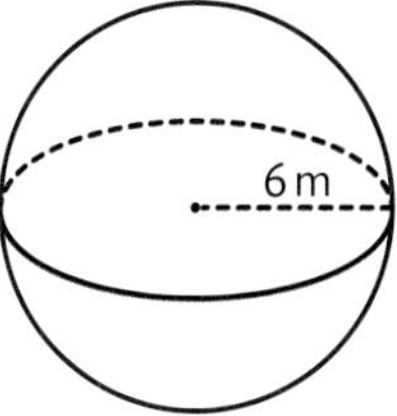


.............................. $m^3$

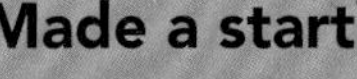

Feeling confident

Exam ready

# Surface area

## 2 Quick quiz

Work out the area of each shape.

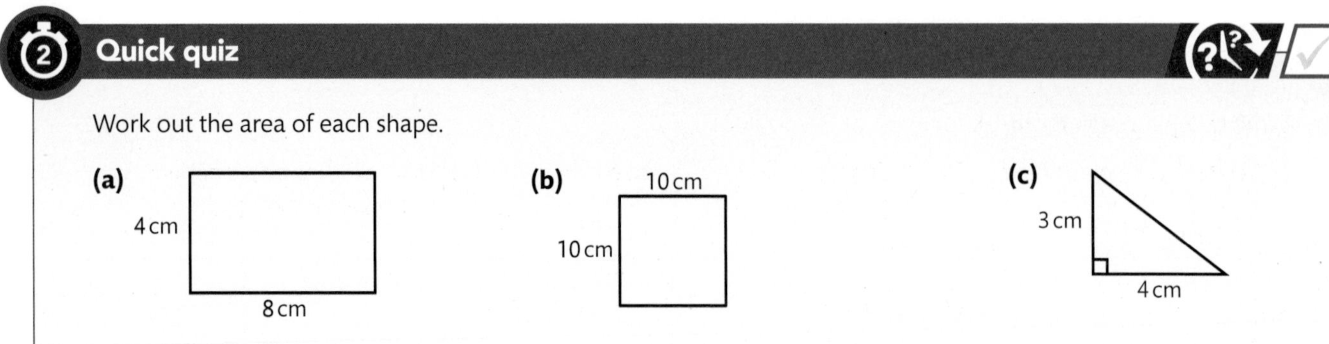


(a) ..............................$cm^2$ (b) ..............................$cm^2$ (c) ..............................$cm^2$

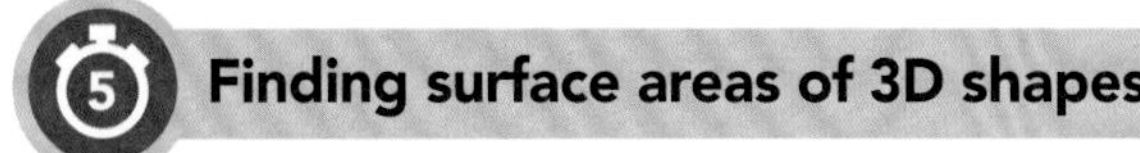

## 5 Finding surface areas of 3D shapes

Grade 4

**1.** Work out the total surface area of this cuboid. **[3 marks]**

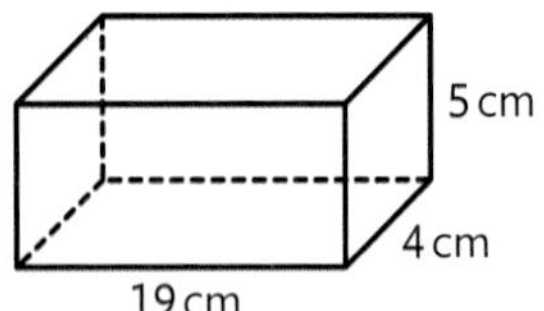


Find the area of all the faces of the cuboid.

Area of base = 19 × 4 = .......... $cm^2$

Area of front = 19 × .......... = .......... $cm^2$

Area of end = .......... × 4 = .......... $cm^2$

Total SA = 2(base + front + end)

= 2(.......... + .......... + ..........)

..............................$cm^2$

**2.** Work out the total surface area of this triangular prism. **[3 marks]**

15 cm
9 cm
12 cm
18 cm

There are five faces in total.

..............................$cm^2$

## 10 Finding surface areas of other 3D shapes

Grade 5

**3.** The curved surface area of a cone = $\pi rl$.

Work out the total surface area of this cone. **[3 marks]**

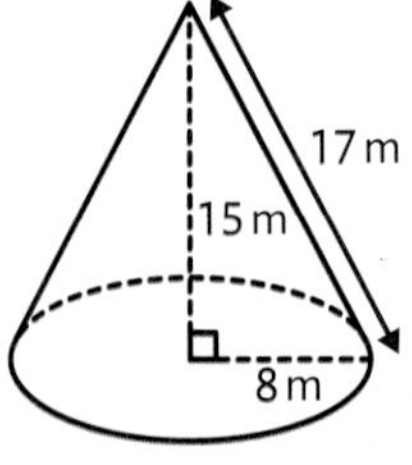


Use $\pi r^2$ to work out the surface area of the base.

..............................$m^2$

**4.** The surface area of a sphere = $4\pi r^2$.

Work out the surface area of this sphere. **[3 marks]**

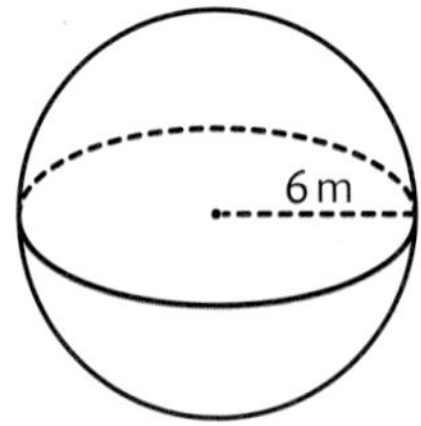


..............................$m^2$

**5.** Work out the total surface area of this hemisphere. **[3 marks]**

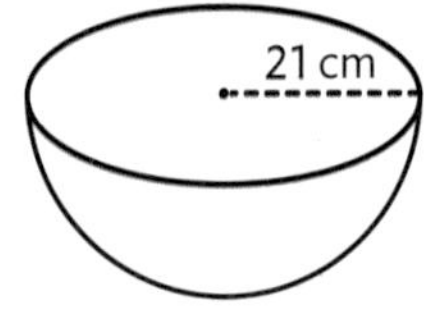


..............................$cm^2$

**6.** This square-based pyramid has four identical triangular faces.

Work out the total surface area of the pyramid. **[3 marks]**

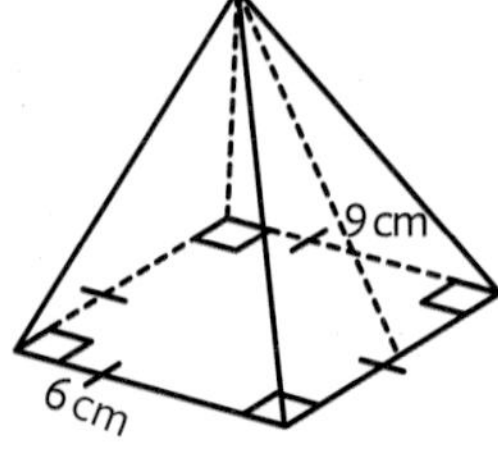


..............................$cm^2$



Made a start | Feeling confident | Exam ready

# Circles and cylinders

## 5 Quick quiz

**1.** Write down the formula for

**(a)** the circumference of a circle with radius *r*

..................................

**(b)** the area of a circle with radius *r*

..................................

**(c)** the volume of a cylinder with base radius *r* and height *h*.

..................................

**2.** A circle has a radius of 4 cm. Write down the area of the circle in terms of $\pi$.

........................

## 5 Composite shapes — Grade 5

**1.** The diagram shows the path of an athlete on a running track.
The path consists of two straight lengths with a semicircle at each end.
Each straight length is 95 metres. Each semicircle has a radius of 33.5 metres.

Calculate the area enclosed by the path.
Give your answer correct to 3 significant figures. **[3 marks]**

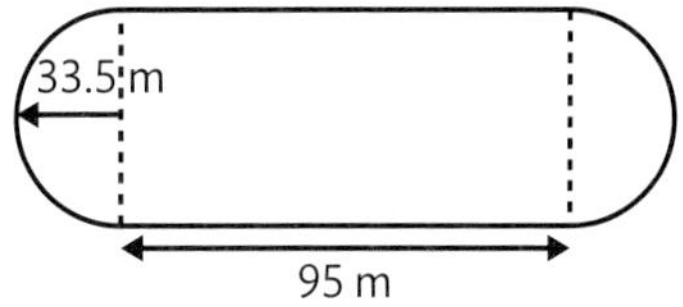


The area of the two semicircles is equal to the area of a whole circle with the same radius.

**Exam focus**
Make sure you round your final answer to 3 significant figures.

Area of semicircular ends = $\pi r^2$ = ........................

Area of rectangle = length × width = ........................

.............................. $m^2$

## 5 Practical problems — Grade 5

**2.** A train has wheels of diameter 1.6 metres.

**(a)** Work out the circumference of one wheel. **[2 marks]**

.............................. m

The train travels 5 km along the track.

**(b)** Work out the number of complete turns made by one wheel of the train. **[2 marks]**

..............................

## 5 Using exact values — Grade 5

**3.** The diagram shows a solid cylinder of radius 10 cm and height *h* cm.
The volume of the cylinder is 4700 $cm^3$.

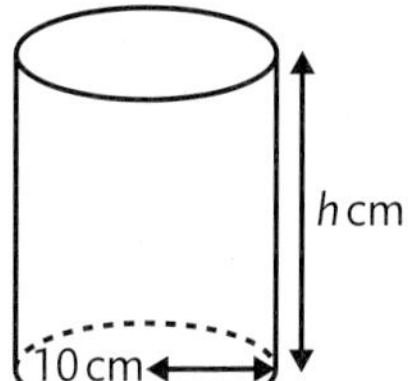


**(a)** Find the height, *h*, of the cylinder. **[3 marks]**

.............................. cm

**(b)** Work out the surface area of the cylinder. **[3 marks]**

.............................. $cm^2$

 Made a start  Feeling confident  Exam ready

# Circles, sectors and arcs

## Quick quiz

Find the circumference and area of a circle with radius

(a) 5 cm
circumference = .................... cm
area = .................... $cm^2$

(b) 15 m
circumference = .................... m
area = .................... $m^2$

(c) 20 mm.
circumference = .................... mm
area = .................... $mm^2$

## Simple arcs and areas — Grade 5

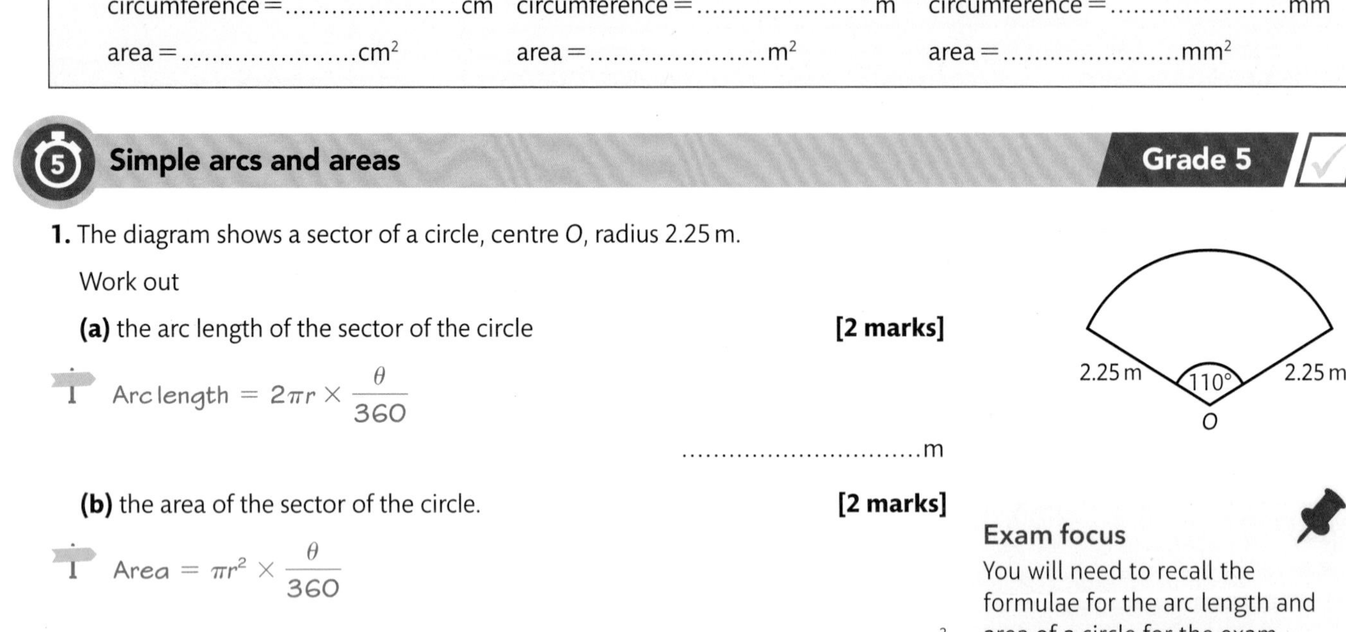


**1.** The diagram shows a sector of a circle, centre $O$, radius 2.25 m.

Work out

**(a)** the arc length of the sector of the circle **[2 marks]**

Arc length $= 2\pi r \times \dfrac{\theta}{360}$

.............................. m

**(b)** the area of the sector of the circle. **[2 marks]**

Area $= \pi r^2 \times \dfrac{\theta}{360}$

.............................. $m^2$

**Exam focus**
You will need to recall the formulae for the arc length and area of a circle for the exam.

## Arc length — Grade 5

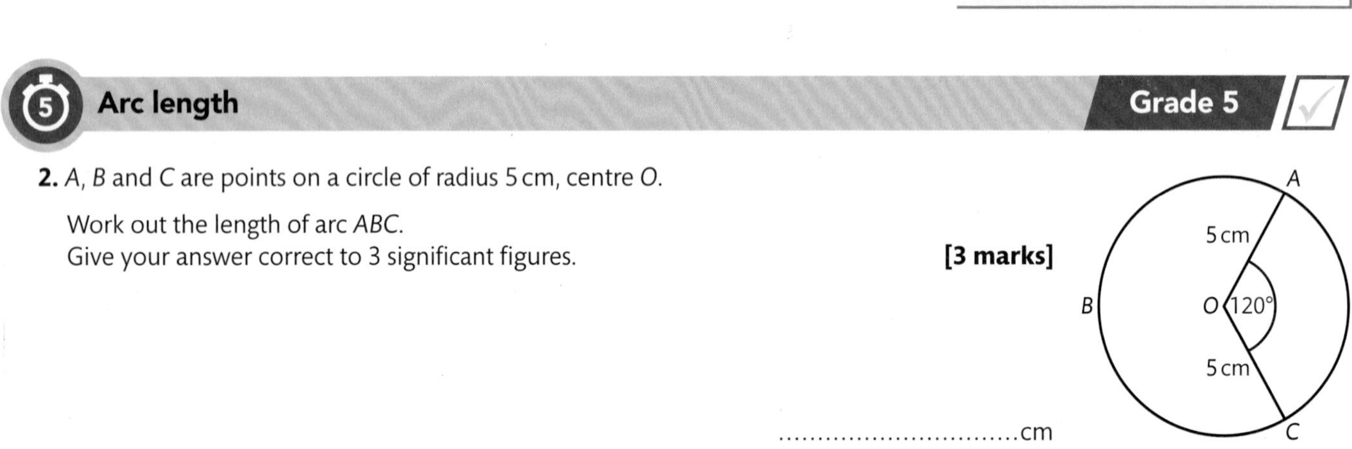


**2.** $A$, $B$ and $C$ are points on a circle of radius 5 cm, centre $O$.

Work out the length of arc $ABC$.
Give your answer correct to 3 significant figures. **[3 marks]**

.............................. cm

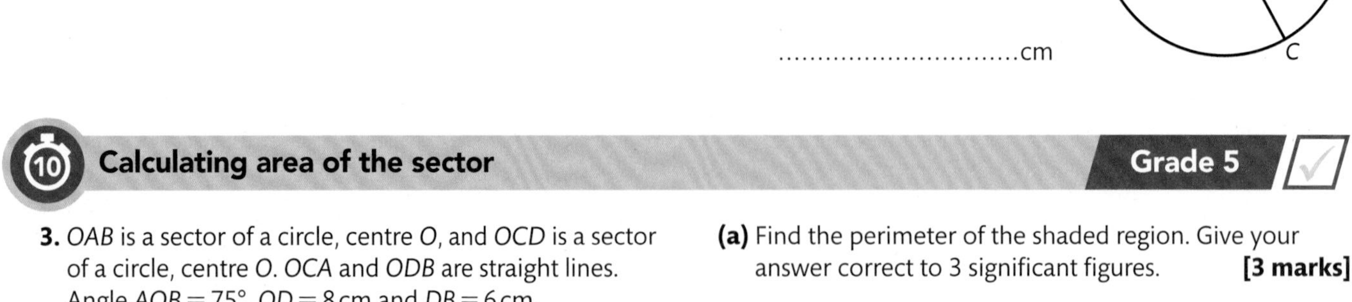

## Calculating area of the sector — Grade 5

**3.** $OAB$ is a sector of a circle, centre $O$, and $OCD$ is a sector of a circle, centre $O$. $OCA$ and $ODB$ are straight lines.
Angle $AOB = 75°$, $OD = 8$ cm and $DB = 6$ cm.

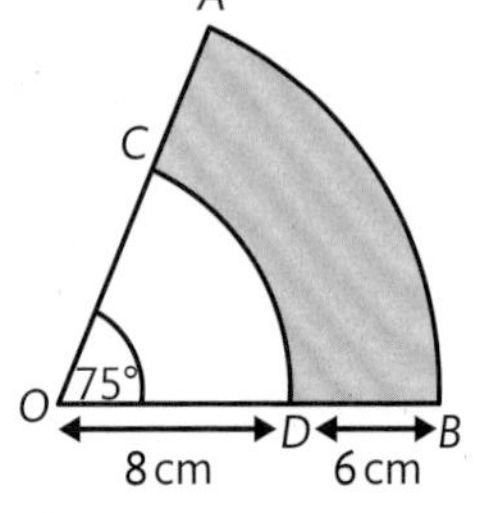


**(a)** Find the perimeter of the shaded region. Give your answer correct to 3 significant figures. **[3 marks]**

.............................. cm

**(b)** Find the area of the shaded region. Give your answer correct to 3 significant figures. **[3 marks]**

.............................. $cm^2$

 Made a start  Feeling confident  Exam ready

# Circle facts

## Quick quiz

Complete the sentences below by circling the correct words.

**(a)** A tangent is a **curved** / **straight** line that touches the circumference of the circle just once.

**(b)** Two tangents intersecting at a point outside the circle are **equal** / **different** in length.

## Using circle facts

**Grade 5**

**1.** *T* is a point on a circle, centre *O*.
*OP* is a straight line.
*STP* is a tangent to the circle.
Angle *TPO* = 52°.

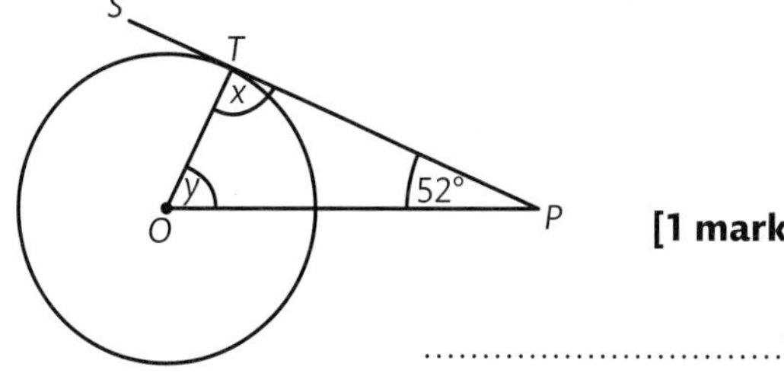


**(a)** Write down the size of the angle marked *x*. **[1 mark]**

................................°

**(b)** Work out the size of the angle marked *y*. **[2 marks]**

The angle between a tangent at a point and the radius at the same point is 90°.

................................°

**2.** *A* and *B* are points on the circumference of a circle, centre *O*.
*AC* and *BC* are tangents to the circle.
Angle *ACB* = 48°

Find the size of angle *x*.
You must give a reason for each step of your working. **[4 marks]**

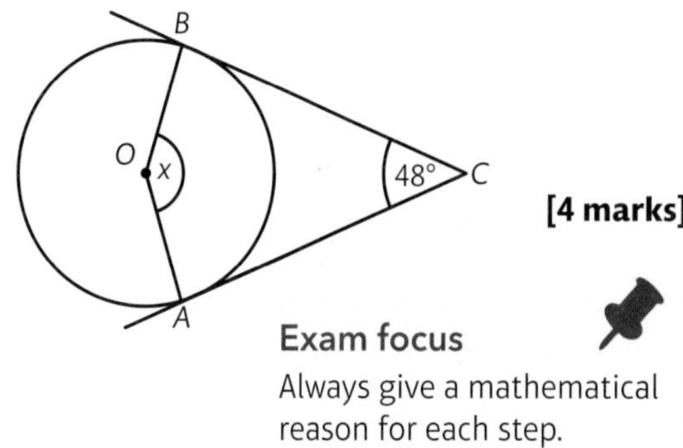


**Exam focus**
Always give a mathematical reason for each step.

................................°

**3.** *A* and *B* are points on the circumference of a circle, centre *O*.
*AT* is a tangent to the circle.
Angle *TAB* = 61°
Angle *BTA* = 43°

**(a)** Explain why angle *OAB* = angle *OBA*. **[2 marks]**

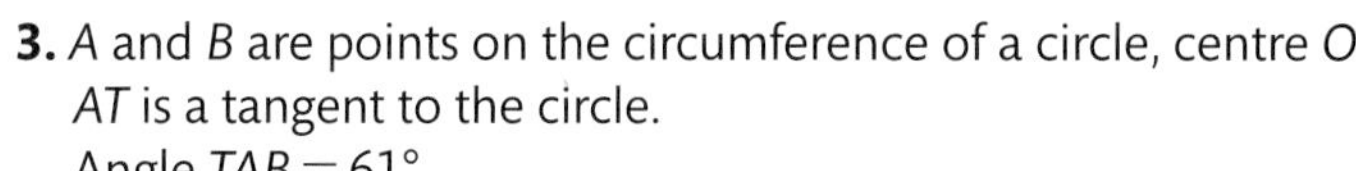

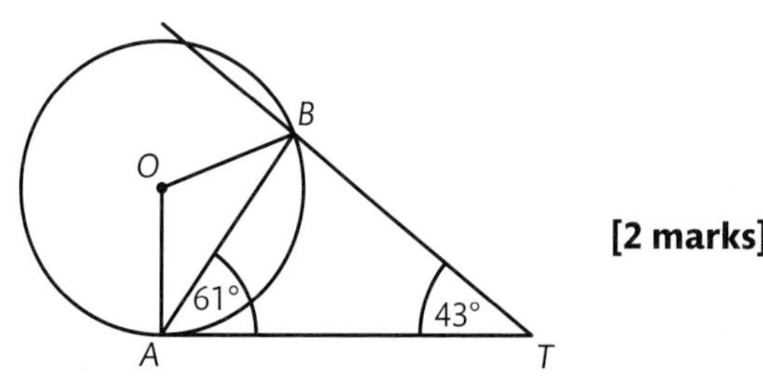


**(b)** Work out the size of angle *OBT*. **[3 marks]**

................................°

# Transformations

## Quick quiz

Write down the names of the four transformations.

.................................... .................................... .................................... ....................................

## Application of transformations

Grade 4

**1. (a)** Rotate triangle A 90° clockwise about the point (0, 1).
Label the new triangle B. **[2 marks]**

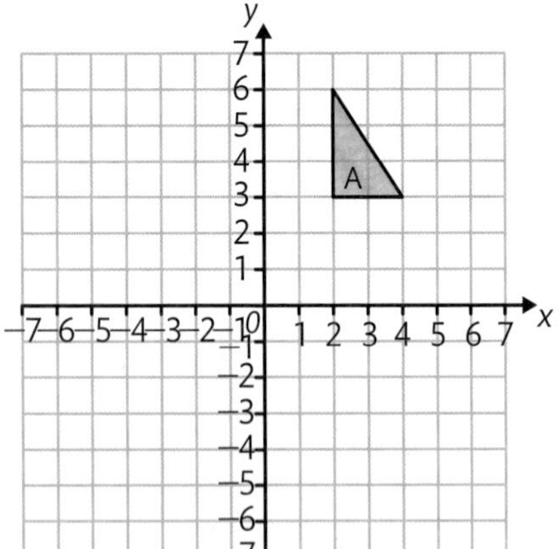

Trace shape A. Keep the paper in place by putting your pencil at (0, 1).

Rotate the tracing 90° clockwise to find the position of the image.

**(b)** Reflect triangle A in the line $x = -1$
Label the new triangle C. **[2 marks]**

The points in a reflected image should be the same distance from the mirror line as the corresponding points in the object, but on the other side of the mirror line.

**(c)** Translate triangle A by $\begin{pmatrix} -4 \\ -7 \end{pmatrix}$
Label the new triangle D. **[2 marks]**

The top number gives the number of units moved on the $x$-axis. A negative number means a move to the left. The bottom number gives the number of units moved on the $y$-axis. A negative number means a move down.

**2.**

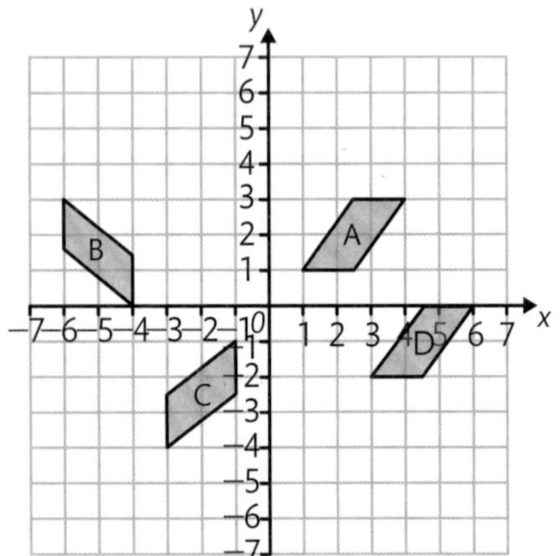

Describe fully the single transformation that maps:

**(a)** shape A onto shape B **[2 marks]**

..........................................................................

**(b)** shape A onto shape C **[2 marks]**

..........................................................................

**(c)** shape A onto shape D. **[2 marks]**

..........................................................................

**Exam focus**
Always label your object and image shapes.

**3.** Shape A has been transformed to get shape B.

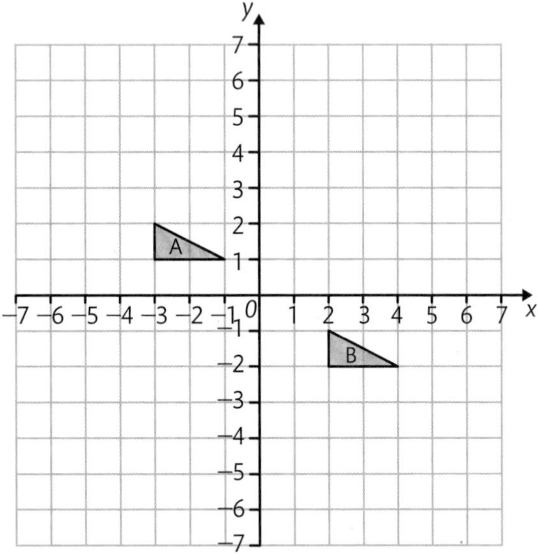

**(a)** Describe fully the single transformation that maps triangle A onto triangle B. **[2 marks]**

..........................................................................

**(b)** Reflect triangle A in the line $x = 1$
Label the new triangle C. **[2 marks]**

**(c)** Rotate triangle A 90° clockwise about the origin.
Label the new triangle D. **[2 marks]**

 Made a start  Feeling confident  Exam ready

# Enlargement

## Quick quiz

Complete the sentences below by circling the correct word.

**(a)** A scale factor greater than 1 means that the image is **smaller** / **larger** than the object.

**(b)** A scale factor between 0 and 1 means that the image is **smaller** / **larger** than the object.

## Centre of enlargement

Grade 4

**1.** On the grid, enlarge the shape by scale factor 0.5, centre (0, 0). **[4 marks]**

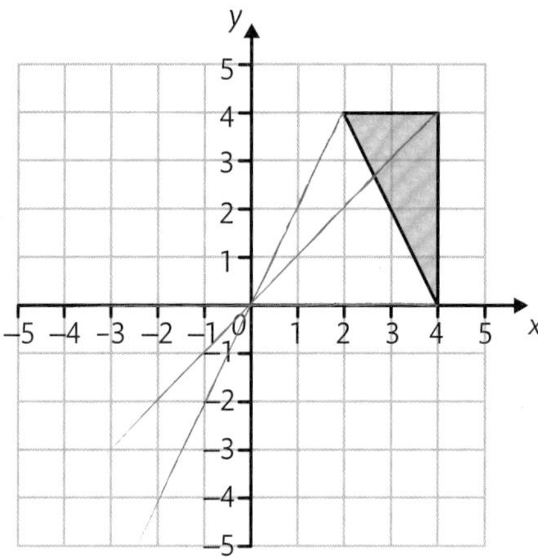

Draw lines from each point of the shape through centre of enlargement (0, 0).

Do not rub out any of the lines you have drawn.

**Exam focus**

Always draw your shape clearly and label it.

## Describing enlargement

Grade 4

**2.** Describe fully the single transformation that maps triangle A onto triangle B. **[3 marks]**

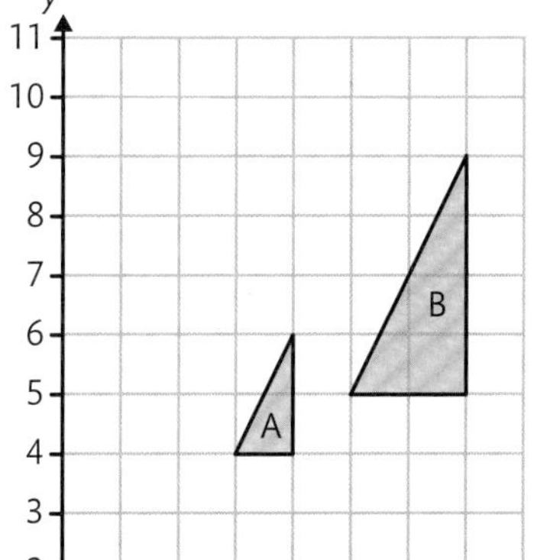

..............................................................................

## Enlarging shapes

Grade 4

**3.** On the grid, enlarge the shape by scale factor 3. **[3 marks]**

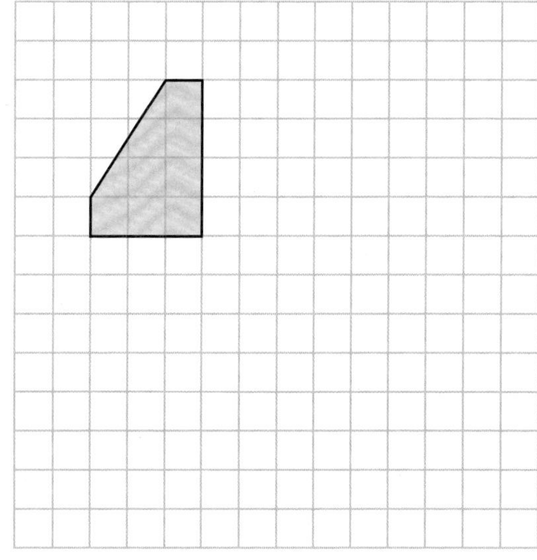

# Bearings

## Quick quiz

Complete the sentences.

**(a)** Bearings are always measured from the .............................. line and given as .............................. digits.

**(b)** The bearing of *B* from *A* is the angle measured clockwise from the north line at point ..............................

**(c)** The bearing of *A* from *B* is the angle measured clockwise from the north line at point ..............................

## Finding bearings

Grade 5

**1.** The diagram shows the positions of a mountain *M*, a climber *C* and a beacon *B*.

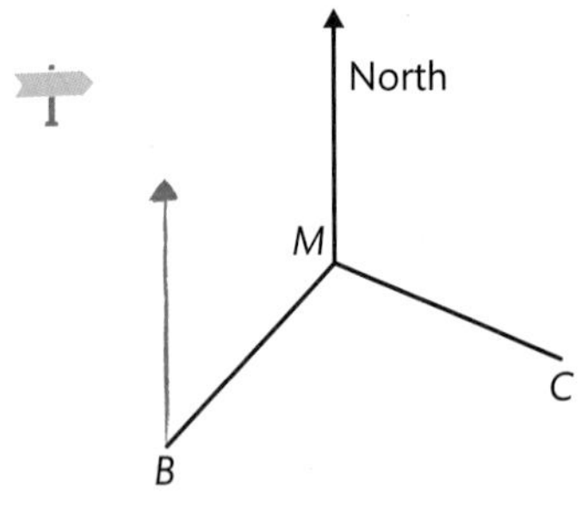


Draw a north line at *B*.

Measure angles to the nearest degree.

**Exam focus**
Always give bearings as three figures.

**(a)** Measure the bearing of *C* from *B*. **[2 marks]**

..............................°

**(b)** Measure the bearing of *M* from *B*. **[1 mark]**

..............................°

**(c)** Explain how you can use your answer to part **(b)** to find the bearing of *B* from *M* without measuring. **[1 mark]**

..............................................................................................................................................

**2.** The diagram shows two points *S* and *T*.
The bearing of *T* from *S* is 053°

Work out the bearing of *S* from *T*. **[2 marks]**

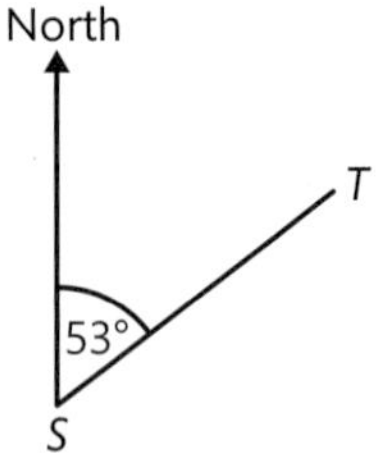


..............................°

## Using bearings

Grade 5

**3.** The diagram shows the positions of three points, *A*, *B* and *C*, on a map.
The bearing of *B* from *A* is 072°
Angle *ABC* is 48°
$AB = CB$

Work out the bearing of *C* from *A*. **[3 marks]**

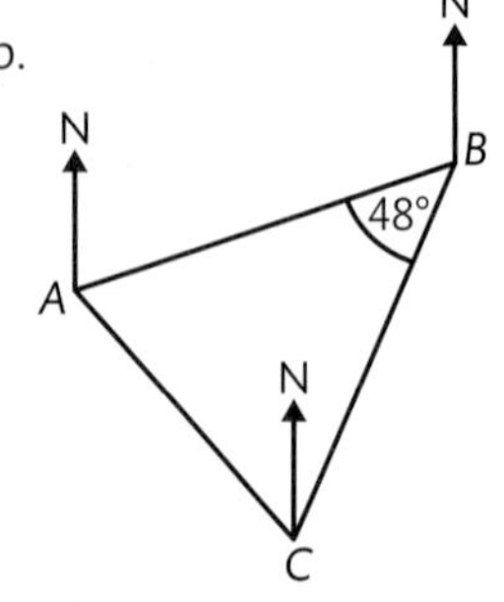


..............................°

Made a start

Feeling confident

Exam ready

# Scale drawings and maps

## Quick quiz

On a map, a scale of 1 cm represents 20 km.

**(a)** What distance does 4.5 cm represent?

................................ km

**(b)** Find the map distance for a real distance of 65 km.

................................ cm

## Distances and bearings

**Grade 5**

**1.** The diagram shows the positions of a lighthouse *L*, a buoy *B* and a ship *S* on a map.

**(a)** Measure the bearing of *L* from *S*. **[1 mark]**

................................ °

Draw a line from *L* to *S*.

**Exam focus**
Leave your construction lines once you have finished the question.

The ship, *S*, sails 125 km on a bearing of 315° from its original position.

**(b)** Find the distance, in km, of the ship from the buoy. **[2 marks]**

New position of ship

125 ÷ 50 = ............. cm

Distance from new position to *B*

= ............. × 50 = ............. km

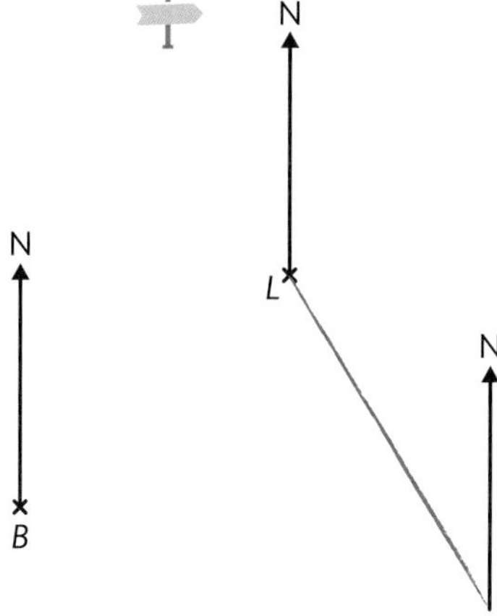


Scale: 1 cm represents 50 km

Change 125 km to cm using the given scale.

Measure the distance from the new position of the ship to the buoy and convert it into km.

................................ km

**2.** The diagram shows the positions of a lighthouse *L* and a port *P*.

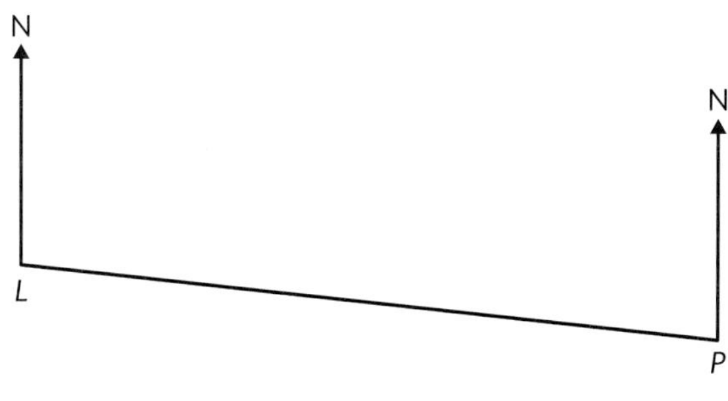


For part **(c)** draw a line on a bearing of 035° from *L*, then measure 2 cm along that line.

Scale: 1 cm represents 10 km

**(a)** Work out the real distance between *L* and *P*. **[1 mark]**

................................ km

**(b)** Measure the bearing of *P* from *L*. **[1 mark]**

................................ °

A ship *S* is 20 km from *L* on a bearing of 035°

**(c)** On the diagram, mark the position of ship *S* with a cross (×). Label it *S*. **[2 marks]**

 Made a start 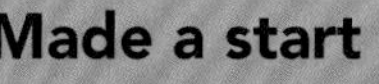  Feeling confident   Exam ready

# Pythagoras' theorem

## 5 Quick quiz

1. Write down Pythagoras' theorem in terms of $a$, $b$ and $c$.

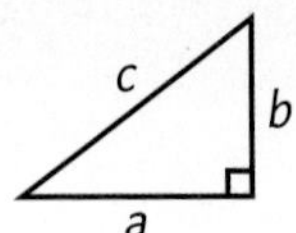


..............................................................

2. Tick the hypotenuse on each right-angled triangle.

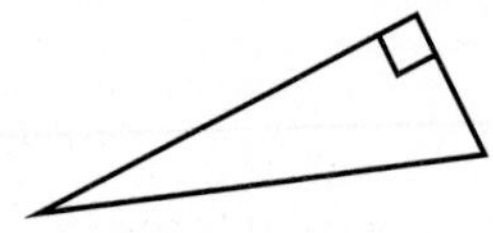

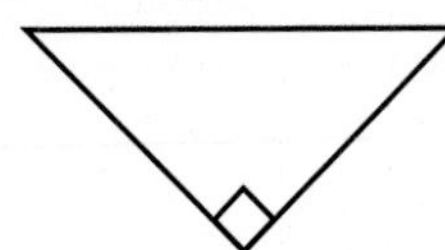

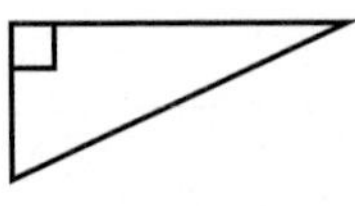

## 15 Using Pythagoras' theorem

Grade 5

1. Work out the unknown sides of the triangles. All lengths are in centimetres. Give your answers correct to 1 decimal place.

(a)

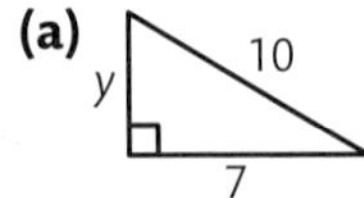


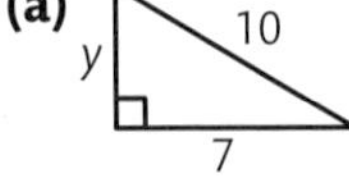

Using Pythagoras' theorem

$10^2 = y^2 + 7^2$

$100 = y^2 +$ .........

$100 -$ ......... $= y^2$

$y^2 =$ .........

$y = \sqrt{\ldots\ldots}$

$y =$ .........

(b) Triangle with sides 3, 8 and $z$.

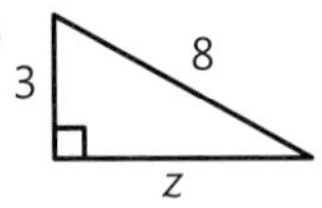

Using Pythagoras' theorem

.........$^2 = z^2 +$ .........$^2$

......... $= z^2 +$ .........

......... $-$ ......... $= z^2$

$z^2 =$ .........

$z = \sqrt{\ldots\ldots}$

$z =$ .........

**Exam focus**
Show each step of your working.

2. The diagram shows a quadrilateral $ABCD$.
$AB = 50$ cm and $AD = 14$ cm.
$BD : BC$ is in the ratio $2 : 3$
Angle $ADB$ = angle $CBD = 90°$

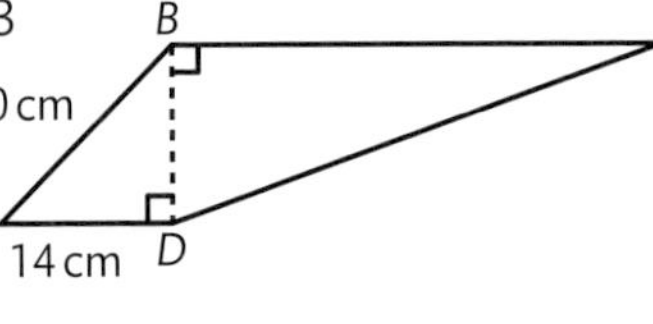


Calculate the length of $CD$.
Give your answer correct to 3 significant figures. **[4 marks]**

$50^2 = 14^2 + BD^2$

$2500 = 196 + BD^2$

$BD^2 = 2500 -$ .........

$BD = \sqrt{\ldots\ldots} =$ .........

$BD : BC = 2 : 3$, so $BC =$ ......... $\times$ .........

In triangle $BDC$, applying Pythagoras' theorem gives ..............................

So $CD^2 =$ .........

Work out the length of $BD$ by applying Pythagoras' theorem to triangle $ABD$.

.............................. cm

3. The diagram shows a rectangular framework.
The framework is made from 5 wooden rods.
The wooden rods weigh 0.25 kg per metre.

Work out the total weight of the framework.
Give your answer in kilograms, correct to 3 significant figures. **[4 marks]**

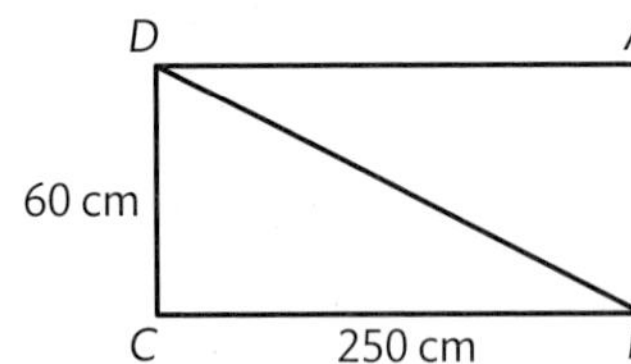


Write down and apply Pythagoras' theorem in triangle $BCD$.

.............................. kg

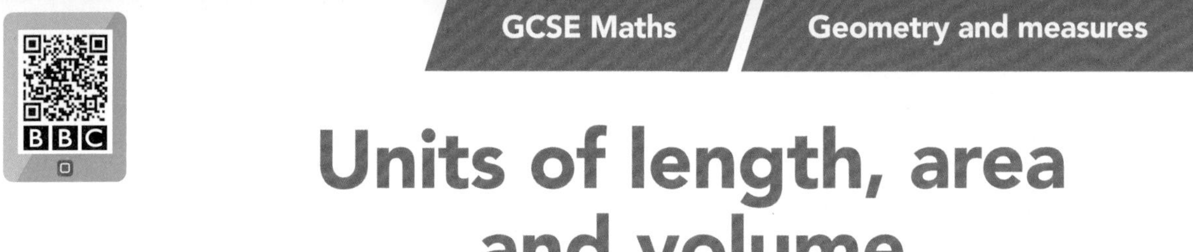

# Units of length, area and volume

## Quick quiz

Complete the conversions.

**(a)** 1 cm = ......... mm **(b)** 1 m = ......... cm **(c)** 1 m = ......... mm **(d)** 1 km = ......... m

## Simple conversions — Grade 5

**1. (a)** Change

**(i)** $2\,m^3$ to $cm^3$ **[2 marks]**

$2 \times 100^3 =$ ..............................

.............................. $cm^3$

**(ii)** $4.5\,km^2$ to $m^2$ **[2 marks]**

$4.5 \times$ ......... $=$ ..............................

.............................. $m^2$

**(b)** A rectangle has an area of $452\,000\,cm^2$. Write this area in $m^2$. **[2 marks]**

$452\,000 \div$ ......... $=$ .........

.............................. $m^2$

Scale factor for volume is the scale factor for length, cubed.

Scale factor for area is the scale factor for length, squared.

**Exam focus**
Remember your metric conversions.

## Using distances — Grade 5

**2.** Mark is on holiday in France.
He is driving to Paris on the motorway.
Mark drives past this road sign.
Mark stops at a service station 35 miles after he sees the road sign.

Paris 283 km

Work out how far Mark still has to drive from the service station to get to Paris.
Give your answer in kilometres.
5 miles ≈ 8 km **[3 marks]**

.............................. km

## Using volumes — Grade 5

**3.** The diagram shows a water butt used to store rainwater.
The container is in the shape of a cylinder of radius 50 cm.
The depth of the rainwater in the water butt is 95 cm.
70 litres of rainwater are taken from the container.

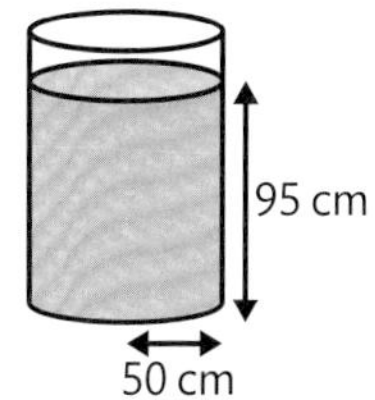


Work out the new depth of the rainwater in the water butt.
Give your answer correct to 1 decimal place.
1 litre = $1000\,cm^3$ **[4 marks]**

.............................. cm

 Made a start 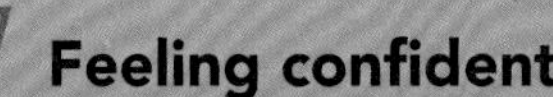 Feeling confident  Exam ready

# Trigonometry: lengths

## Quick quiz

Write each of the following in terms of opposite, adjacent and hypotenuse.

**(a)** $\sin\theta = \frac{\ldots\ldots}{\ldots\ldots}$ **(b)** $\cos\theta = \frac{\ldots\ldots}{\ldots\ldots}$ **(c)** $\tan\theta = \frac{\ldots\ldots}{\ldots\ldots}$

## Finding lengths

**Grade 4**

**1.** Calculate the value of $x$.
Give your answer correct to 3 significant figures. **[2 marks]**

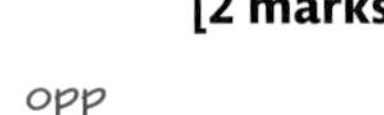


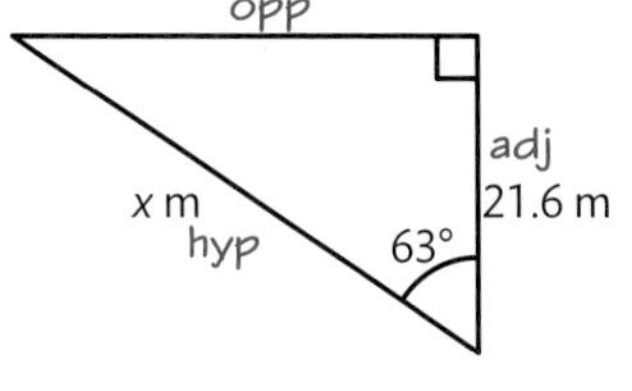


..............................

Write down SOH CAH TOA.

Label the sides as hyp, opp and adj.

Choose the correct trigonometrical ratio.

**2.** Find

**(a)** $x$ **[2 marks]**

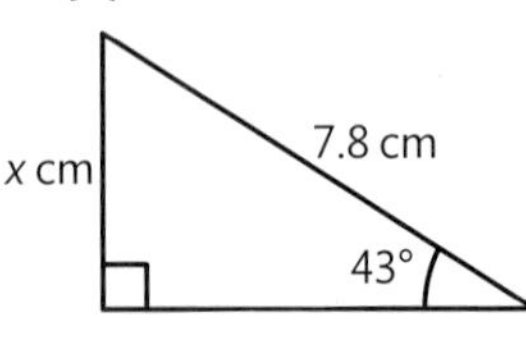


.............................. cm

**(b)** $PR$ **[2 marks]**

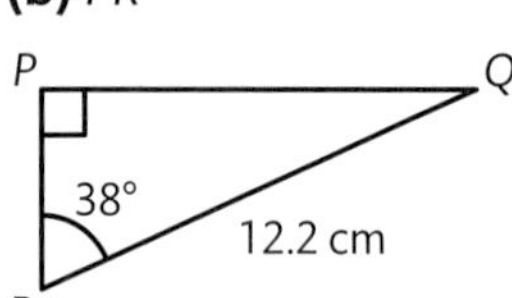


.............................. cm

**(c)** $x$ **[2 marks]**

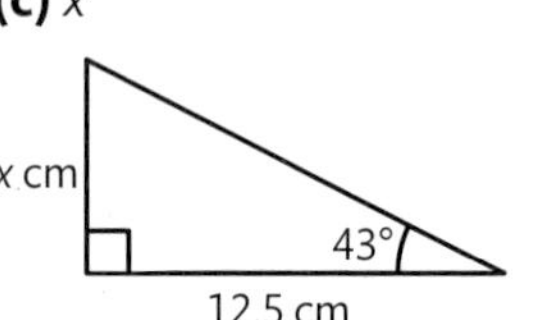


.............................. cm

## Using trigonometry

**Grade 5**

**3.** $PSR$ is a straight line.
Angle $PSQ = 90°$
$PS = 9.2$ cm
Angle $QPS = 42°$ and angle $SQR = 46°$

Work out the length of $QR$.
Give your answer correct to 3 significant figures. **[4 marks]**

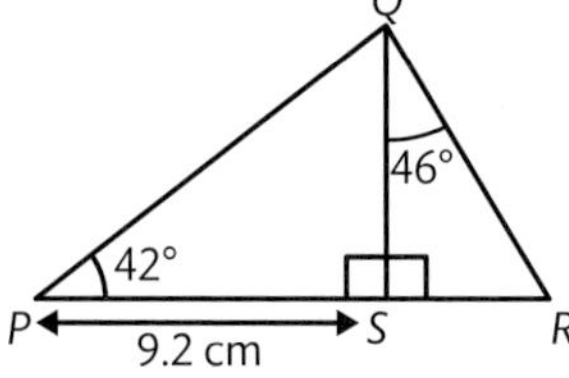


.............................. cm

**4.** The diagram shows triangle $ABC$.
Angle $CBA = 90°$ and angle $BAC = 36°$
$AC = 96$ m
$D$ is the point on $AB$ such that angle $BDC = 53°$

Calculate the length of $BD$.
Give your answer correct to 3 significant figures. **[4 marks]**

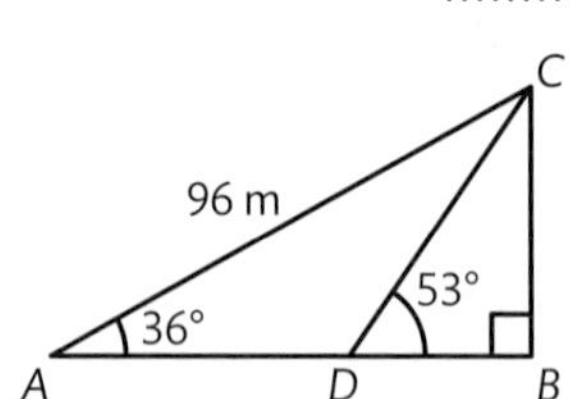


.............................. m



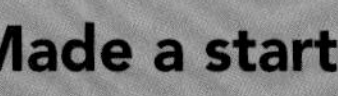 Made a start  Feeling confident  Exam ready

# Trigonometry: angles

## Quick quiz

Work out the sizes of these angles.

**(a)** tan $\theta = 3.45$, $\theta =$ ........ °

**(b)** sin $\theta = 0.78$, $\theta =$ ........ °

**(c)** cos $\theta = 0.34$, $\theta =$ ........ °

## Finding angles

Grade 4

**1.** Work out the value of *x*.
Give your answer correct to 1 decimal place. **[2 marks]**

You know the adjacent and opposite angles.

adj = 28.5 and opp = 19.4

SOH CAH TOA

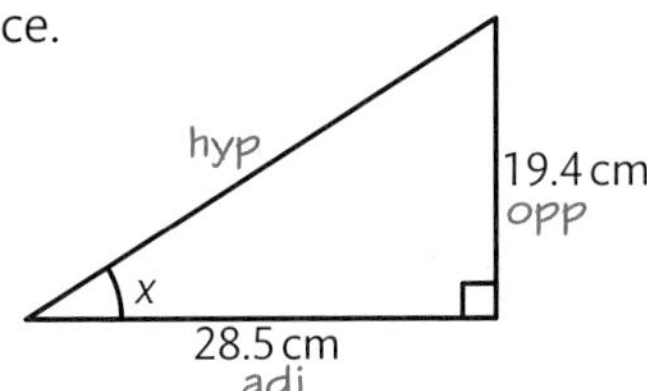


........ $x =$ $\frac{........}{........}$

................................ °

## Using trigonometry

Grade 5

**2.** The diagram shows triangle *ABC*.
*D* is the point on *AB* such that *CD* is perpendicular to *AB*.

*AC* = 9.4 cm, *AD* = 5.2 cm and *BD* = 7.8 cm.

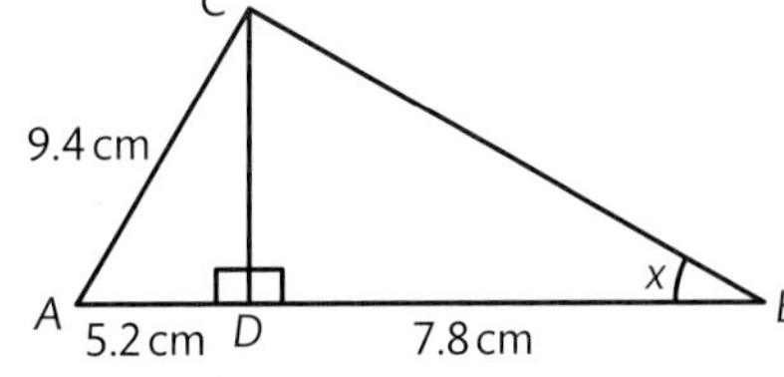


**(a)** Find the length of *CD*. **[2 marks]**

................................cm

**(b)** Find the size of angle *x*. **[2 marks]**

................................ °

**3.** In the diagram, *ABC* is a right-angled triangle.
*D* is a point on *AB*.
*AD* = 11.3 cm, *DB* = 6.5 cm and *AC* = 19.6 cm.

Work out the size of the angle labelled *x*.
Give your answer correct to 1 decimal place. **[4 marks]**

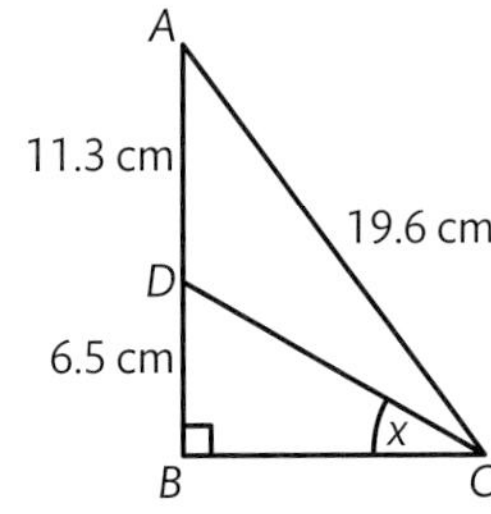


................................ °

# Trigonometry techniques

## Quick quiz

Write down the values of

**(a)** tan 60° ............................ **(b)** sin 45° ............................ **(c)** cos 30° ............................

## Real-life problems with trigonometry

Grade 5

**1.** Leinani walks from point $A$ 20 km east.
Jerry walks from point $A$ 40 km on a bearing of $\theta$.
Jerry is now directly due north of Leinani.

Work out the value of $\theta$. **[3 marks]**

**Problem solving**

You can draw your own diagram using the information given in the question.

Write all the angles on the diagram and then work out the bearing.

Write down SOH CAH TOA.

Label the sides as hyp, opp and adj.

hyp = ........ km and opp = ........ km

SOH CAH TOA

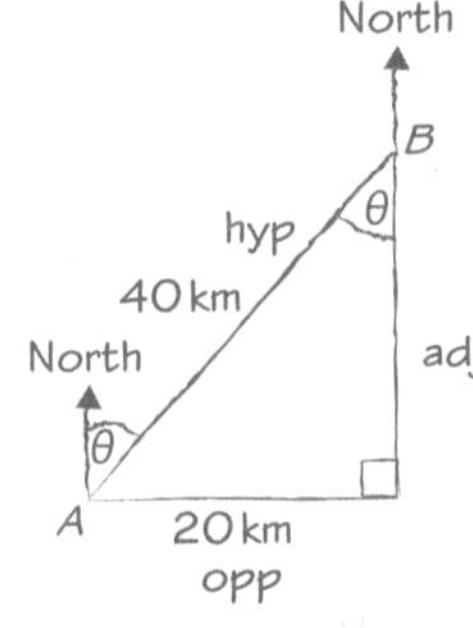


..............................°

**2.** The diagram shows a ladder leaning against a vertical wall.
The ladder stands on horizontal ground.
The length of the ladder is 6 m.
The bottom of the ladder is 3 m from the bottom of the wall.
The ladder is safe to use if the angle marked $x$ is more than 65°.

Is the ladder safe to use?
You must show all your working.

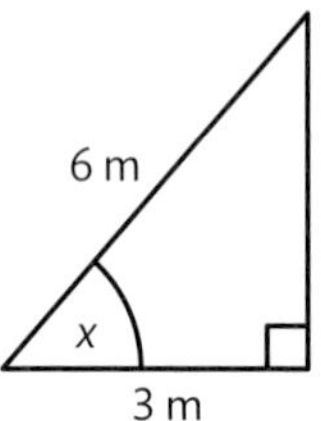


**[3 marks]**

..............................

## Using trigonometry

Grade 5

**3.** $ABE$ and $ACD$ are right-angled triangles.
Angle $BAE = 30°$
$BE = 10$ m
$BC = 30$ m

Work out the length of $CD$. **[4 marks]**

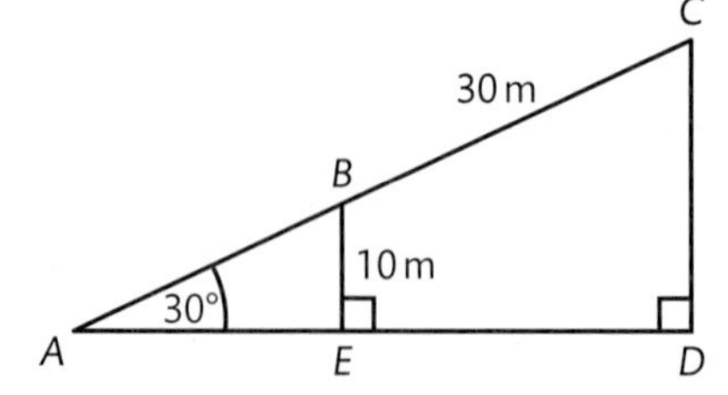


.............................. m

 Made a start  Feeling confident  Exam ready

# Time and timetables

## 2 Quick quiz

Complete these sentences.

**(a)** There are ............................ minutes in one hour. **(b)** There are ............................ hours in one day.

## 10 12- and 24-hour time

Grade 1

**1.** Ajay drives to the gym on his way home from work.
The table shows some information about his journey.

| | Leaves work | Arrives at the gym | Leaves the gym |
|---|---|---|---|
| **Time** | 17:40 | 18:20 | 19:35 |

**(a)** How many minutes does it take Ajay to get to the gym from work? **[1 mark]**

................................minutes

**(b)** How many minutes does Ajay spend at the gym? **[1 mark]**

................................minutes

**2.** Jamie has a clock on the wall in his house. The time shown is in the evening.

**(a)** Write the time in the 24-hour format. **[1 mark]**

Add 12 hours if the time is p.m.

.......... 15

................................

**(b)** The news started 20 minutes earlier than the time shown on the clock. What time did the news start? **[1 mark]**

20..........

Use the 24-hour format.

................................

**(c)** The news ends 35 minutes after the time shown on the clock. What time does the news end? **[1 mark]**

................................

## 10 Timetables

Grade 2

**3.** Here is part of a train timetable from Newcastle to London.

| Newcastle | 06:56 | 07:30 | 08:28 |
|---|---|---|---|
| Durham | 07:09 | 07:42 | 08:41 |
| York | 07:56 | 08:33 | 09:27 |
| London | 10:08 | 10:39 | 11:45 |

A train leaves Newcastle at 07:30.

**(a)** At what time should this train get to London? **[1 mark]**

................................

Omar gets to the station in Durham at 08:06.
He wants to catch the next train to York.

**(b)** How many minutes should he have to wait for this train? **[1 mark]**

................................minutes

A train leaves York at 08:33.

**(c)** How many minutes should this train take to get from York to London? **[1 mark]**

................................minutes

**4.** Here is part of a train timetable from Liverpool to London.

| Liverpool | 09:47 | 10:17 | 10:47 |
|---|---|---|---|
| Crewe | 10:21 | 10:51 | 11:21 |
| Stafford | 10:40 | 11:10 | 11:40 |
| London | 11:59 | 12:29 | |

A train leaves Crewe at 10:21.

**(a)** At what time should this train get to London? **[1 mark]**

................................

Nell catches the train from Stafford at 11:10.

**(b)** How many minutes should it take her to travel from Stafford to London? **[1 mark]**

................................minutes

**(c)** Complete the timetable by working out what time the last train should reach London. **[1 mark]**

# Reading scales

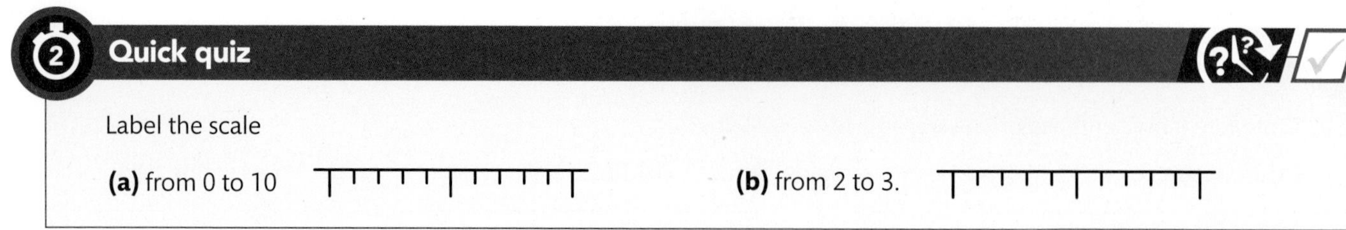

## Quick quiz

Label the scale

**(a)** from 0 to 10

**(b)** from 2 to 3.

## Scales with integers

Grade 1 

**1. (a)** Write down the number shown by the arrow on each scale.

**(i)** 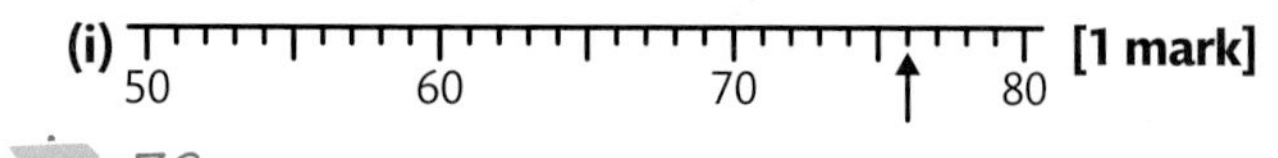 **[1 mark]**

76

There are 10 marks between 70 and 80 so each mark is worth 1 unit.

................................

**(ii)** 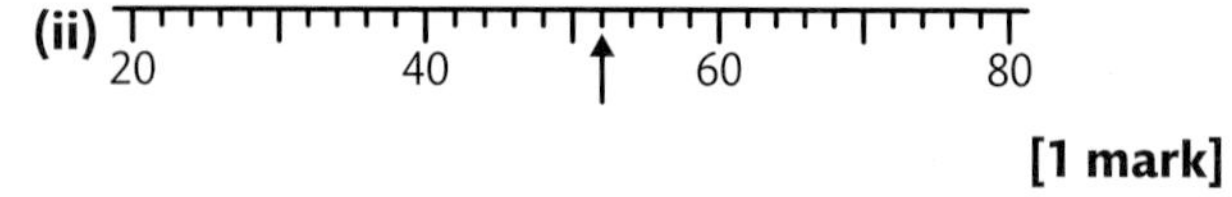

**[1 mark]**

................................

**(b)** Draw an arrow (↓) on the thermometer to show 22 °C.

**[1 mark]**

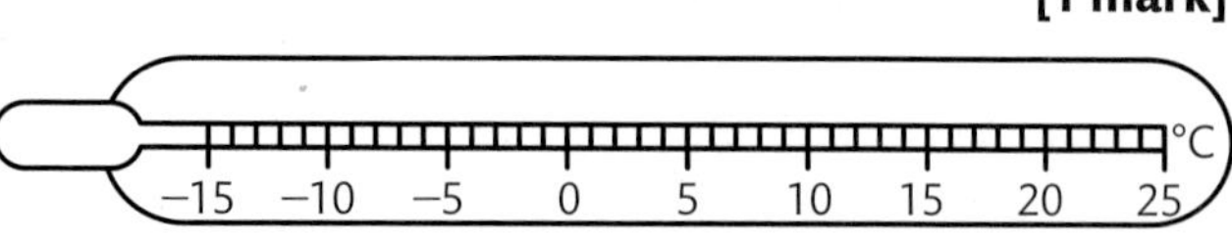

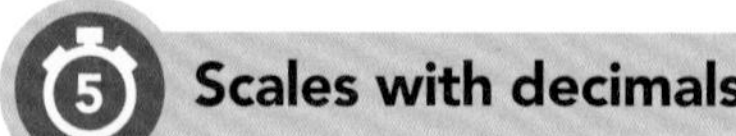

## Scales with decimals

Grade 1 

**2.** Write down the number marked with the arrow on each scale.

**(a)** 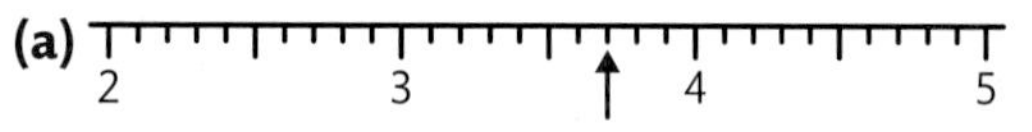

**[1 mark]**

................................

**(b)**

**[1 mark]**

................................

**3.** Draw an arrow (↓) on the scale to show

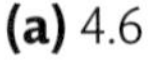

**(a)** 4.6 **[1 mark]**

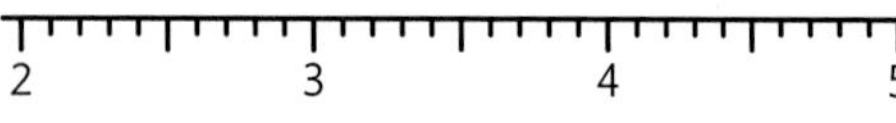

**(b)** 6.24 **[1 mark]**

## Using scales

Grade 1 

**4.** Normal body temperature is 36.8 °C.
Jeremy's body temperature drops by 1.4 degrees.

Show Jeremy's new body temperature with an arrow (↓) on the thermometer. **[2 marks]**

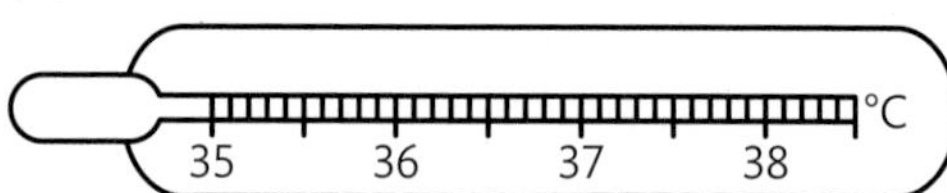

36.8 − 1.4 = ..........

**Exam focus**

You can calculate the answer and then mark the arrow or count back on the scale. Make sure the arrow is drawn clearly.

**5.** The diagram shows a scale with 3 blocks of wood.

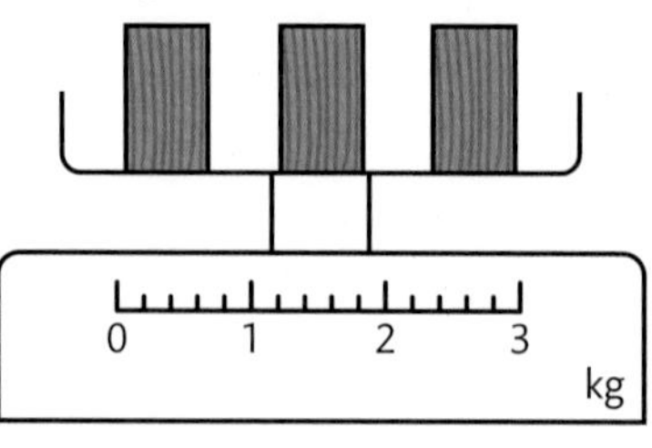


Each block of wood weighs 0.8 kg.

Show the total weight of the 3 blocks of wood with an arrow (↑) on the scale. **[2 marks]**

# Symmetry

## 2 Quick quiz

Write the names of the two types of symmetry.

**(a)** ................................ symmetry **(b)** ................................ symmetry

## 5 Symmetry — Grade 1

**1. (a)** Draw two different lines of symmetry on the pentagon. **[1 mark]**

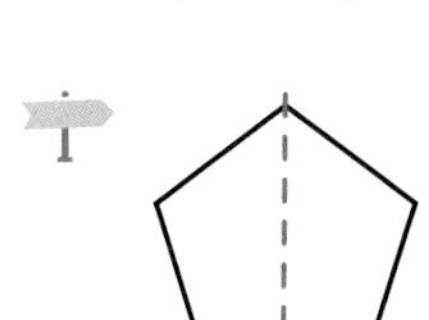

**(b)** What is the order of rotational symmetry of this pentagon? **[1 mark]**

Turn the shape through 360° and count how many times the shape looks like the original shape.

................................

**2. (a)** Draw all the lines of symmetry on this rhombus. **[1 mark]**

**(b)** Write down the order of rotational symmetry of the rhombus. **[1 mark]**

Draw lines so that one half of the shape is a mirror image of the other half.

................................

**3. (a)** Draw all the lines of symmetry on this square. **[1 mark]**

**(b)** Write down the order of rotational symmetry of a square. **[1 mark]**

................................

## 5 Shading shapes — Grade 1

**4. (a)** On the grid, shade in one more square so that the completed shape has one line of symmetry. **[1 mark]**

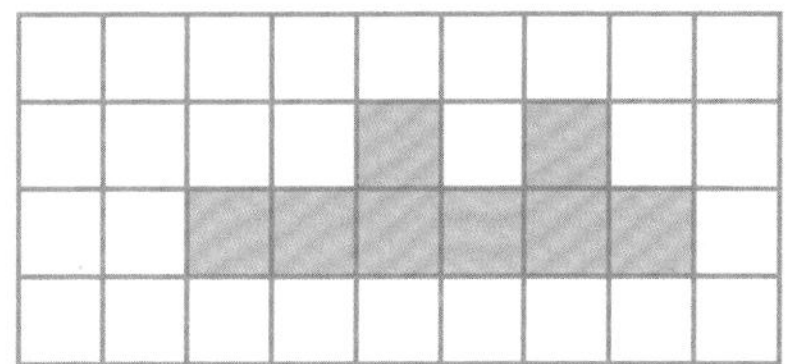

**(b)** On the grid, shade in two more squares so that the completed shape has rotational symmetry of order 2. **[1 mark]**

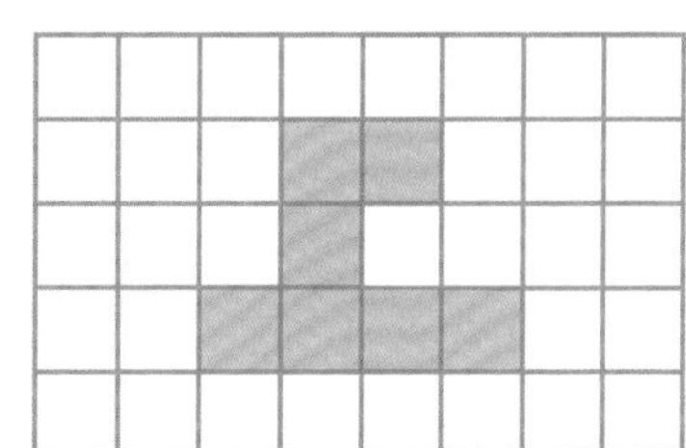

## 5 Identifying shapes — Grade 1

**5.** Here are four shapes.

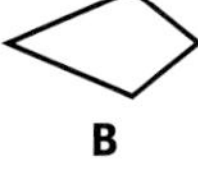

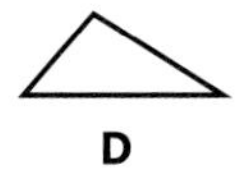


**(a)** How many lines of symmetry does each shape have? **[1 mark]**

**A** = ............................ **B** = ............................

**C** = ............................ **D** = ............................

One of the shapes has rotational symmetry of order 2

**(b)** Write down the letter of this shape. **[1 mark]**

................................

**6.** Here are five shapes.

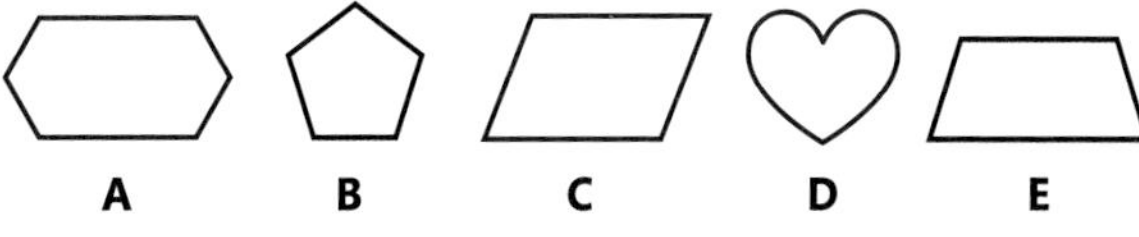


One of these shapes has exactly two lines of symmetry.

**(a)** Write down the letter of this shape. **[1 mark]**

................................

**(b)** Write down the order of rotational symmetry of shape **E**. **[1 mark]**

................................

# Quadrilaterals

## 2 Quick quiz

Complete the sentence.

A quadrilateral is a ..........-sided two-dimensional shape. The interior angles of a quadrilateral always add up to ..........°.

## 5 Identifying four-sided shapes — Grade 1

**1.** Write down the names of two quadrilaterals that have 4 right angles. **[2 marks]**

................................ ................................

**Exam focus**
Always use the correct mathematical name.

**2.** Write down the mathematical name of these quadrilaterals.

**(a)** **[1 mark]** ................................

**(b)** **[1 mark]** ................................

## 10 Drawing four-sided shapes — Grade 1

**3.** Use the grid provided to draw

**(a)** a kite **[1 mark]**

**Exam focus**
Draw the shapes using a ruler and pencil.

**(b)** a trapezium. **[1 mark]**

## 5 Properties of quadrilaterals — Grade 1

**4.** These are the names of five types of quadrilateral: trapezium parallelogram square rhombus kite

**(a)** From the list, write down the names of two quadrilaterals in which all four sides are the same length. **[1 mark]**

................................ ................................

**(b)** From the list, write down the name of the quadrilateral that has only one pair of parallel sides. **[1 mark]**

................................

One of these quadrilaterals has:
- two pairs of equal adjacent sides
- one pair of opposite equal angles
- diagonals that cross at 90° and bisect each other.

**(c)** Write down the name of this quadrilateral. **[1 mark]**

Trapezium Parallelogram Square Rhombus Kite

................................

**Problem solving**
Work through the shapes to decide which one has all the properties.

Trapeziums and parallelograms do not have any equal adjacent sides.

Made a start

Feeling confident

Exam ready

# Plans and elevations

## Quick quiz

One of these could **not** be the net of a cube. Circle it.

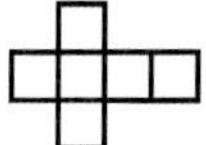 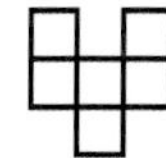 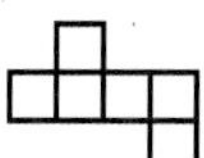

## Drawing shapes

Grade 2

**1.** The diagram shows a shape made from 7 small cubes.

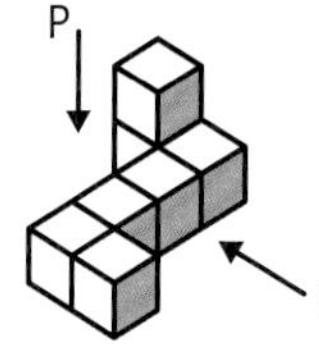


**(a)** On the grid, draw the plan view. **[1 mark]**

When you draw plans and elevations, you need to use lines to represent changes in height or depth.

**(b)** On the grid, draw the front elevation. **[1 mark]**

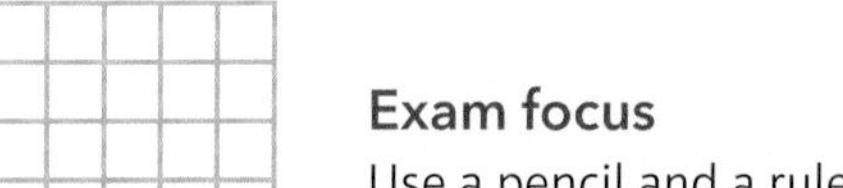

**Exam focus**

Use a pencil and a ruler to draw the elevations.

**2.** The diagram shows a shape made up of 9 small cubes.

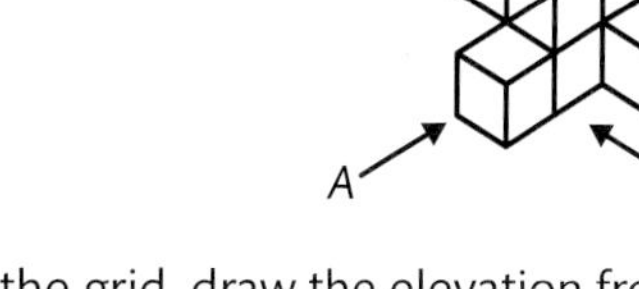


On the grid, draw the elevation from

**(a)** *A* **[1 mark]**

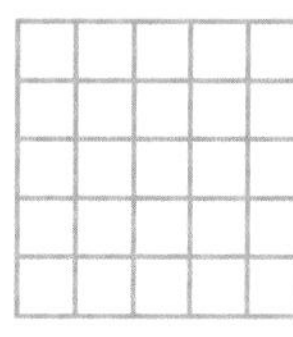

**(b)** *B*. **[1 mark]**

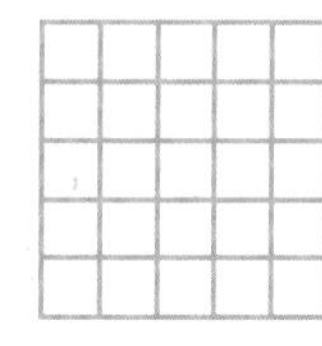

## Plans and elevations

Grade 2

**3.** The diagram shows the plan and front elevation of a solid shape.

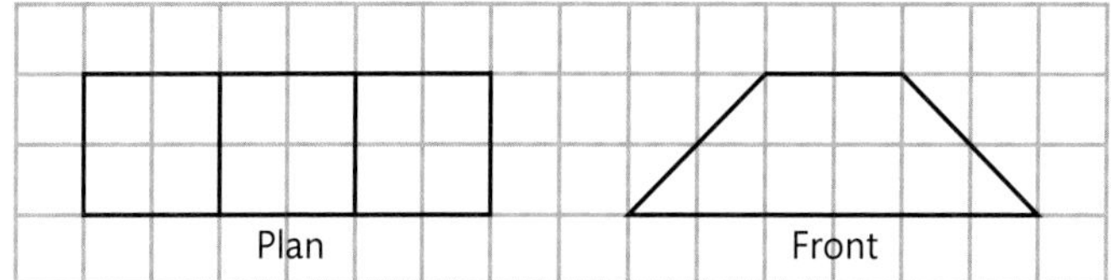


**(a)** On the grid below, draw the side elevation of the shape. **[2 marks]**

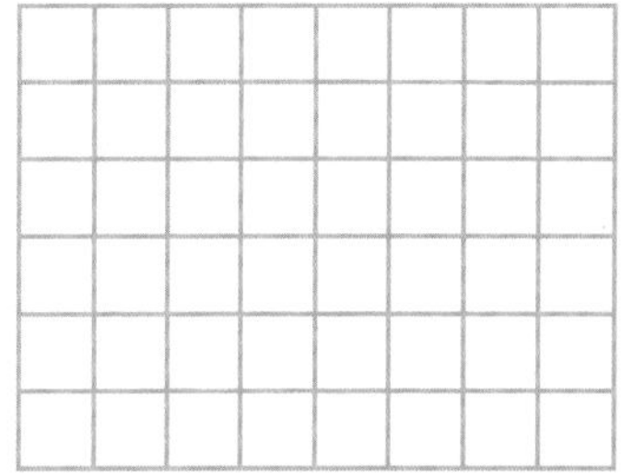

**(b)** Sketch the solid shape in the space provided below. **[2 marks]**

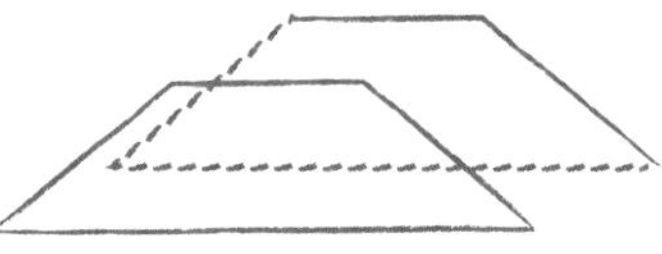

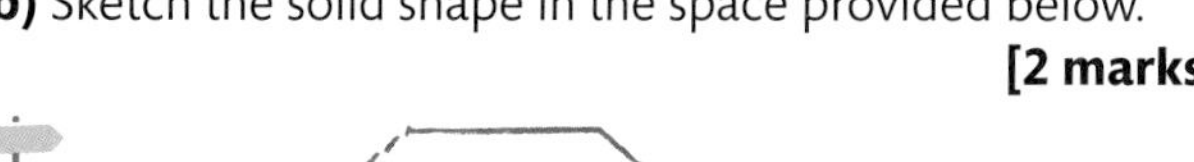

Draw the front elevation first. The back of the shape will have the same outline, but moved to the side and up. You can use dotted lines to show hidden edges.

 Made a start 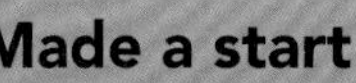 Feeling confident  Exam ready

# Similarity and congruence

## Quick quiz

Write 'similar' or 'congruent' next to the correct description.

**(a)** exactly the same size and shape .................... **(b)** one shape is an enlargement of the other ...................

## Identifying similar and congruent shapes

Grades 1–2

**1.** These eight shapes are drawn on squared paper.

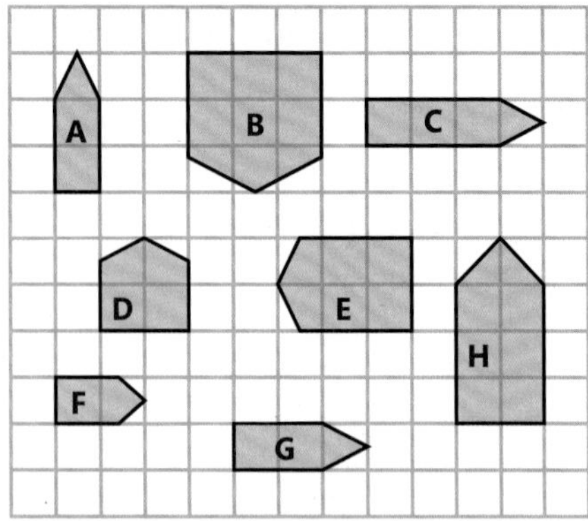


Two of these shapes are congruent.

**(a)** Write down the letters of these two shapes. **[1 mark]**

Congruent shapes can be rotated or reflected.

.............................. ..............................

Shape **F** is similar to one of the other shapes.

**(b)** Which shape? **[1 mark]**

..............................

**2.** These nine triangles are drawn on squared paper.

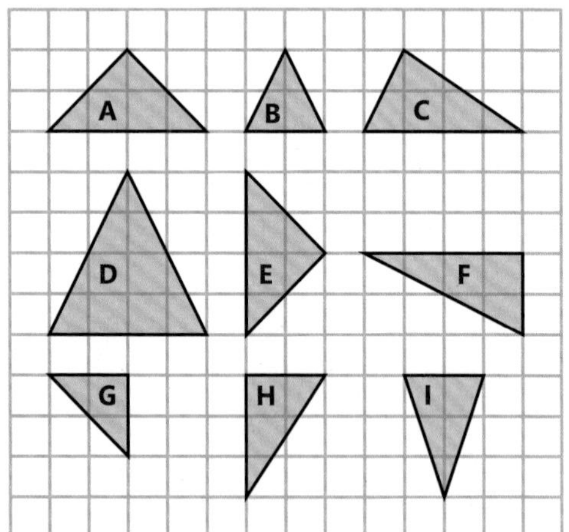


Two of these shapes are congruent.

**(a)** Write down the letters of these two shapes. **[1 mark]**

.............................. ..............................

Triangle **B** is similar to one of the other triangles.

**(b)** Which triangle? **[1 mark]**

..............................

**3.** These six shapes are drawn on squared paper.

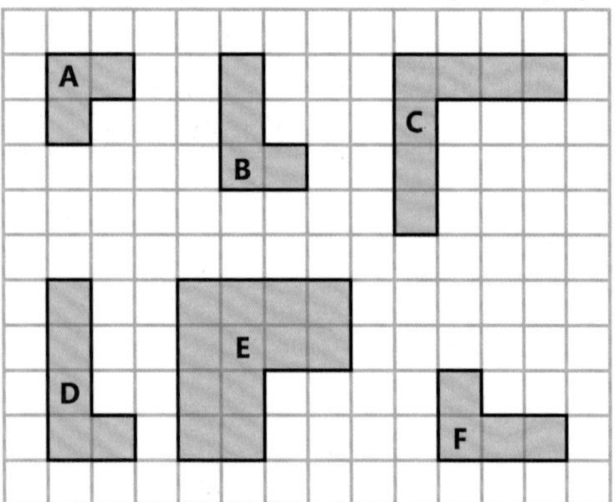


Two of the shapes are congruent.

**(a)** Write down the letters of these two shapes. **[1 mark]**

.............................. ..............................

One of the shapes is similar to shape **E**.

**(b)** Write down the letter of this shape. **[1 mark]**

..............................

**4.** These six shapes are drawn on squared paper.

Two of the shapes are congruent.

**(a)** Write down the letters of these two shapes. **[1 mark]**

.............................. ..............................

One of the shapes is similar to shape **A**.

**(b)** Write down the letter of this shape. **[1 mark]**

..............................

Made a start

Feeling confident

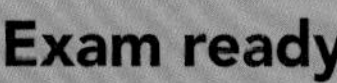

Exam ready

# Similar shapes

## Quick quiz

Complete the sentence below.

A ——— 10 cm ——— B    C ——— 4 cm ——— D

The line AB is ...................... times as long as the line CD.

## Using similarity

Grade 4

**1.**

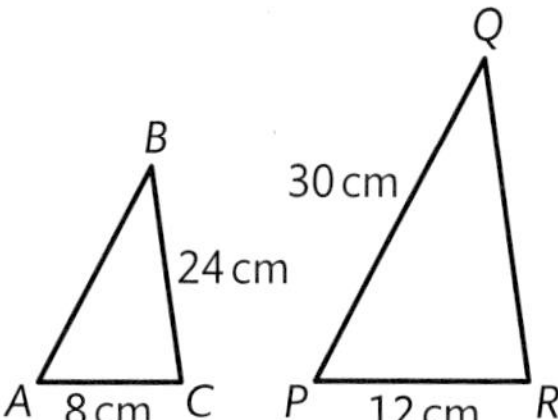


Triangles ABC and PQR are mathematically similar.

Angle A = angle P
Angle B = angle Q
Angle C = angle R
AC = 8 cm, BC = 24 cm,
PR = 12 cm and PQ = 30 cm.

**Exam focus**
The scale factors for each side are equal for similar shapes.

**(a)** Work out the length of QR. **[2 marks]**

...................... cm

**(b)** Work out the length of AB. **[2 marks]**

...................... cm

**2.** ABCD and EFGH are two rectangles.

E F
A B
D C
H G

Rectangle EFGH is 45 cm by 30 cm. There is a space 5 cm wide between rectangle ABCD and rectangle EFGH.

Are rectangle ABCD and rectangle EFGH mathematically similar? You must show how you got your answer. **[3 marks]**

$AB = 45 - 5 - 5 =$ .........

$AD = 30 -$ ......... $-$ ......... $=$ .........

$\frac{EH}{AD} =$ .........

$\frac{EF}{AB} =$ .........

Find the scale factor by dividing EH by AD. Check it is the same as EF divided by AB.

...............................

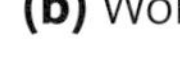

## Finding lengths

Grade 4

**3.** Triangle ABC is similar to triangle ADE.

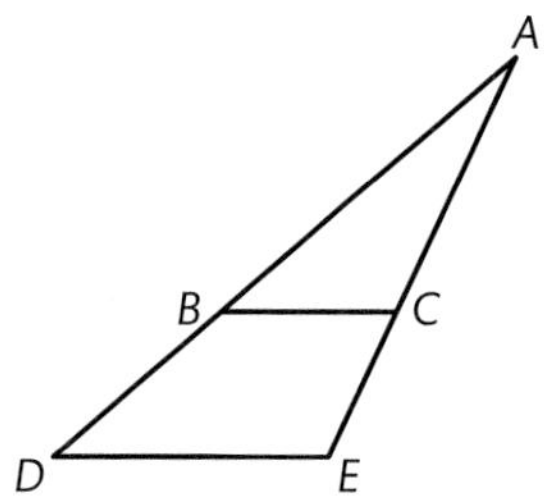


AC = 45 cm, CE = 18 cm and BC = 37.5 cm

Work out the length of DE. **[3 marks]**

...................... cm

**4.** AB is parallel to DE.
ACE and BCD are straight lines.
AB = 12 cm, AC = 16 cm,
CD = 27 cm and DE = 18 cm.

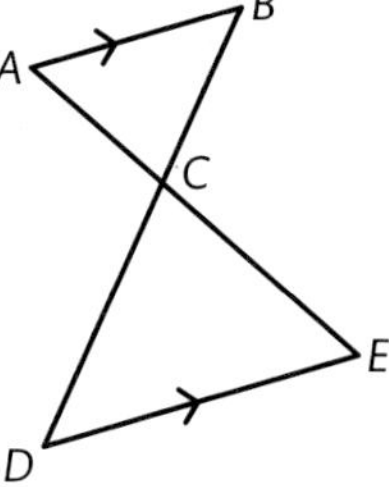


**(a)** Calculate the length of CE. **[2 marks]**

...................... cm

**(b)** Calculate the length of BC. **[2 marks]**

...................... cm

# Congruent triangles

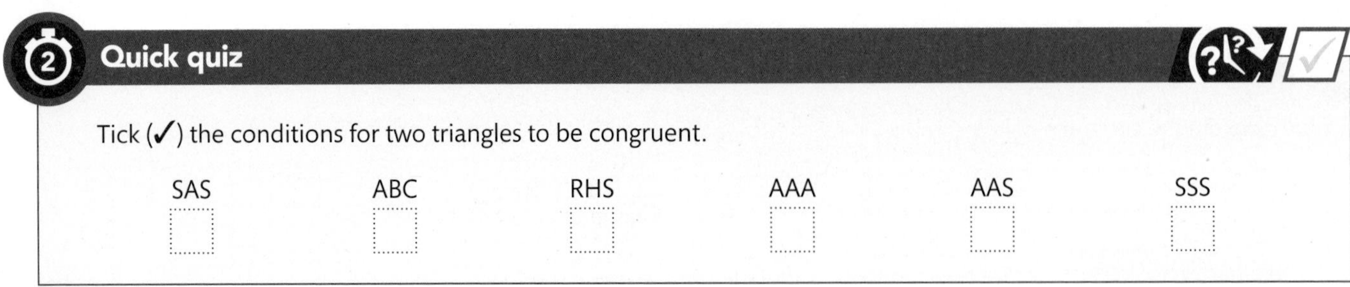

## Quick quiz

Tick (✓) the conditions for two triangles to be congruent.

| SAS | ABC | RHS | AAA | AAS | SSS |
|---|---|---|---|---|---|
| ☐ | ☐ | ☐ | ☐ | ☐ | ☐ |

## Identifying conditions of congruency

Grade 4

**1.** State the condition of congruency for each pair.

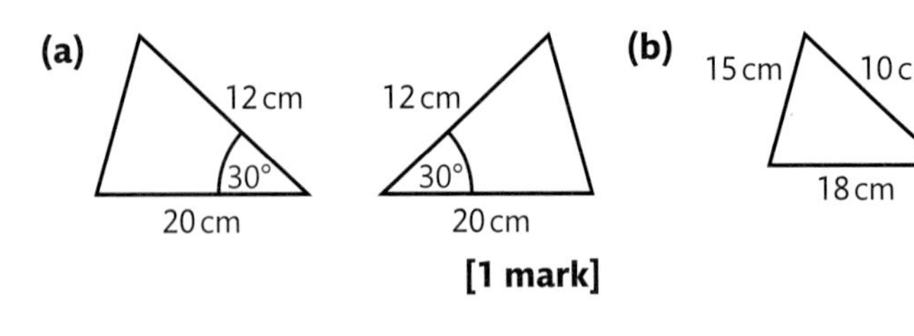


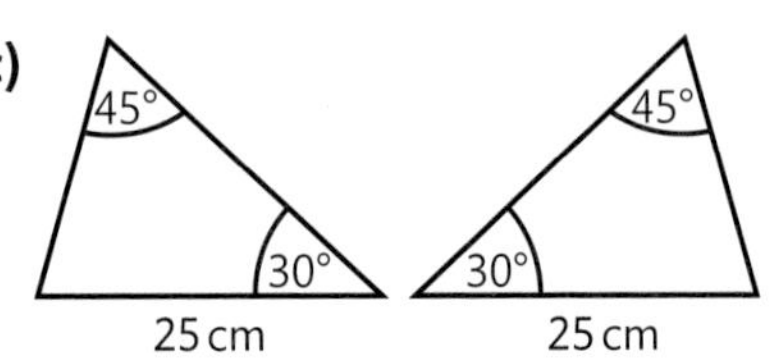


(a) **[1 mark]** (b) **[1 mark]** (c) **[1 mark]**

(a) ........SAS........ (b) .............................. (c) ..............................

The parts of the triangle that are labelled are Side, Angle, Side.

**Exam focus**
Make sure you know the different congruency conditions (SAS, RHS, SSS, AAS, ASA).

## Showing congruency

Grade 5

**2.** *ABCD* is a parallelogram.

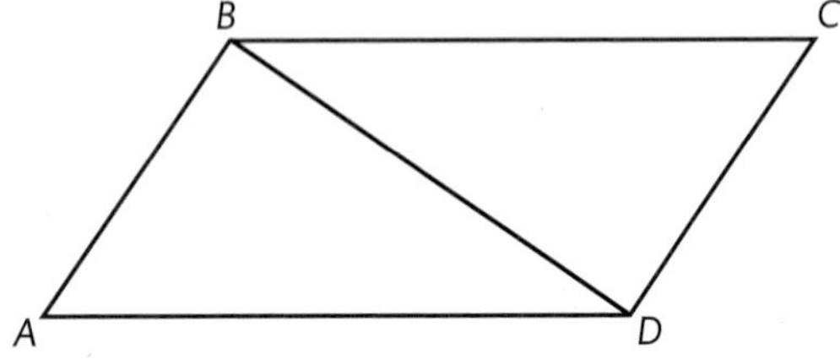


Explain why triangles *ABD* and *BCD* are congruent.

**[3 marks]**

**Exam focus**
Write down the condition of congruency you have used.

..............................................................................

**3.** In the diagram, the lines *AC* and *BD* intersect at *E*.



*AB* and *CD* are parallel and *AB* = *CD*.

Explain why triangles *ABE* and *CDE* are congruent.

**[4 marks]**

..............................................................................

**4.** *ABC* is an isosceles triangle in which *AC* = *BC*.
*D* and *E* are points on *BC* and *AC* such that *CE* = *CD*.

Show that triangles *ACD* and *BCE* are congruent.

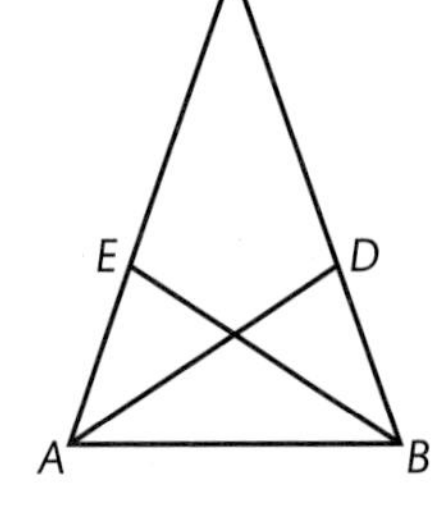


**[4 marks]**

**5.** The diagram shows a rhombus *ABCD*. The diagonals intersect at *E*.

Show that triangles *ADE* and *BCE* are congruent.

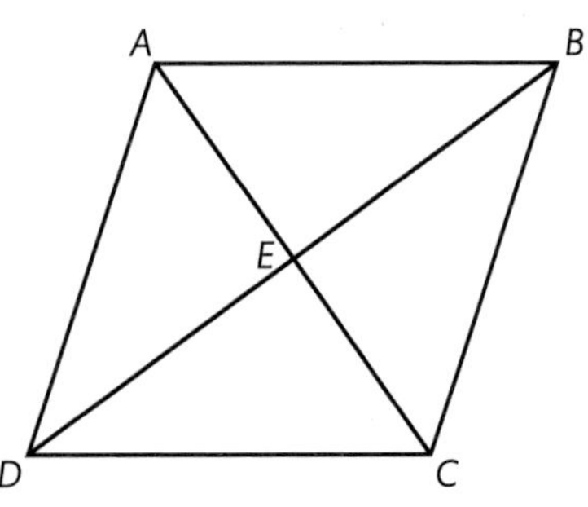


**[4 marks]**

 Made a start  Feeling confident  Exam ready

# Line segments

## 2 Quick quiz

**1.** Find the value of $x$.

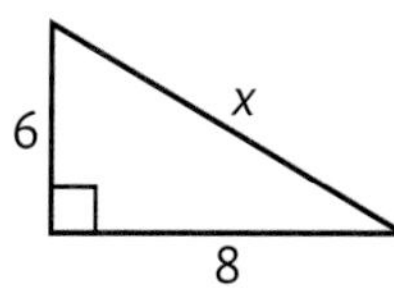


Use Pythagoras' theorem.

..............................

**2.** Find the value of $y$.

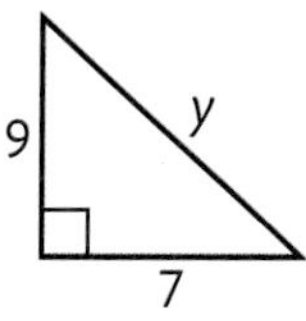


..............................

## 20 Finding lengths and midpoints

Grade 5 

**1.**

Midpoint = $\left(\frac{x_2 + x_1}{2}, \frac{y_2 + y_1}{2}\right)$

Draw a right-angled triangle and then use Pythagoras' theorem.

$A$ is the point with coordinates (1, 2).
$B$ is the point with coordinates (5, 4).

**(a)** Find the coordinates of the midpoint of the line segment $AB$.

**[2 marks]**

$x$-coordinate $= \frac{1}{2} \times$ (......... + .........) = .........

$y$-coordinate $= \frac{1}{2} \times$ (......... + .........) = .........

Midpoint = (........., .........)

(........., .........)

**(b)** Calculate the length $AB$.
Give your answer correct to 3 significant figures.

**[2 marks]**

$AB = \sqrt{(............)^2 + (............)^2}$

$= \sqrt{............^2 + ............^2}$

$= \sqrt{.........} =$ ...........

..............................

**2.** $A$ is the point with coordinates (2, 3).
$B$ is the point with coordinates (7, 8).

**(a)** Find the coordinates of the midpoint of the line $AB$. **[2 marks]**

(........., .........)

**(b)** Calculate the length $AB$.
Give your answer correct to 3 significant figures. **[2 marks]**

..............................

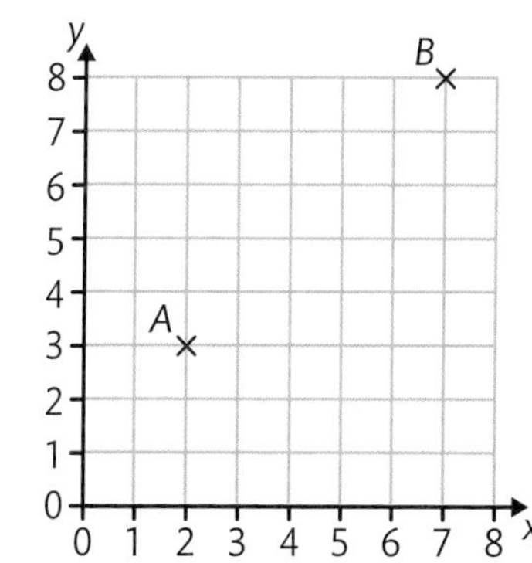


**3.** $P$ is the point with coordinates (–2, 10).
$Q$ is the point with coordinates (5, 6).

**(a)** Find the coordinates of the midpoint of the line $PQ$. **[2 marks]**

(........., .........)

**(b)** Calculate the length $PQ$.
Give your answer correct to 3 significant figures.

**[2 marks]**

..............................

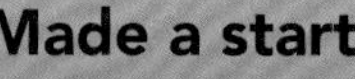
Made a start

Feeling confident

Exam ready

# Vectors

## Quick quiz

Complete the sentences.

**1.** Vectors are quantities that have both .............................. and ..............................

**2.** $\begin{pmatrix} x \\ y \end{pmatrix}$ is called a .............................. vector.

## Column vectors

**Grade 5**

**1.** $\mathbf{a} = \begin{pmatrix} 4 \\ -6 \end{pmatrix}$ and $\mathbf{b} = \begin{pmatrix} -3 \\ 1 \end{pmatrix}$

$\begin{pmatrix} x \\ y \end{pmatrix}$ represents a vector.

Find

**(a)** $\mathbf{a} + \mathbf{b}$ **[2 marks]**

$\mathbf{a} + \mathbf{b} = \begin{pmatrix} 4 \\ -6 \end{pmatrix} + \begin{pmatrix} -3 \\ 1 \end{pmatrix}$

$= \begin{pmatrix} 4 - 3 \\ -6 + 1 \end{pmatrix}$

..............................

**(b)** $\mathbf{b} - \mathbf{a}$ **[2 marks]**

$\mathbf{b} - \mathbf{a} = \begin{pmatrix} -3 \\ 1 \end{pmatrix} - \begin{pmatrix} 4 \\ -6 \end{pmatrix}$

..............................

**(c)** $2\mathbf{a} - 3\mathbf{b}$ **[2 marks]**

$2\mathbf{a} = 2 \times \begin{pmatrix} 4 \\ -6 \end{pmatrix}$

..............................

**(d)** $4\mathbf{b} - 5\mathbf{a}$ **[2 marks]**

**Exam focus**
Give your answer as a vector.

..............................

## Finding and using vectors

**Grade 5**

**2.** The diagram shows a parallelogram, *ABCD*.
*M* is the midpoint of *AD*.

$\overrightarrow{AM} = \mathbf{a}$ and $\overrightarrow{AB} = \mathbf{b}$

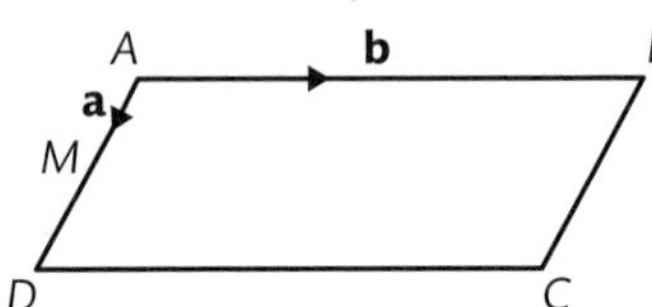


Find, in terms of **a** and/or **b**,

**(a)** $\overrightarrow{AD}$ **[1 mark]**

..............................

**(b)** $\overrightarrow{AC}$ **[1 mark]**

..............................

**(c)** $\overrightarrow{MB}$. **[1 mark]**

..............................

**3.** The diagram shows a trapezium *OPQR*.
*PQ* is parallel to *OR*.

$\overrightarrow{OP} = 2\mathbf{b}$ $\overrightarrow{PQ} = 2\mathbf{a}$ $\overrightarrow{OR} = 6\mathbf{a}$

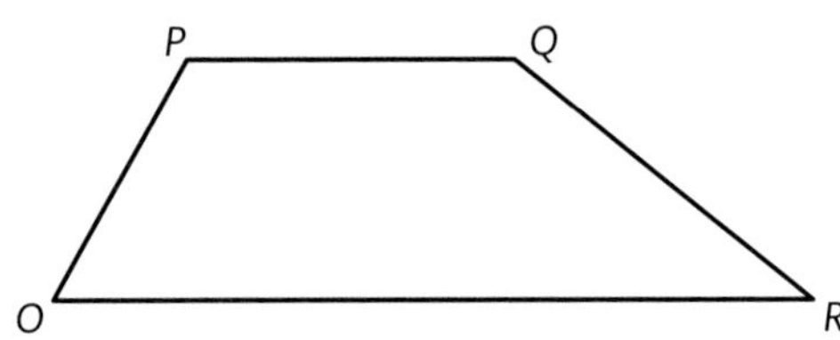


Find, in terms of **a** and/or **b**,

**(a)** $\overrightarrow{QP}$ **[1 mark]**

..............................

**(b)** $\overrightarrow{OQ}$ **[1 mark]**

..............................

**(c)** $\overrightarrow{QR}$. **[1 mark]**

..............................

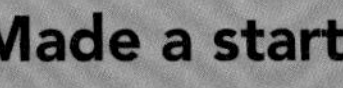

Made a start

Feeling confident

Exam ready

# Geometry and measures

## Surface area and volume

Grade 4 

**1.** The total surface area of a cube is 384 cm².

Work out the volume of the cube. **[4 marks]**

First, calculate the surface area of one face of the cube by dividing 384 cm² by 6, the total number of faces.

Find the length of the cube by using the surface area of one face of the cube.

Volume of a cube $= l^3 = l \times l \times l$

................................ cm³

## Triangles

Grade 4 

**2.** The size of the largest angle in a triangle is 5 times the size of the smallest angle.
The other angle is 18° less than the largest angle.

Work out, in degrees, the size of each angle in the triangle. You must show your working. **[5 marks]**

................................°

## Trigonometry and Pythagoras

Grade 5 

**3.** *ABC* is a triangle.

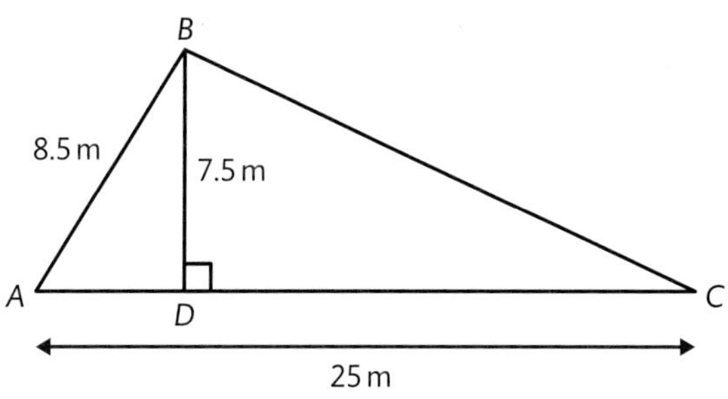


Work out the size of angle *BCD*.
Give your answer correct to 1 decimal place. **[5 marks]**

................................°

# Introduction to probability

## 2 Quick quiz

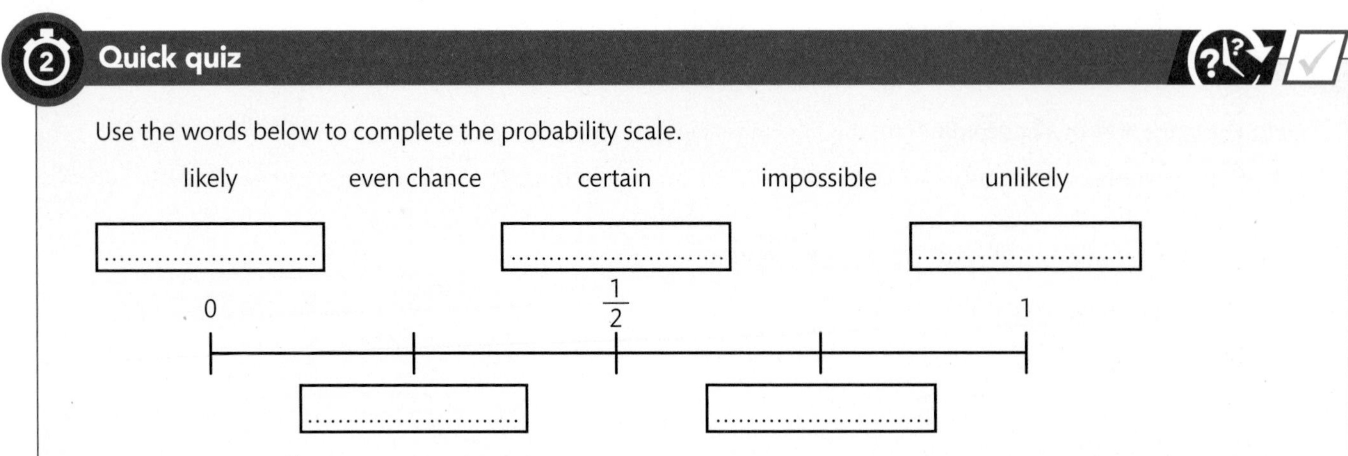

Use the words below to complete the probability scale.

likely even chance certain impossible unlikely



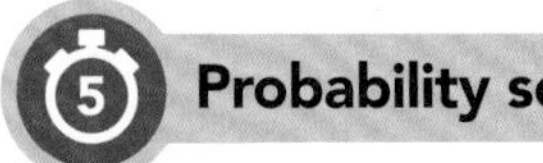

## 5 Probability scales

Grade 1

**1.** Kaida rolls a normal 6-sided dice once.

On the probability scale below, mark with a cross (×) the probability that Kaida gets a 7. **[1 mark]**

**2.** Meela has a fair 6-sided spinner. The sides of the spinner are numbered 3, 3, 3, 4, 4, 6, as shown.

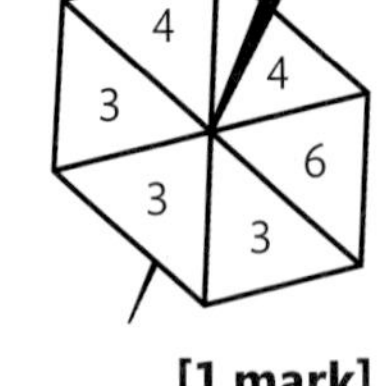


From the list below, circle the word that best describes the likelihood that the spinner will land on 3. **[1 mark]**

impossible unlikely even likely certain

## 10 Sample space diagrams

Grade 3

**3.** Three cards are numbered 1, 3 and 4. Three discs are numbered 2, 4 and 6.

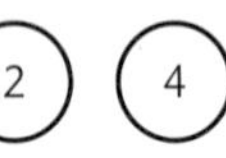

A game consists of picking one card at random and one disc at random. The number on the card is added to the number on the disc.

**(a)** Complete the table to show all the possible totals. **[2 marks]**

| | | Disc | | |
|---|---|---|---|---|
| | | **2** | **4** | **6** |
| Card | **1** | 3 | | |
| | **3** | | | |
| | **4** | | | |

**(b)** What is the probability of getting a total that is an odd number? **[2 marks]**

There are 9 equally likely outcomes. Count the number of outcomes that produce an odd number and divide this by 9.

...............................

**4.** Two bags, **A** and **B**, each contain four numbered discs that are all the same size.

A disc is drawn at random from bag **A** and a disc is drawn at random from bag **B**. A score is obtained by multiplying the numbers on the two discs.

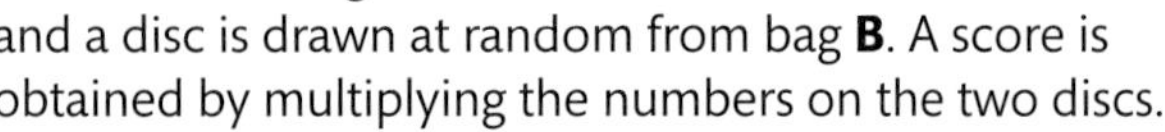

**(a)** Complete the table to show all the possible scores. **[2 marks]**

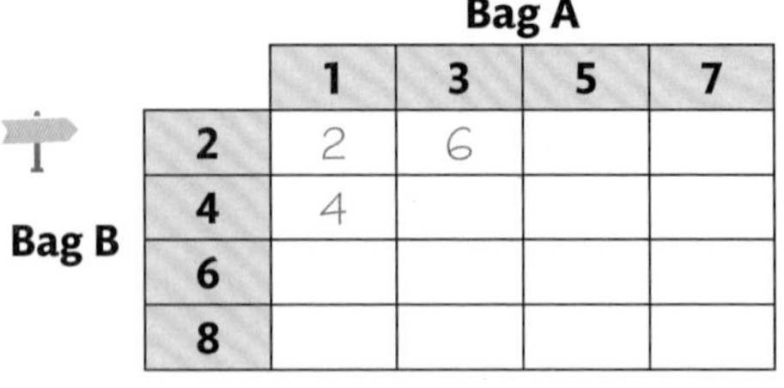

| | | Bag A | | | |
|---|---|---|---|---|---|
| | | **1** | **3** | **5** | **7** |
| Bag B | **2** | 2 | 6 | | |
| | **4** | 4 | | | |
| | **6** | | | | |
| | **8** | | | | |

**(b)** Find the probability of scoring more than 20. **[2 marks]**

...............................

# More about probability

## Quick quiz

1. For any event, the total probability of all the possible outcomes adds up to ......................
2. On a given day, the probability that it snows is 0.35. Find the probability that it does not snow on this day. ......................
3. A number is selected at random from the following list: 5 7 8 2 4 3

   Find the probability that the number picked is

   **(a)** even ...................... **(b)** prime ...................... **(c)** a square number. ......................

## Using tables

**Grade 5**

**1.** Jordan plays a game in which he throws a hoop at a target.
The table shows information about the probability of each possible score.

| **Score** | 0 | 1 | 2 | 3 | 4 |
|---|---|---|---|---|---|
| **Probability** | $x$ | $2x$ | 0.20 | 0.12 | 0.23 |

The probabilities of all possible outcomes total 1.

Jordan is twice as likely to score 1 point as to score 0 points.

**(a)** Work out the value of $x$. **[3 marks]**

Set up an equation in $x$ and then solve it.

.........$x$ = ......... ...............................

Jordan plays the game twice.

**(b)** Work out the probability that he scores 1 both times. **[2 marks]**

**Exam focus**
Give probabilities as decimals or fractions.

...............................

## Finding probability

**Grade 5**

**2.** The probability that a lorry will pass an emissions test is 0.90. Three lorries are tested.

**(a)** Work out the probability that all three of these lorries will pass the emissions test. **[2 marks]**

...............................

**(b)** Work out the probability that none of these lorries will pass the emissions test. **[2 marks]**

P(pass) = 1 - P(not pass)

...............................

**3.** Peter throws an ordinary fair dice twice. Work out the probability that he gets the number 4 both times. **[2 marks]**

...............................

**4.** There are 11 yellow counters, 6 blue counters and some red counters in a box.
Minah selects one of these counters at random.
The probability that Minah selects a blue counter is $\frac{1}{5}$

Work out the probability that Minah selects a red counter. **[3 marks]**

...............................

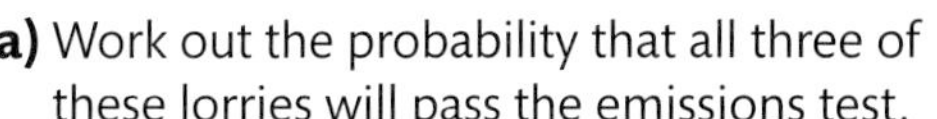

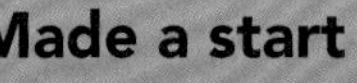
Made a start

Feeling confident

Exam ready

# Relative frequency

## Quick quiz

1. A coin is tossed 20 times and a head is obtained 8 times.
   Write down the relative frequency for the number of heads. ........................
2. Complete the sentence.
   As you increase the number of times the coin is tossed, the relative frequency gets closer to the theoretical ..................................

## Probability and relative frequency

**Grade 5**

**1.** A box contains 30 plastic plates. The table shows information about the radii of the plates.

| **Radius of plastic plate (cm)** | 3 | 4 | 5 | 6 | 7 |
|---|---|---|---|---|---|
| **Frequency** | 4 | 7 | 6 | 8 | 5 |

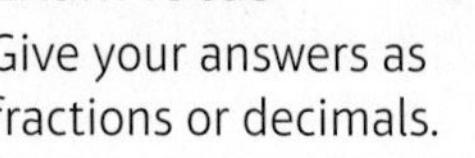

**Exam focus**
Give your answers as fractions or decimals.

A plate is taken at random from the box. Work out the probability that the radius of the plate is

**(a)** 3 cm **[1 mark]** **(b)** not 5 cm **[2 marks]** **(c)** more than 5.5 cm. **[2 marks]**

Probability = $\frac{\square}{30}$

How many plates have a radius of 3 cm?

Probability = $\frac{\square}{30}$

Add up the frequencies for the other radii.

Probability = $\frac{\square}{30}$

**2.** There are 80 tiles in a bag. There are five different colours of tile. The table shows information about the tiles in the bag.

| **Colour of tile** | Red | Yellow | Blue | Green | Black |
|---|---|---|---|---|---|
| **Frequency** | 14 | 17 | 23 | 16 | 10 |

A tile is taken at random from the bag. Work out the probability that the tile is

**(a)** yellow or blue **[2 marks]** **(b)** not black. **[2 marks]**

........................ ........................

Nyasha takes a tile from the bag at random. She records the colour of the tile and then replaces the tile in the bag. Anjali then takes a tile from the bag at random.

**(c)** Work out the probability that Nyasha takes a red tile and Anjali takes a green tile. **[3 marks]**

........................

**3.** Jake rolls a biased dice 60 times and records two 6s. Sarah rolls the dice 300 times and records five 6s. Jake and Sarah use their results to estimate the probability that the dice will land on a 6.

Who has the more reliable result? You must justify your answer. **[2 marks]**

........................................................................................................................

# Venn diagrams

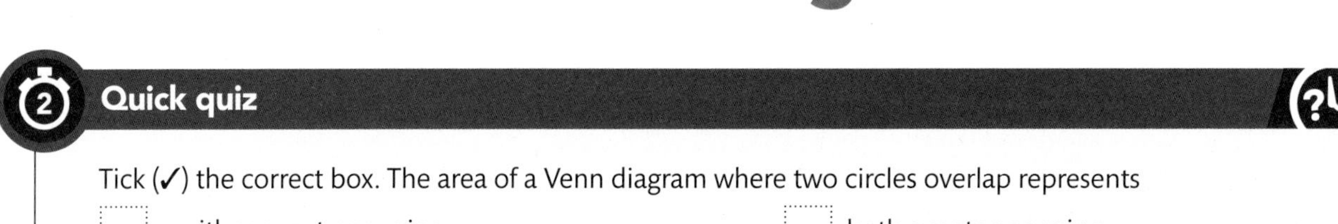

## Quick quiz

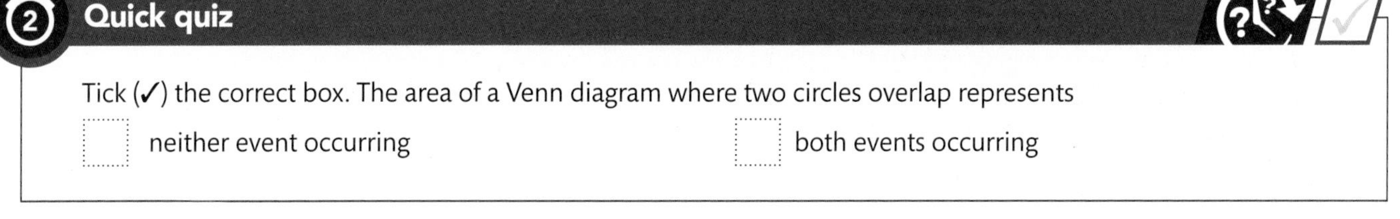

Tick (✓) the correct box. The area of a Venn diagram where two circles overlap represents

☐ neither event occurring ☐ both events occurring

## Using Venn diagrams

Grade 5

**1.** In Year 12, there are 60 students. 20 of the students study textiles, 15 of the students study food science and 9 of the students study both.

> Students who study both subjects are represented in the overlap.

**(a)** Show this information on a Venn diagram. **[3 marks]**

ℰ T F 9

> **Exam focus**
> The whole Venn diagram needs to be labelled with the symbol ℰ.

One of the 60 students is selected at random.

**(b)** Work out the probability that the student

**(i)** studies textiles but not food science **[2 marks]**

........................

**(ii)** studies neither subject. **[2 marks]**

........................

> To work out the number of students who study only textiles subtract 9 from the total number of students who study textiles.

**2.** A survey of 30 people showed that 17 jog, 15 walk, and 7 jog and walk.

**(a)** Draw a Venn diagram to represent this information. **[4 marks]**

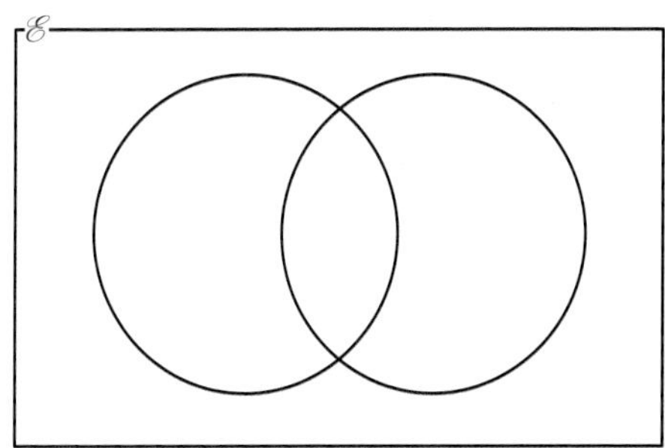


**(b)** Work out the probability that a person selected randomly from the survey

**(i)** takes neither of these types of exercise **[2 marks]**

........................

**(ii)** only jogs or walks, but not both. **[2 marks]**

........................

**3.** ℰ = {integers between 0 and 20 inclusive}
$A$ = {factors of 50}
$B$ = {multiples of 5}

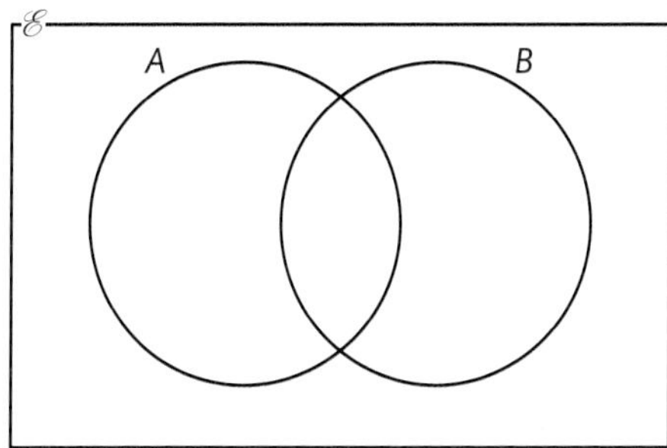


**(a)** Complete the Venn diagram to represent this information. **[3 marks]**

**(b)** List the members of the set $A \cap B$. **[3 marks]**

........................

> The integers from 0 to 20 should each appear exactly once on your completed Venn diagram.

 Made a start  Feeling confident 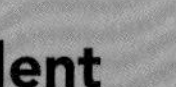 Exam ready 

# Tree diagrams

## Quick quiz

Tick (✓) the correct box.

Probabilities can be represented on a ☐ pictogram ☐ tree diagram ☐ sample space diagram.

## Completing and interpreting tree diagrams

**Grade 5**

**1.** In a bag, there are 6 black counters and 4 green counters. Andrea takes a counter at random and records the colour. She puts the counter back in the bag. She then takes another counter from the bag and records the colour.

**(a)** Complete the tree diagram. **[2 marks]**

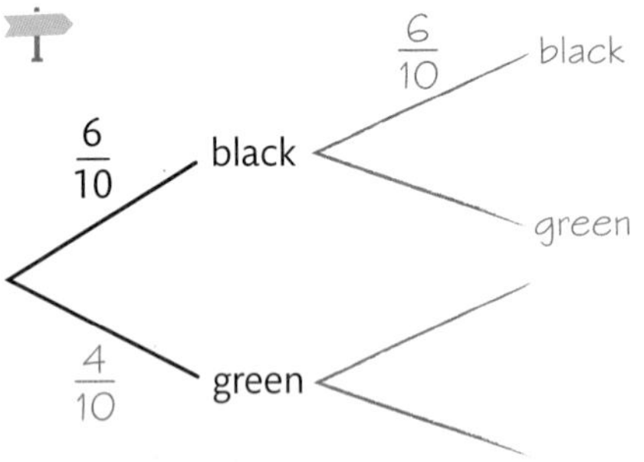

$\frac{6}{10}$ black — $\frac{6}{10}$ black; green

$\frac{4}{10}$ green — ; 

Write the probabilities on the branches.

Leave the probabilities as fractions.

The probabilities on each pair of branches add up to 1

**Exam focus**
You multiply along the branches.

**(b)** Work out the probability that both counters will be black. **[2 marks]**

..............................

**(c)** Work out the probability that exactly one of the counters will be black. **[3 marks]**

..............................

**2.** A spinner can land on green or on red. The probability that the spinner will land on green is 0.7. The spinner is spun twice.

**(a)** Complete the probability tree diagram. **[2 marks]**

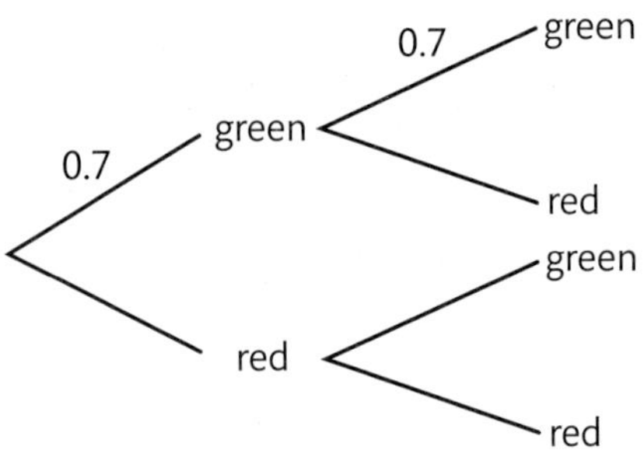

0.7 green — 0.7 green; red

red — green; red

**(b)** Work out the probability that the spinner will land on green twice. **[2 marks]**

..............................

**(c)** Work out the probability that the spinner lands on two different colours. **[3 marks]**

..............................

 Made a start 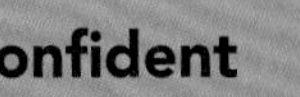 Feeling confident  Exam ready

# Probability

## Probability

Grade 5 

1. There are 11 counters in a bag. 8 of the counters are red. 3 of the counters are yellow.
Sandeep takes a counter at random and records the colour.
He puts the counter back into the bag.
He then takes another counter at random and records the colour.

Work out the probability that Sandeep takes

(i) two red counters. You must show your working. **[2 marks]**

..............................

Draw a tree diagram.

Write the probabilities on each branch.

**Exam focus**

Multiply along the branches and add up the probabilities of the different outcomes.

(ii) one counter of each colour. You must show your working. **[3 marks]**

..............................

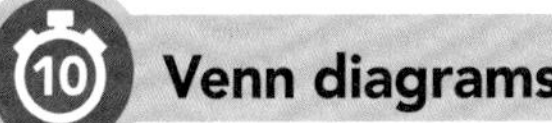

## Venn diagrams

Grade 5 

2. $\mathscr{E}$ = {the first 12 square numbers}
$A$ = {1, 4, 16, 25, 36, 144}
$B$ = {9, 16, 36, 49}

(a) Complete the Venn diagram to represent this information. **[4 marks]**

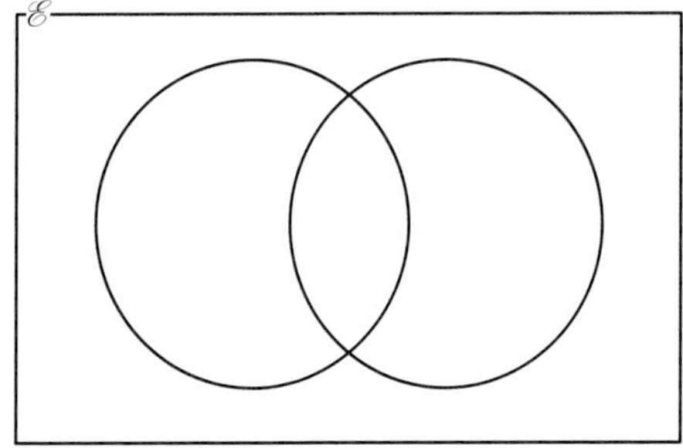

A number is selected at random from the universal set, $\mathscr{E}$.

(b) What is the probability that the number is in the set $A \cup B$? **[2 marks]**

..............................

(c) What is the probability that the number is in the set $A \cap B$? **[2 marks]**

..............................

$A \cup B$ means all the elements that are in $A$, or $B$, or both.

## Relative frequency

Grade 5 

3. Here is a four-sided spinner. The spinner is biased.

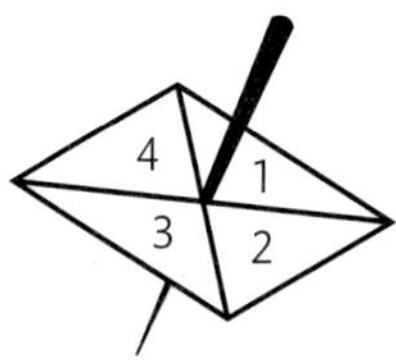


The table shows the probabilities that the spinner will land on 2 or 3.

| **Number** | **1** | **2** | **3** | **4** |
|---|---|---|---|---|
| **Probability** | | 0.35 | 0.25 | |

The probability that the spinner will land on 1 is the same as the probability that the spinner will land on 4.

(a) Work out the probability that the spinner will land on 1. **[3 marks]**

..............................

Joshua is going to spin the spinner 280 times.

(b) Work out an estimate for the number of times the spinner will land on 2 **[2 marks]**

..............................

# Averages and range

## Quick quiz

Match each word to the correct definition.

| mode | median | mean | range |
|---|---|---|---|

| | | | |
|---|---|---|---|
| the middle number in a set of data, when the data has been written in ascending order | the difference between the largest and smallest values | all the values added together and divided by the number of values | the number or item which occurs most often |

## Finding averages from discrete data — Grades 1–4

**1.** Here is a list of numbers:

4 8 5 11 10 5 9 3 4 14 4

**(a)** Write down the mode. **[1 mark]**

3 4 4 4 5 5 8 9 10 11 14

Write the numbers in order of size.

..........................

**(b)** Work out the median. **[2 marks]**

..............................

**(c)** Work out the mean. **[2 marks]**

..............................

**(d)** Work out the range. **[2 marks]**

..............................

## Using the mean, mode and median — Grades 3–4

**2.** Ryan recorded the heights, in cm, of 11 tomato plants growing in his potting shed. Here are his results:

23 18 25 28 11 14 26 22 14 25 25

**(a)** Write down the mode. **[1 mark]**

.............................. cm

**(b)** Find the median height. **[2 marks]**

.............................. cm

**(c)** Work out the mean height. **[2 marks]**

.............................. cm

**(d)** Work out the range. **[2 marks]**

.............................. cm

**3.** Uri measures the weights, to the nearest kg, of the parcels delivered to a business one day. Here are his results:

4 2 7 5 4 8 15 7 5 2 7

**(a)** Write down the mode. **[1 mark]**

.............................. kg

**(b)** Work out the mean weight. **[2 marks]**

.............................. kg

The business wants to know how much an average parcel weighs. Uri suggests that the median would be a better average to use for this set of data.

**(c)** Explain why Uri is correct. **[2 marks]**

..............................................................................

..............................................................................

## Using the combined mean — Grade 5

**4.** Their trainer recorded the times it took each of Ada, Charlie, Osman and Diego to run a race. The mean of their times is 13.5 seconds. Ed also ran the race. The combined mean time for all 5 people was 14 seconds.

Work out the time it took Ed to run the race. **[3 marks]**

**Problem solving**

If four people have a mean time of 13.5 seconds, the total time for all four people is $4 \times 13.5$

.............................. seconds

Made a start | Feeling confident | Exam ready

# Pictograms

## Quick quiz

If ■ represents 5 then

■■ represents ..................... ■■■ represents ..................... ■■■■■■ represents .....................

## Interpreting pictograms

Grade 1

1. Alex asks his friends to tell him which sport they like best out of football, badminton, tennis and cricket.
The pictogram shows how many friends chose football, how many chose badminton and how many chose tennis.

| Sport | Number of friends |
|---|---|
| Football | ● ● ● |
| Badminton | ● ◖ |
| Tennis | ● ● ◜ |
| Cricket | |

Key ● represents 4 friends

(a) How many chose football? **[1 mark]**

3 whole symbols represent 3 × .......... = ..........

...............................

10 of his friends chose cricket.

(b) Use this information to complete the pictogram. **[1 mark]**

1 symbol represents 4 friends, so 10 friends will be represented by .......... ÷ .......... = .......... symbols

(c) Work out the total number of friends Alex asked. **[2 marks]**

Adding the votes for all the sports: football + badminton + tennis + cricket =

...............................

## Using pictograms

Grade 1

2. The pictogram shows the numbers of tins of tomatoes sold in a shop on Monday, Tuesday and Wednesday last week.

| Day | Number of tins |
|---|---|
| Monday | ◇ ◇ ◇ ◇ |
| Tuesday | ◇ ◁ |
| Wednesday | ◇ ◇ ◇ ◇ |
| Thursday | |
| Friday | |

Key ◇ represents 10 tins

On Thursday, 30 tins of tomatoes were sold in the shop and on Friday, 25 tins of tomatoes were sold in the shop.

(a) Use this information to complete the pictogram. **[2 marks]**

(b) How many more tins were sold on Wednesday than on Tuesday? **[2 marks]**

...............................

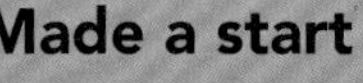

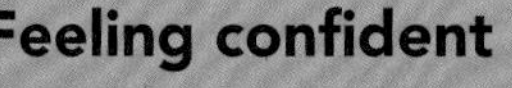

Made a start | Feeling confident | Exam ready

# Line graphs

## Quick quiz

Look at this set of data: 14 18 16 12 13 19 24 36 36

Work out

**(a)** the mode ................................ **(b)** the median ................................ **(c)** the mean. ................................

## Interpreting line graphs

Grade 5

1. Shauna asked some people how many driving tests they had each taken. The table gives information about her results.

| Number of driving tests | 1 | 2 | 3 | 4 | 5 |
|---|---|---|---|---|---|
| Frequency | 11 | 9 | 6 | 4 | 3 |

**(a)** Complete the bar-line graph for the information in the table. **[2 marks]**

**Exam focus**

Make sure you know the difference between the mean, mode and median.

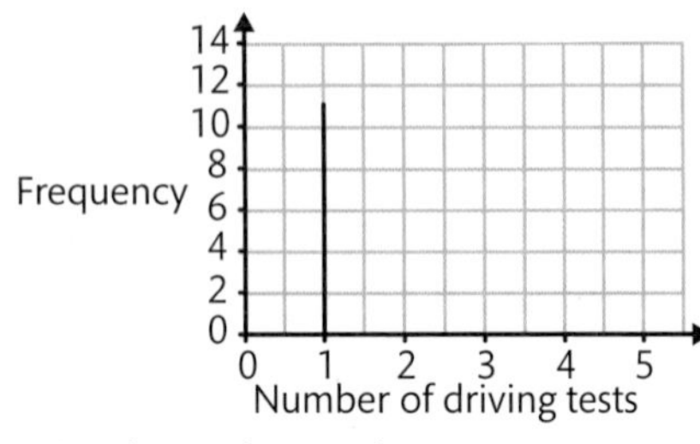


**(b)** Write down the mode. **[1 mark]**

The mode is represented by the tallest line.

................................

**(c)** Work out the mean number of driving tests. **[3 marks]**

$$\text{Mean} = \frac{(1 \times 11) + (2 \times \ldots\ldots) + (3 \times \ldots\ldots) + (4 \times \ldots\ldots) + (5 \times \ldots\ldots)}{33}$$

................................

To find the mean, find the total number of tests and divide the answer by the total number of people taking the tests.

## Interpreting time series graphs

Grade 5

2. The time series graph gives some information about the number of televisions sold in a shop in each quarter of 2010 and 2011.

**(a)** Work out the total number of televisions sold in quarter 1 of 2010 and quarter 1 of 2011. **[2 marks]**

................................

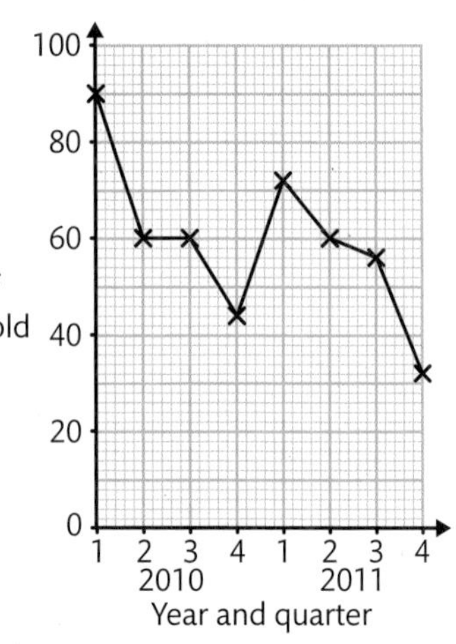


**(b)** Describe the trend in the number of televisions sold in the shop from 2010 to 2011. **[1 mark]**

................................................................................................

................................................................................................

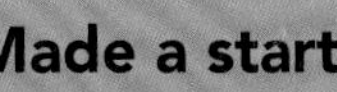

Made a start Feeling confident Exam ready

# Pie charts

## Quick quiz

Work out

(a) $\frac{20}{30} \times 360$ ..........................
(b) $\frac{42}{60} \times 360$ ..........................
(c) $\frac{70}{90} \times 360$ ..........................

## Drawing pie charts

Grade 2

**1.** Chenoa asked 60 students to name their favourite drink. Here are her results.

| Favourite drink | Frequency | Angle |
|---|---|---|
| Cola | 15 | |
| Orange squash | 20 | |
| Sparkling water | 25 | |

Draw an accurate pie chart for her results. **[3 marks]**

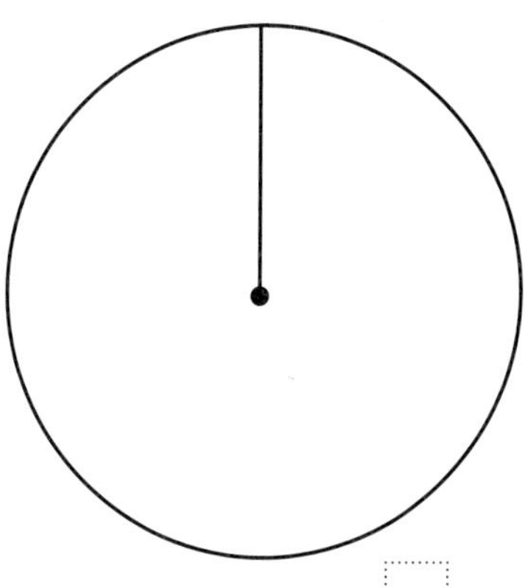

The angles at the centre of a pie chart add up to 360°.

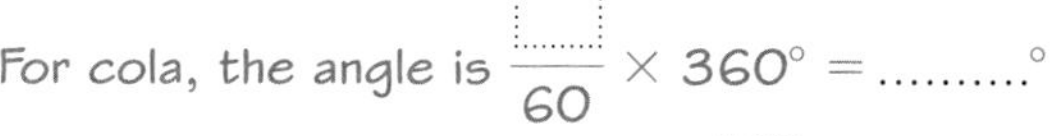

For cola, the angle is $\frac{\square}{60} \times 360° =$ ..........°

For orange squash, the angle is $\frac{\square}{60} \times 360° =$ ..........°

For sparkling water, the angle is $\frac{\square}{60} \times 360° =$ ..........°

**2.** Ali asked 72 people which foreign language they studied at school. Here are his results.

| Language | Frequency |
|---|---|
| Latin | 15 |
| French | 10 |
| Spanish | 20 |
| Italian | 27 |

Draw an accurate pie chart for his results. **[3 marks]**

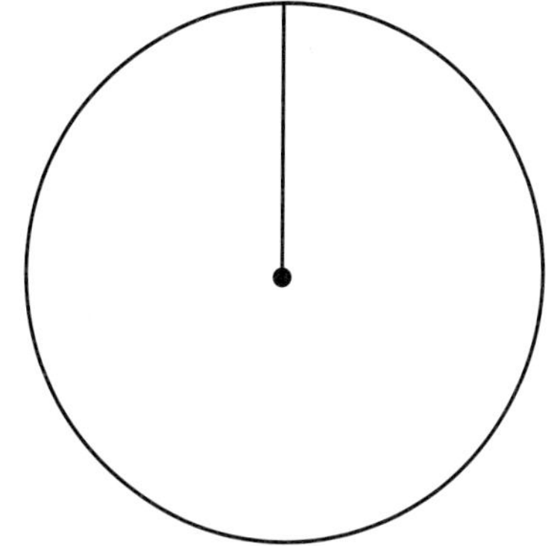

**Exam focus**
Label each sector clearly.

Add a column to the table to work out the angles:

$$\frac{\text{frequency for this sector}}{\text{total frequency}} \times 360°$$

## Interpreting pie charts

Grade 2

**3.** The pie chart gives some information about the number of birds that Renu saw in her garden one day.

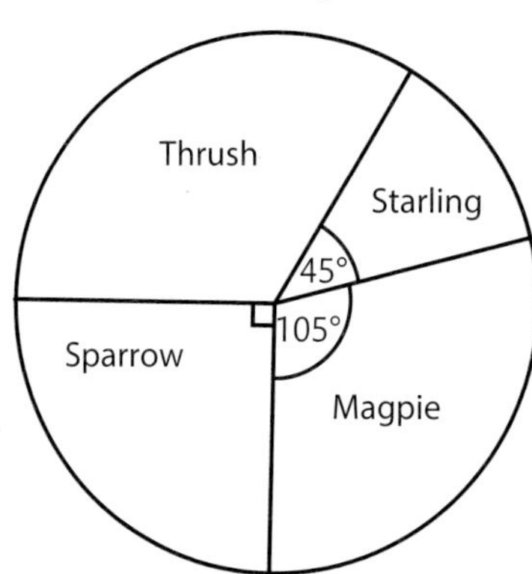


Renu saw 21 magpies on that day.

**(a)** How many starlings did Renu see on that day?

**[3 marks]**

..............................

**(b)** How many sparrows did Renu see on that day?

**[2 marks]**

..............................

**(c)** Work out the total number of birds she saw on that day.

**[2 marks]**

..............................

# Stem-and-leaf diagrams

## Quick quiz

Write down the following numbers in ascending order.

**(a)** 6 5 2 1 3 9 2

........ ........ ........ ........ ........ ........ ........

**(b)** 8 9 5 6 7 7 5

........ ........ ........ ........ ........ ........ ........

## Drawing stem-and-leaf diagrams

**Grade 3**

**1.** Sifiso catches 20 fish.

Here are the masses, in grams, of the fish he caught.

40 51 47 37 43 65 52 38
54 63 68 41 56 48 56 38
45 59 40

Draw an ordered stem-and-leaf diagram for these masses. **[3 marks]**

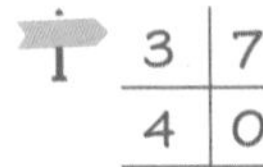

| | |
|---|---|
| 3 | 7 |
| 4 | 0 7 3 |
| 5 | 1 |
| 6 | 5 |

Step 1: Draw an unordered stem and leaf diagram.

Step 2: Draw the ordered stem and leaf diagram.

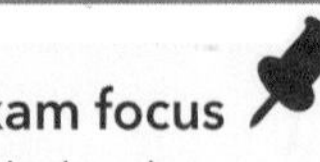

**Exam focus**
Include a key.

Key

**2.** Here are the heights, in centimetres, of 16 children.

113 137 125 140 137 119
138 139 115 127 123 128
123 120 141

Draw an ordered stem-and-leaf diagram for these heights. **[3 marks]**

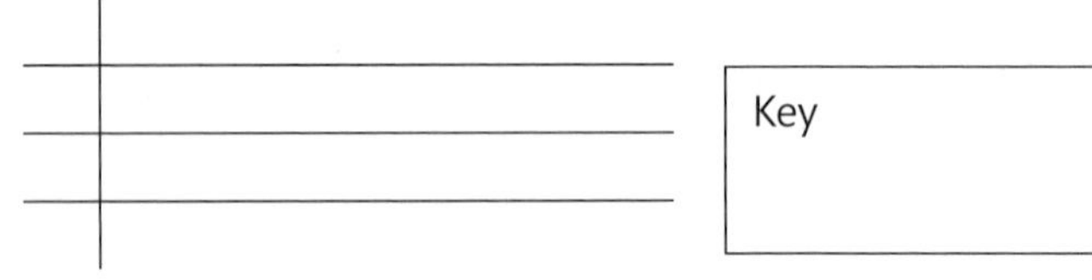

Key

**3.** Nicholas plays 15 games of ten-pin bowling.

Here are his scores.

62 49 65 56 69 65 56 53
79 66 55 69 67 61 73

Draw an ordered stem-and-leaf diagram for these scores. **[3 marks]**

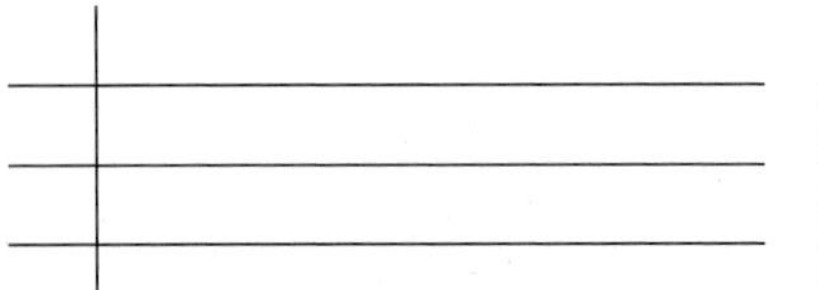

Key

**4.** Here are the heights, in centimetres, of 20 plants.

63 74 68 86 88 74 91 83
61 94 71 82 85 93 90 86
77 81 78 86

Draw an ordered stem-and-leaf diagram for these heights. **[3 marks]**

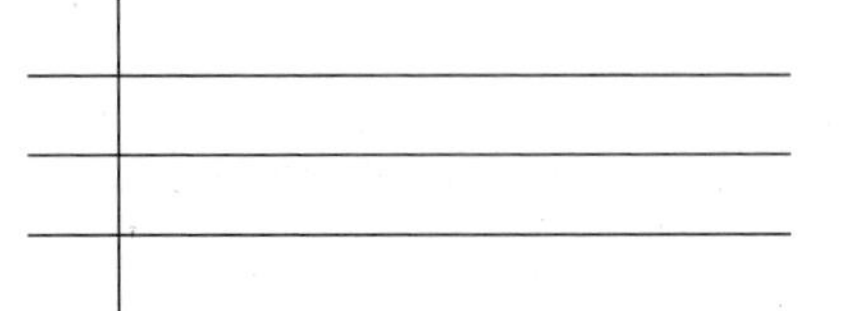

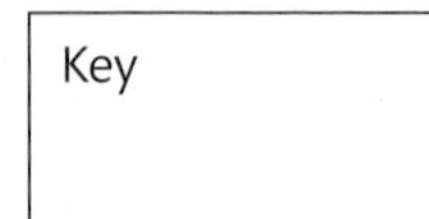

Key

Key



Made a start Feeling confident Exam ready

# Scatter graphs

## Quick quiz

Write down the type of correlation shown when data on a scatter graph is going

**(a)** upwards from left to right .............................. **(b)** downwards from left to right. ..............................

## Interpreting scatter graphs

**Grade 5**

**1.** Jorell recorded the heights in centimetres and the weights in kilograms of 9 different students. The scatter graph shows information about his results.
One of the points is an outlier.

An outlier is a point that does not follow the trend of the data.

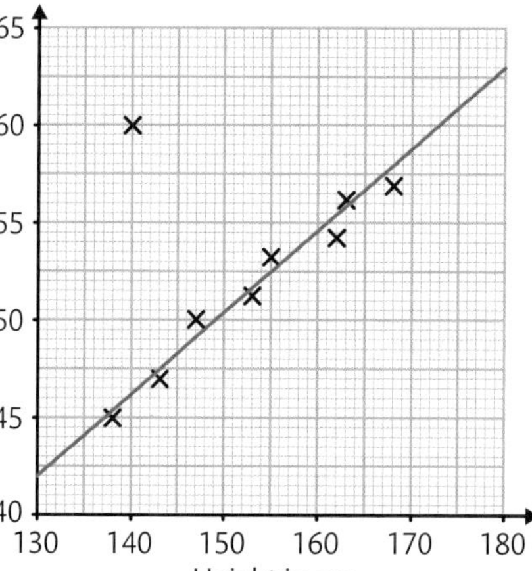


**(a)** Write down the coordinates of the outlier. **[1 mark]**

..............................

**(b)** For all the other points

**(i)** draw the line of best fit **[1 mark]**

**(ii)** describe the correlation. **[1 mark]**

..............................

'Describe the correlation' means say whether it is positive or negative.

A student is 180 cm tall.

**(c)** Estimate the weight of this student. **[1 mark]**

.............................. kg

**(d)** Is this estimate reliable? Give a reason for your answer. **[1 mark]**

..............................................................................................................................

## Drawing scatter graphs

**Grade 5**

**2.** The table shows information about 8 apartments in a city. The table shows the distance, in miles, from the city centre and the monthly rent, in pounds, of each apartment.

| **Distance from city centre (miles)** | 3.4 | 1.4 | 0.6 | 2.4 | 1.8 | 0.9 | 4.1 | 3.2 |
|---|---|---|---|---|---|---|---|---|
| **Monthly rent (£)** | 130 | 330 | 510 | 280 | 400 | 440 | 120 | 140 |

**(a)** Draw a scatter graph for the information in the table. **[3 marks]**

**(b)** Describe and interpret the correlation. **[2 marks]**

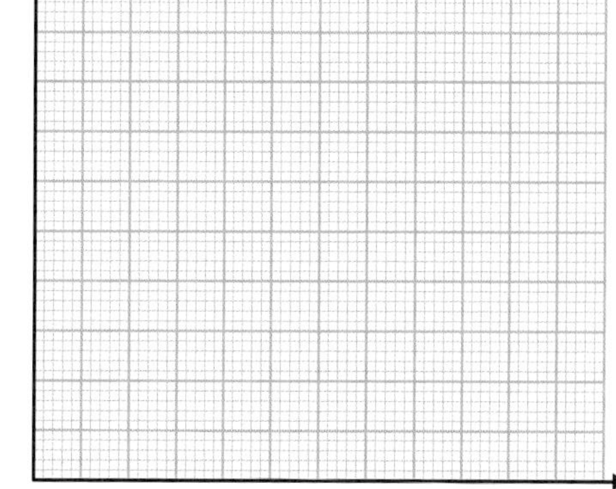

..............................................................................................

..............................................................................................

An apartment is 2.8 miles from the city centre.

**(c)** Estimate the monthly rent for this apartment. **[1 mark]**

£..............................

**(d)** Is this estimate reliable? Give a reason for your answer. **[1 mark]**

..............................................................................................................................

 Made a start 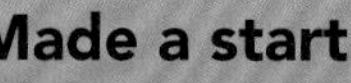  Feeling confident Exam ready

# Frequency tables

## 5 Quick quiz

Look at this set of data: 3 3 5 5 5 5 8 8 8 9 10 12 14 15 16

Work out

**(a)** the mode ........................ **(b)** the median ........................ **(c)** the mean. ........................

## 5 Averages from a frequency table

**Grade 4**

**1.** The table gives information about the numbers of medals gained by the boys at a running club.

| Number of medals | Frequency | $fx$ |
|---|---|---|
| 0 | 19 | |
| 1 | 16 | |
| 2 | 9 | |
| 3 | 7 | |
| 4 | 4 | |

$fx$ = frequency × number

Add another column to work out $fx$.

The mode is the number that occurs most often. It has the highest frequency.

The median is the middle number in the ordered data.

**(a)** Write down the mode. **[1 mark]**

...............................

**(b)** Work out the median. **[1 mark]**

Total frequency = 19 + 16 + 9 + 7 + 4 = .............

Median = $\frac{1}{2}(55 + 1)$ = ........th value = .............

...............................

**(c)** Work out the mean number of medals. **[2 marks]**

Mean = $\frac{\text{total of all data values}}{\text{number of data values}} = \frac{\sum fx}{\sum f} = \frac{\text{..........................}}{\text{..........................}}$

...............................

## 10 Averages from a grouped frequency table

**Grade 5**

**2.** David asked some people how many minutes they each took to get to work. The table shows some information about his results.

| Number of minutes, $t$ | Frequency, $f$ |
|---|---|
| $0 \leqslant t < 10$ | 7 |
| $10 \leqslant t < 20$ | 11 |
| $20 \leqslant t < 30$ | 16 |
| $30 \leqslant t < 40$ | 19 |
| $40 \leqslant t < 50$ | 12 |

**(a)** Find the class interval that includes the median. **[1 mark]**

...............................

**(b)** Write down the modal class. **[1 mark]**

...............................

**(c)** Work out an estimate for the mean time taken. **[3 marks]**

............................... minutes

**(d)** Explain why your answer to part **(c)** is an estimate. **[1 mark]**

.............................................................................................

.............................................................................................

.............................................................................................

 Made a start  Feeling confident  Exam ready

# Two-way tables

## Quick quiz

Fill in the gaps.

**(a)** 60 − 42 = ........................ **(b)** ........................ + 21 = 33 **(c)** 70 − 31 − 23 = ........................

## Completing two-way tables

**Grade 2**

**1.** 90 students each study one language. The two-way table shows some information about these students.

| | Latin | Spanish | German | Total |
|---|---|---|---|---|
| **Female** | 20 | | | 46 |
| **Male** | | 19 | | |
| **Total** | | 23 | 35 | 90 |

**Exam focus**
Use the totals to check your completed two-way table.

**(a)** Complete the table. **[3 marks]**

Number of male students = 90 − 46 = ...............

Total number who study Latin = 90 − ............... − ............... = ...............

Number of males that study Latin = ............... − ............... = ...............

Each row or column should add up to the total.

Leave your answer as a fraction.

One of these students is picked at random.

**(b)** Write down the probability that the student studies Spanish. **[1 mark]**

...............................

## Drawing two-way tables

**Grade 3**

**2.** 60 students attending an after-school club are each asked to choose a piece of fruit. They can choose a banana, an orange or a pear.
There are 25 boys.
24 students chose a banana. 11 of them were girls.
9 boys chose an orange.
13 girls chose a pear.

**(a)** Draw a two-way table to show this data. **[4 marks]**

**(b)** How many students chose a pear? **[1 mark]**

...............................

A student is selected at random.

**(c)** What is the probability that this student is a boy who chose a pear? **[1 mark]**

...............................

**3.** 100 students take part in lunchtime sports activities at a school. They can choose swimming, badminton or tennis.
32 students choose swimming. 17 of them are girls.
25 students choose badminton. 14 of them are girls.
There are 45 boys altogether.

**(a)** Draw a two-way table to show this information. **[4 marks]**

**(b)** A student is selected at random. Find the probability that this student is

**(i)** a girl who goes swimming **[1 mark]**

...............................

**(ii)** a boy who chose tennis. **[1 mark]**

...............................

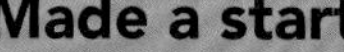
Made a start

Feeling confident

Exam ready

# Sampling

## Quick quiz

Tick (✓) the correct box. A sample is random when

☐ all the individuals in the population have an equal chance of being chosen

☐ the population is divided into strata and then each person has an equal chance of being chosen from the strata.

## Data collection — Grade 5

**1.** Keith wants to find out the types of film people like best. He is going to ask whether they prefer thriller films, horror films, science fiction films or musicals.

**(a)** Design a suitable table for a data collection sheet he could use to collect this information. **[2 marks]**

| | Thriller | Horror | | |
|---|---|---|---|---|
| Tally | | | | |
| | | | | |

Draw a table and write down the headings.

**Exam focus**
Give clear and concise answers.

Keith collects his data by asking 10 people outside the cinema on a Friday night.
This might not be a good way to find out the types of film people like best.

**(b)** Give two reasons why. **[2 marks]**

1. ..............................

2. ..............................

## Samples and surveys — Grade 5

**2.** A machine produces 2000 bolts each day. Tara wants to take a random sample of 20 of these bolts.

Describe a method she could use to select the sample. **[2 marks]**

..............................

..............................

**3.** Govind is doing a survey to find out how many magazines people buy.
He chooses 5 of his friends at school to fill out his survey.

This may not be a good sample to use. Give two reasons why. **[2 marks]**

1. ..............................

2. ..............................

**4.** Penn Council wants to produce a newsletter for adults living in Penn. The council wants to find out which local issues the adults are most concerned about. They decide to ask a sample of the adults. The council sends a survey to all the adults living in Wells Street.

Discuss whether or not this would be a good sample. **[2 marks]**

..............................

..............................

 Made a start 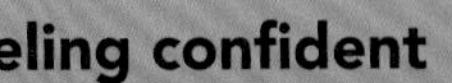 Feeling confident  Exam ready

# Analysing data

## 2 Quick quiz

The median time for boys to walk home is 23 minutes and the median time for girls to walk home is 18 minutes.

Fill in this contextualised comparison.

On average it takes boys .............................. to get home than girls.

## 5 Comparing data — Grade 3

**1.** Merindah recorded the shoe size of each of the boys in her class.
Here are the shoe sizes she recorded:

5   6   7   5   6   7   5   10   8   9

For the shoe sizes of the girls in her class, the mean is 5.2 and the range is 3.

Compare the shoe sizes of the boys and the girls. **[4 marks]**

The mean for the boys is ..............................

The range for the boys is ......... − ......... = .........

.....................................................................................................

.....................................................................................................

Work out the mean shoe size for the boys.

Work out the range of the shoe sizes for the boys.

Make comparisons by using words such as 'greater than' or 'less than'.

**Exam focus**

Compare the mean and the range. Ensure that one of the comments is written in context.

## 5 Interpreting discrete data — Grade 3

**2.** Amrit played 15 computer games. Here are the points she scored in each game:

28   29   29   29   30   31   31   33   34   34   34   37   38   39   39

Seke plays the same 15 computer games. The median number of points Seke scored is 34 and the range is 18.

Who is more consistent at scoring points, Amrit or Seke? You must give a reason for your answer. **[3 marks]**

.....................................................................................................

.....................................................................................................

## 5 Interpreting statements — Grade 5

**3.** Adam carried out a survey of 30 people. He found that they had a mean age of 36 years and a median age of 32 years.
Adam then surveys one more person. This person has an age of 40.
Adam decides to include this age so he works out the mean age and median age of 31 people. Here are two statements about the ages of the 31 people.

Statement 1: The mean age of the 31 people is more than 36 years.
Statement 2: The median age of the 31 people is less than 32 years.

Comment on both statements. You must give reasons for your answers. **[2 marks]**

.....................................................................................................

.....................................................................................................

.....................................................................................................

# Statistics

## 5 Pictograms

Grade 1 

1. Some children were asked to name their favourite colour out of red, yellow, green and pink.
The incomplete pictogram shows how many children chose red, how many chose yellow and how many chose green.

| Colour | Number of children |
|---|---|
| Red | ○ ○ ○ |
| Yellow | ○ ○ ◖ |
| Green | ○ ○ ○ ○ ○ |
| Pink | |

Key ○ represents 4 children

6 children said pink.

**(a)** Complete the pictogram. **[1 mark]**

1 symbol represents 4 children.

So 6 children will be represented by ........ ÷ 4 = ........ symbols.

Use the key to calculate how many shapes you need to draw.

**(b)** How many more children chose green than yellow? **[1 mark]**

...............................

Find the difference between the number of children who chose green and the number who chose yellow.

**(c)** Work out how many children were asked to name their favourite colour. **[2 marks]**

...............................

Work out the total number of children.

## 10 Stem-and-leaf diagrams

Grade 3 

2. Daisy recorded the number of phone cards sold in a shop for each of 27 days. Here are her results:

| | | | | | | | | |
|---|---|---|---|---|---|---|---|---|
| 15 | 20 | 31 | 24 | 32 | 28 | 36 | 37 | 25 |
| 21 | 19 | 28 | 51 | 23 | 43 | 49 | 26 | 48 |
| 31 | 35 | 33 | 41 | 18 | 46 | 34 | 39 | 47 |

**(a)** Draw an ordered stem-and-leaf diagram for this information. You must include a key. **[3 marks]**

**(b)** Work out the median. **[2 marks]**

...............................

**(c)** Work out the range. **[2 marks]**

...............................

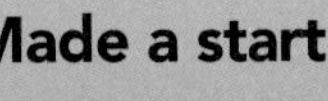
Made a start

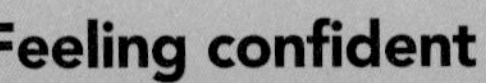
Feeling confident

Exam ready

# Problem-solving strategies

## Using areas in context

Grade 4

**1.** The diagram shows the end wall of Taimoor's garden shed.

Taimoor is going to paint the wall.
He uses tins of spray paint.
Each tin will cover 2 $m^2$ of the wall.
Each tin of paint normally costs £6.50
Taimoor gets a discount of 20% off the cost of the paint.
Taimoor has £50 to spend.

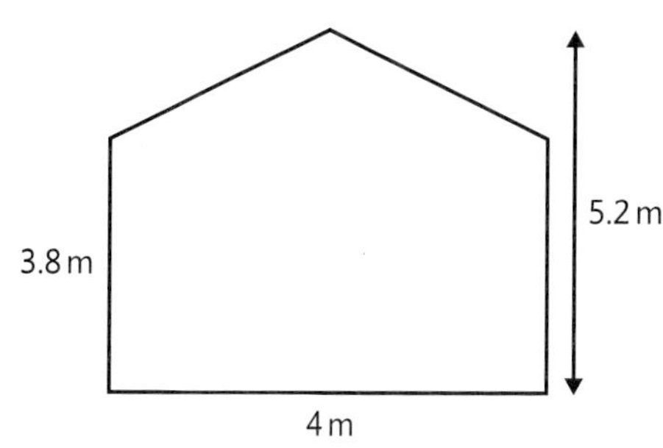


Does Taimoor have enough money to buy all the paint he needs?
You must show all your working. **[5 marks]**

**What is my plan to solve the problem?**

| | |
|---|---|
| **1. What do I have to do?** | *I will need to work out the area of the triangle. I will need to work out the area of the rectangle. I will need to work out the discount. I can then work out the cost of the paint and compare the cost with £50 to see if Taimoor has enough money.* |
| **2. What information do I need?** | *I need to work out the height of the triangle.* |
| **3. What mathematics can I do?** | *I need to recall the formulae for the area of a triangle and the area of a rectangle. I need to use percentages.* |
| **4. Is my solution correct?** | *I will do my calculations in a logical way so that each step acts as a building block.* |
| **5. Have I completed everything?** | *I will check that the answer is sensible.* |

| | |
|---|---|
| **I need to work out the height of the triangle.**<br><br>Height of triangle = 5.2 − 3.8<br><br>Height of triangle = ......... m | **I need to work out the area of the triangle.**<br><br>Area of triangle = $\frac{1}{2}$ × base × height<br><br>Area of triangle = $\frac{1}{2}$ × 4 × ......... = ......... $m^2$ |
| **I need to work out the area of the rectangle.**<br><br>Area of rectangle = length × width<br><br>Area of rectangle = 3.8 × 4 = ......... $m^2$ | **I need to work out the total area of the wall.**<br><br>Total area = area of triangle + area of rectangle<br><br>Total area = ......... + ......... = ......... $m^2$ |
| **I need to work out the cost of the paint.**<br><br>Number of tins of paint = ......... ÷ 2 = .........<br><br>Cost = ......... × £6.50 = £......... | **I need to work out the cost with the discount.**<br><br>Discounted price = £......... × 0.8<br><br>Discounted price = £......... |
| **I need to compare the cost of the tiles with the amount of money Taimoor has.**<br><br>Cost of the paint is ......... than £50 | **My conclusion:**<br><br>Taimoor ........................................................ money. |

# Solving number problems

## Using composite shapes

Grade 5

**1.** The diagram shows a play area in the shape of a square *ABCD* and a semicircle.

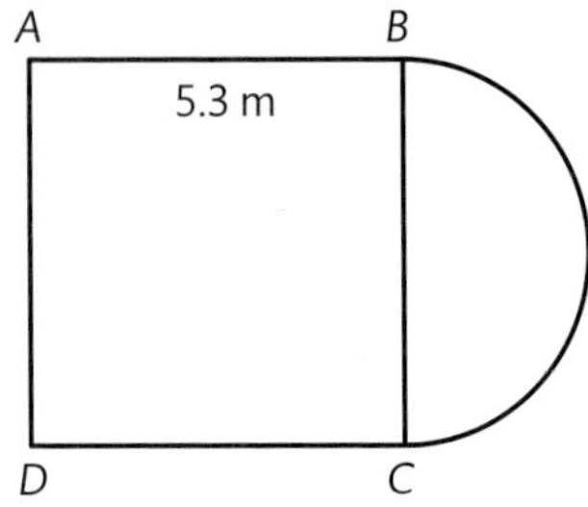


*BC* is the diameter of the semicircle.

$AB = 5.3\,\text{m}$

Len is going to cover the play area with wood chips. The wood chips are sold in packs.
One pack of wood chips will cover $3.5\,\text{m}^2$. A pack of wood chips normally costs £23.60.
Len gets a discount of 24% off the cost of the wood chips.
Len has £220 to spend.

Does Len have enough money to buy all the wood chips he needs?
You must show your working. **[5 marks]**

.................................

## Finding interest

Grade 5

**2.** Romik has £9000 to invest for 4 years in a savings account. He has a choice of two different accounts.

| **Account A** | **Account B** |
|---|---|
| 2% per year compound interest | Receive £150 interest each year |

Romik wants to have as much money as possible at the end of the 4 years.

In which account should he invest his £9000? **[4 marks]**

.................................

 Made a start  Feeling confident Exam ready

# Solving graphical problems

## Conversion graphs

Grade 5

**1.** You can use this graph to convert gallons to litres and vice versa.

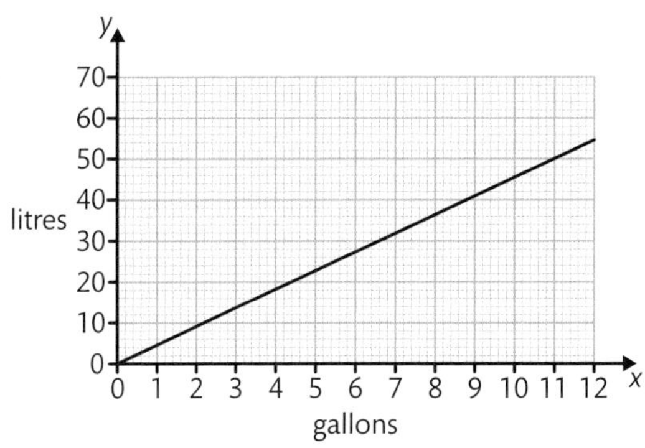


You can use a calculator for question **1(b)**.

**(a)** Convert 20 litres to gallons. **[1 mark]**

................................ gallons

**(b)** The fuel tank of a lorry holds 460 litres of diesel when completely full. The fuel tank is empty. Alexa puts 95 gallons of diesel in the fuel tank.

Is the fuel tank completely full? You must show how you get your answer. **[3 marks]**

................................

## Quadratic graphs

Grade 5

**2.** Mark wants to find out the maximum area, in m², of a rectangle with a fixed perimeter. He uses the formula $A = 12x - x^2$ where $x$ is the width of the rectangle.

**(a)** Complete the table of values for $A = 12x - x^2$

| $x$ | 0 | 2 | 4 | 6 | 8 | 10 | 12 |
|---|---|---|---|---|---|---|---|
| $A$ | 0 | | 32 | | | 20 | |

**(b)** On the grid, draw the graph of $A = 12x - x^2$ for values of $x$ from 0 to 12 **[2 marks]**

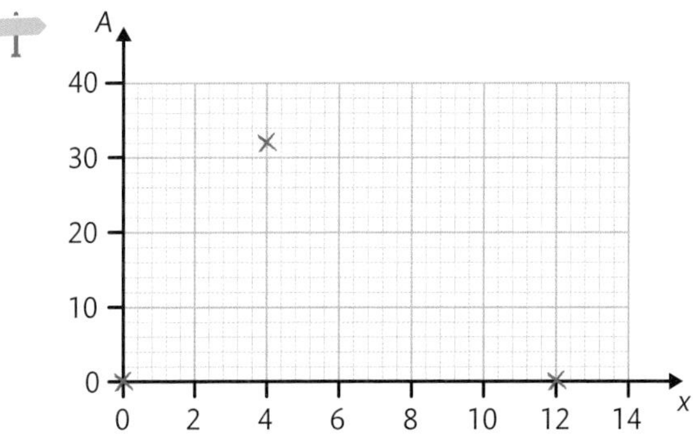


**(c)** Write down the coordinates of the turning point. **[2 marks]**

................................

**(d)** Interpret your answer from part **(c)**. **[2 marks]**

................................................................................................

................................................................................................

 Made a start  Feeling confident  Exam ready

# Solving geometric problems

## Using constructions

**Grade 4**

**1.** Here is a scale drawing of a rectangular garden *ABCD*.

Scale: 1 cm represents 1 metre

Ann wants to plant a sunflower in the garden, so that it is

at least 6 m from point *C*,
nearer to *AB* than to *AD*
and less than 4 m from *DC*.

On the diagram, shade the region where Ann can plant the sunflower. **[4 marks]**

## Using trigonometry

**Grade 5**

**2.** The diagram shows a frame made out of metal bars.
Angle *ACB* = angle *BAD* = 90°
*AB* = 10 m and *BC* = 15 m
The metal bar costs £12.85 per metre.

Work out the total cost of the metal frame. **[5 marks]**

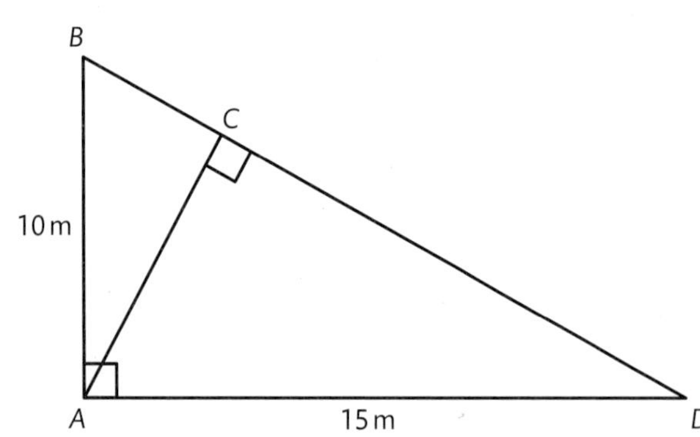


**Problem solving**

1. Work out the perimeter of the shape.
2. Then work out the length of *AC*.
3. Add your results together to find the total length required.
4. Finally, multiply the total length by the cost for one metre.

£..............................

 **Made a start**  **Feeling confident**  **Exam ready**

# Solving algebraic problems

## Using algebra

Grade 4 

**1.** The width of a rectangle is $x$ cm.
The length of the rectangle is $x + 5$ cm.

$(x + 5)$ cm

$x$ cm

**Problem solving**

Write a formula for the perimeter and then rearrange it to make $x$ the subject.

Then, use your value of $x$ to work out the lengths in cm.

Finally, work out the area.

The perimeter of the rectangle is 46 cm.

Work out the area of the rectangle. **[4 marks]**

................................cm$^2$

## Simultaneous equations

Grade 5 

**2.** Cindy buys 2 tins of paint and 5 tins of varnish for £22.75
Darren buys 2 tins of paint and 3 tins of varnish for £17.25

Use your calculator for this question.

Work out the cost of one tin of paint and the cost of one tin of varnish.
Give your answers in pounds and pence. **[4 marks]**

Paint: £................................ Varnish: £................................

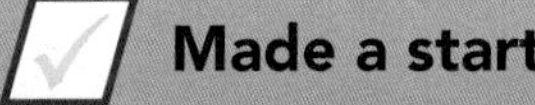

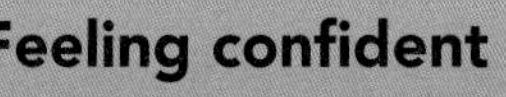
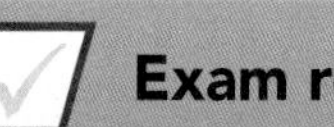

Made a start | Feeling confident | Exam ready

# Solving statistical problems

## Scatter graphs — Grade 5

**1.** The scatter graph shows the air temperature, $y$ °C, at eight different heights, $x$ km, above sea level.

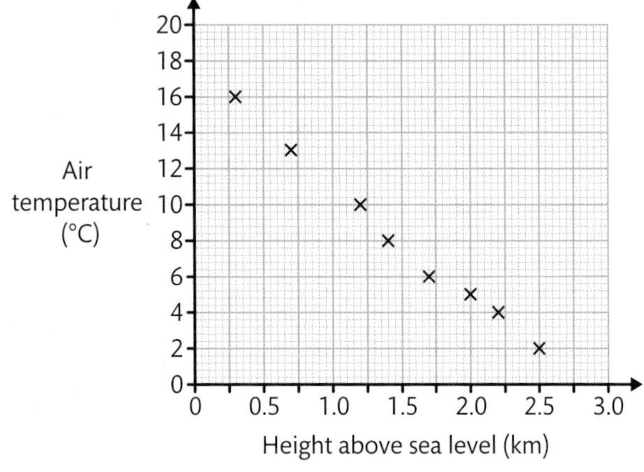


**(a)** Using the scatter graph, write down the air temperature recorded at a height of 2.0 km above sea level. **[1 mark]**

................................°C

**(b)** Describe the correlation between the air temperature and the height above sea level. **[1 mark]**

....................................

**(c)** Find an estimate of the height above sea level at which the air temperature is 0.5 °C. **[2 marks]**

................................km

## Using Venn diagrams — Grade 5

**2.** 60 children were asked about which pets they like.
25 children like dogs and 31 children like cats.
21 children like both dogs and cats.

**(a)** Complete the Venn diagram to represent this information. **[4 marks]**

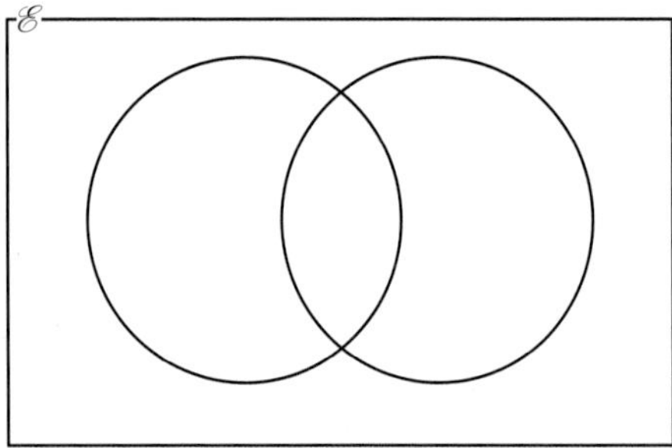


A child is picked at random.

**(b)** Find the probability that the child does not like either dogs or cats. **[1 mark]**

................................

Made a start | Feeling confident | Exam ready

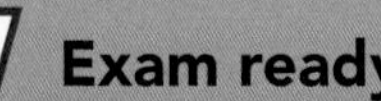

# Non-calculator practice paper

## Mathematics

### Non-calculator (Foundation Tier)

Time: 1 hour 30 minutes
Total marks: 80. Answer all questions.
You must have: ruler, protractor, pair of compasses, pen, HB pencil, eraser.
Calculators must not be used.

**Exam focus**
For your GCSE you will sit three exams. You **must not** use a calculator in Paper 1.

1. **(a)** Write 4.8 metres in centimetres. **(1 mark)**
   **(b)** Write 4600 g in kilograms. **(1 mark)**

2. Work out $5 - 18 \div 9$ **(1 mark)**

3. Solve $4y = 15$ **(1 mark)**

4. Write down the number that is half way between $-8$ and 2 **(1 mark)**

5. Here are the first four terms of a sequence: 3 7 11 15
   Write down the next two terms of the sequence. **(1 mark)**

6. Here is a pentagon.
   All measurements are in centimetres. The perimeter of the pentagon is $P$ cm.
   Find a formula for $P$ in terms of $x$. Write your formula in its simplest form. **(3 marks)**

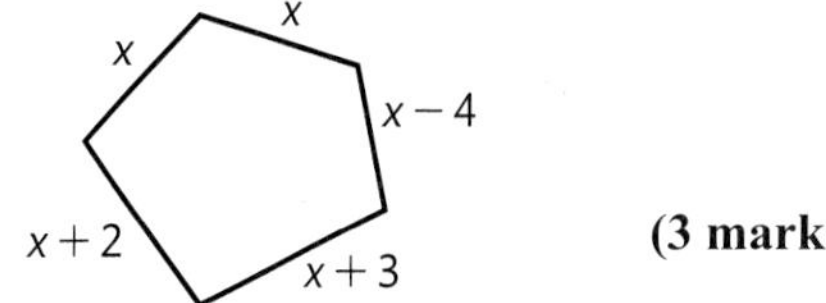


7.

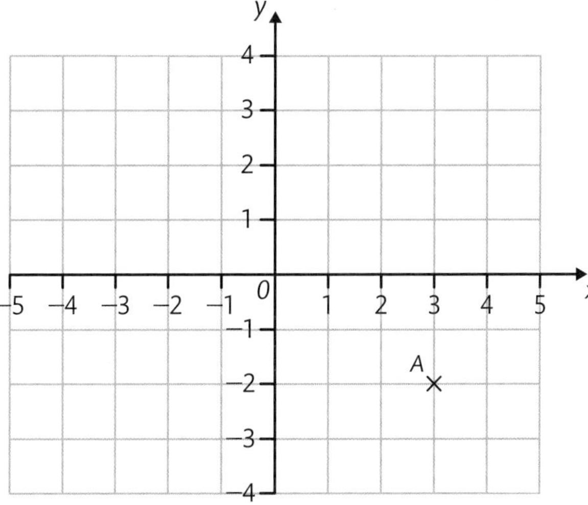


**(a)** Write down the coordinates of the point $A$. **(1 mark)**
**(b)** **(i)** Plot the point with the coordinates $(-1, 2)$. Label the point $B$. **(1 mark)**
**(ii)** Does point $B$ lie on the straight line $y = 2x - 1$? You must show your working. **(1 mark)**

8. The diagram shows an isosceles triangle.
   All measurements are in centimetres. Work out the perimeter of the triangle. **(4 marks)**

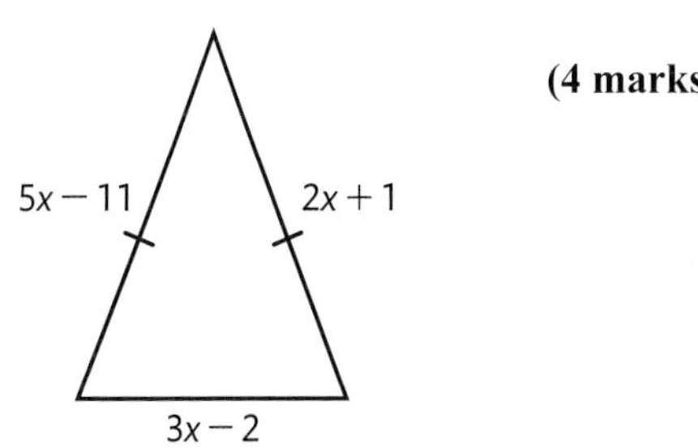

9. The length of a rectangle is two centimetres greater than the width of the rectangle.
The area of the rectangle is $24\,\text{cm}^2$. Draw the rectangle on the centimetre grid. **(2 marks)**

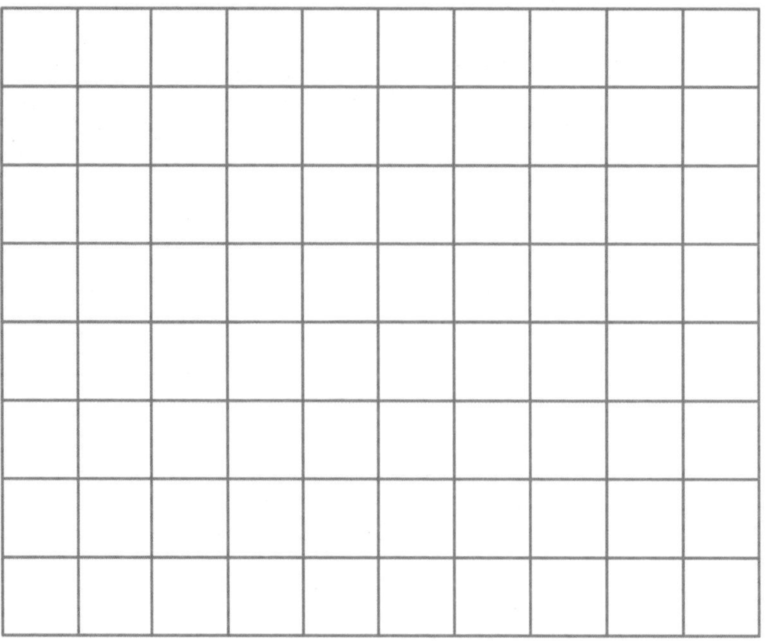

10. James and Asha each took five tests. Their results are shown below.

| **James** | 15 | 14 | 13 | 16 | 17 | 14 |
|---|---|---|---|---|---|---|
| **Asha** | 7 | 17 | 12 | 19 | 9 | 15 |

**(a)** Who had the least consistent results, James or Asha? Give a reason for your answer. **(1 mark)**

James works out his mean test result. He works out the mean to be 20
**(b)** Without working out the mean, say whether James is correct. Give a reason for your answer. **(1 mark)**

11. A school is organising a trip to the beach. The total number of people going on the trip is 71
Each minibus can carry 15 people.

**(a)** Work out the smallest number of minibuses needed for the school trip. **(2 marks)**

Two more teachers join the school trip.
**(b)** Does the school need more minibuses for the trip? You must give a reason for your answer. **(1 mark)**

12. 50 adults were asked if they were left-handed or right-handed. Here are the results.
30 of the adults were male. 12 of the female adults were right-handed. 16 of the adults who are left-handed are male.
**(a)** Use the information to complete the two-way table.

| | **Left-handed** | **Right-handed** | **Total** |
|---|---|---|---|
| **Male** | | | 30 |
| **Female** | | | |
| **total** | | | |

**(3 marks)**

One of the adults is selected at random.

**(b)** Write down the probability that this adult is a male. **(1 mark)**
**(c)** Write down the probability that this adult is a right-handed female. **(1 mark)**

13. The volume of a cube is $64\,\text{cm}^3$. Work out the surface area of the cube. **(4 marks)**

14. Here are two fractions: $\frac{4}{7}$ $\frac{5}{9}$

Which fraction is bigger? You must show your working. **(3 marks)**

15. There are white beads, blue beads and grey beads in a box.
number of white beads : blue beads : grey beads = 4 : 5 : 6
Write down the fraction of the beads that are **not** grey. Give your answer in its simplest form. **(2 marks)**

**16.** Mirlande booked a family holiday. The total cost of the holiday was £4500 plus VAT at 20%. She paid a deposit of £1200. Then she paid the remaining amount of money in 6 equal monthly payments. Work out the amount of each monthly payment. **(4 marks)**

**17.** There are 3 counters in a bag. One counter is yellow, one counter is green and one counter is red. Consuelo takes a counter at random from the bag. She puts the counter back in the bag. Then Consuelo takes a counter at random from the bag again. Work out the probability of both counters being the same colour. **(2 marks)**

**18.** Alan, Ramah and Carol share £350 in the ratio 2 : 3 : 5. How much does Ramah get? **(2 marks)**

**19.** Here are the ingredients to make 6 scones:

| 110 g flour, 20 g butter, 80 ml milk and 2 tablespoons of sugar |
|---|

Angela wants to make 15 scones. Work out how much of each ingredient she needs. **(3 marks)**

**20.** Priya and Lesedi work out $\dfrac{890}{5.03^2 + 4.9}$

Priya works out an answer of 2.9469 and Lesedi works out an answer of 29.469
One of these answers is correct. Use approximations to find out which answer is correct. **(3 marks)**

**21.** Work out $\dfrac{0.03 \times 0.004}{0.02}$

Give your answer in standard form. **(3 marks)**

**22.** **(a)** Work out $\dfrac{7}{8} \times \dfrac{3}{4}$ **(1 mark)**

**(b)** Work out $\dfrac{4}{5} - \dfrac{1}{3}$ **(2 marks)**

**(c)** Write down the value of $16^{\frac{1}{2}}$ **(1 mark)**

**(d)** Write down the value of $3^{-2}$ **(1 mark)**

**23.** Write 48 as a product of its prime factors. **(2 marks)**

**24.** Manu has five more marbles than Ben. Emma has three times as many marbles as Manu. The total number of marbles is 50. Work out the percentage of marbles that Manu has. **(4 marks)**

**25.** $ABCD$ and $EFG$ are parallel lines.
$BC = CF$. Angle $EFB = 65°$

Work out the size of the angle marked $x$.
Give reasons for each stage of your working. **(4 marks)**

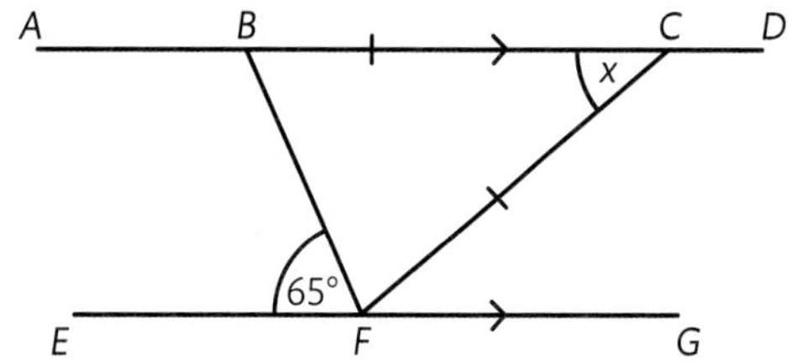


**26.** The diagram shows the plan of a floor.
Martina is going to paint the floor. She needs 1 litre of paint for 2.5 m² of floor.
There are 1.5 litres of paint in each tin of paint. Martina has 5 tins of paint.
Does Martina have enough paint for the floor? You must show your working. **(5 marks)**

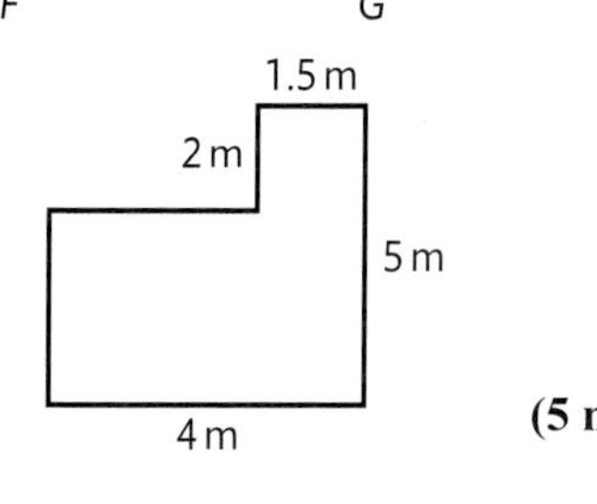


**27.** The table shows information about the ages of 20 teachers.

| **Age, $x$ (years)** | $25 < x \leqslant 35$ | $35 < x \leqslant 45$ | $45 < x \leqslant 55$ | $55 < x \leqslant 65$ |
|---|---|---|---|---|
| **Frequency** | 4 | 7 | 6 | 3 |

**(a)** Work out the estimate for the mean of the ages. **(3 marks)**

Another teacher who is 60 years old is to be included in the table.
**(b)** Will that affect the mean? You must justify your answer. **(1 mark)**

**28.** In a sale, the normal price of a jacket is reduced by 30%.
The sale price of a jacket is £77. Work out the normal price of the jacket. **(2 marks)**

# Calculator practice paper

## Mathematics

### Calculator (Foundation Tier)

Time: 1 hour 30 minutes
Total marks: 80. Answer all questions.
You must have: calculator, ruler, protractor, pair of compasses, pen, HB pencil, eraser.

**1.** Write 35% as a decimal. **(1 mark)**

**2.** Write 4789 correct to the nearest 1000 **(1 mark)**

**3.** **(a)** Simplify $4n \times 5m$ **(1 mark)**
**(b)** Simplify $p \times p \times p$ **(1 mark)**
**(c)** Simplify $2x + 3x - x$ **(1 mark)**

**4.** Anjali buys some buttons, some zips, some packs of needles and some reels of cotton.
She buys 5 buttons at 30p each, 3 zips at 90p each and 4 packs of needles at 65p per pack.
Each reel of cotton costs 55p. Anjali spends a total of £11.20 on these sewing materials.
Work out how many reels of cotton Anjali buys. **(3 marks)**

**5.** Devon thinks of a number.
$\frac{3}{4}$ of Devon's number is 60
Work out $\frac{2}{5}$ of Devon's number. **(2 marks)**

**6.** 60 students were asked to name their favourite sandwiches. The table shows the results.

| **Sandwich** | **Chicken** | **Cheese** | **Egg** | **Prawn** |
|---|---|---|---|---|
| **Frequency** | 15 | 10 | 23 | 12 |

**(a)** What fraction of the 60 students did **not** choose egg as their favourite? **(2 marks)**
**(b)** Draw a pie chart for the information in the table. **(4 marks)**

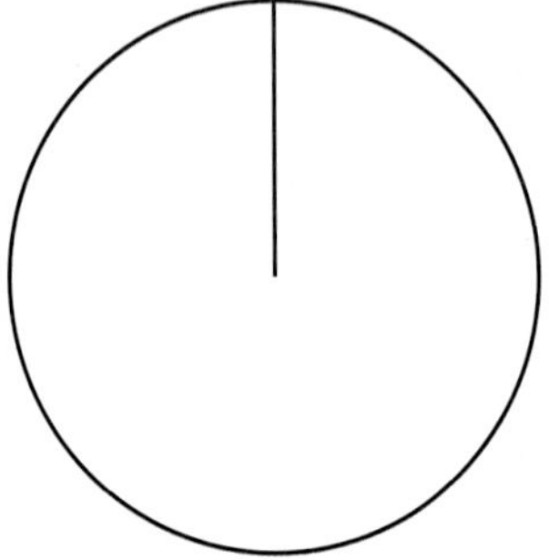

**7.** Asahi and Jill share some money in the ratio 8 : 7
**(a)** What fraction of the money does Jill get? **(1 mark)**

Lucy and Zack share some chocolates. Zack gets $\frac{1}{5}$ of the chocolates.
**(b)** Write down the ratio of the number of chocolates Lucy gets to the number of chocolates Zack gets. **(1 mark)**

**8.** Javed has a bottle of water. There are 3 litres of water in the bottle. Javed also has some empty cups. Each cup can be completely filled with 175 ml of water. How many cups can be completely filled with water from the bottle? **(3 marks)**

**9.** A gold bar has a mass of 7.5 kg. The density of gold is 19.3 g/cm$^3$.
Work out the volume of the gold bar. Give your answer correct to 3 significant figures. **(3 marks)**

**10.** The pictogram gives information about the number of books sold in each of 4 months.

| Month | Number of books sold |
|---|---|
| August | |
| September | |
| October | |
| November | |
| December | |

| Key |
|---|
| represents 4 books |

**(a)** How many books were sold in August? **(1 mark)**

**(b)** How many more books were sold in November than in September? **(2 marks)**

In December, 15 books were sold.
**(c)** Show this information in the pictogram. **(1 mark)**

**11.** In the diagram, *BCD* is a straight line.
*ABC* is a triangle.

Is triangle *ABC* an isosceles triangle?
Give a reason for each stage of your working. **(4 marks)**

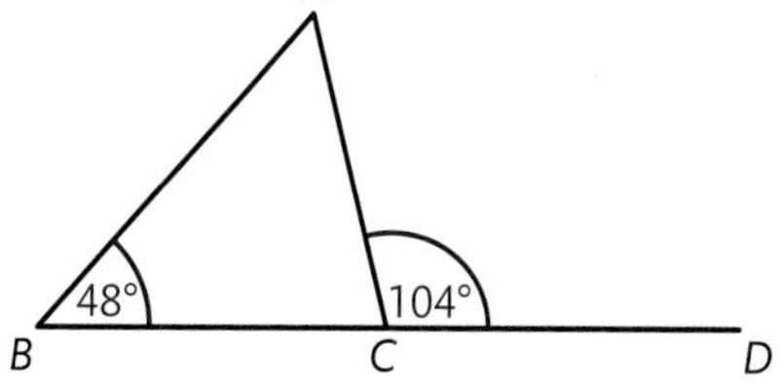


**12.** The diagram shows a building and a man. The man is of normal height.
The man and the building are drawn to the same scale.
Estimate the height of the building. **(2 marks)**

**13.** Here is a list of numbers:
31  32  33  34  35  36  37  38  39

From the numbers in the list, write down

**(a)** a square number **(1 mark)**
**(b)** a number that is a multiple of **both** 4 and 8 **(1 mark)**
**(c)** a prime number. **(1 mark)**

**14.** Rebecca is going to buy 125 pens. Here is some information about the cost of pens in two shops.

| **Pens for U** | **Petersons** |
|---|---|
| Box of 25 pens for £2.49 | Box of 10 pens for £1.60<br>Buy 2 boxes, get 1 box free. |

Rebecca wants to buy the pens as cheaply as possible.
Which shop should Rebecca buy the 125 pens from? You must show your working. **(4 marks)**

**15.** 4.5 kg of tomatoes cost £5.94. Work out the cost of 6.5 kg of tomatoes. **(2 marks)**

**16.** On the grid, draw the graph of $y = 4x + 2$ from $x = -1$ to $x = 3$ **(3 marks)**

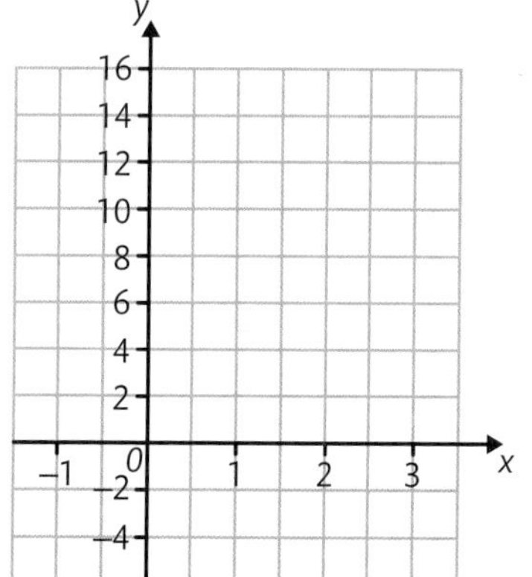

**17.** **(a)** Factorise $6x - 12$ **(1 mark)**
**(b)** Factorise fully $3a^2b + 12ab^2$ **(2 marks)**

**18.** **(a)** Write $5.8 \times 10^{-3}$ as an ordinary number. **(1 mark)**
**(b)** Work out the value of $(3.5 \times 10^3) \times (8.4 \times 10^4)$. Give your answer in standard form. **(2 marks)**

**19.** A biased 5-sided spinner is spun. The table shows the probabilities that the spinner will land on 1, 2, 3 or 4

| **Spinner** | 1 | 2 | 3 | 4 | 5 |
|---|---|---|---|---|---|
| **Probability** | 0.20 | 0.30 | 0.25 | 0.10 | |

Joe spins the spinner once.
**(a)** Work out the probability that the spinner will land on 5 **(2 marks)**

Manraj is going to spin the spinner 80 times.
**(b)** Work out an estimate for the number of times the spinner will land on 2 **(2 marks)**

**20.** Here are the first four terms of an arithmetic sequence: 5 11 17 23

**(a)** Find, in terms of $n$, an expression for the $n$th term of this arithmetic sequence. **(2 marks)**
**(b)** Is 121 a term of this arithmetic sequence? You must explain your answer. **(2 marks)**

**21.** In Wolverhampton, 1 litre of petrol costs 109.4p. In Washington D.C., 1 US gallon of petrol costs \$2.85
1 US gallon = 3.875 litres
£1 = \$1.45
In which city is petrol better value for money, Wolverhampton or Washington D.C.?
You must show your working. **(3 marks)**

**22.** In the diagram, $ABC$ and $EDC$ are straight lines. $EA$ is parallel to $DB$.
$EC = 16.2$ cm
$DC = 10.8$ cm
$DB = 5.2$ cm

**(a)** Work out the length of $AE$. **(2 marks)**

$AC = 12.3$ cm
**(b)** Work out the length of $AB$. **(2 marks)**

**23.** Jason wants to invest £35 000 for 3 years in a bank.

| **Wolves Bank** | **Bankworld** |
|---|---|
| Compound Interest<br>2% for each year | Compound Interest<br>4.2% for the first year<br>0.8% for each extra year |

Which bank will give Jason more interest at the end of 3 years?
You must show your working. **(3 marks)**

**24.** A number, $n$, is rounded to 2 decimal places. The result is 8.34
Using inequalities, write down the error interval for $n$. **(2 marks)**

**25.** Solve $x^2 + 3x - 40 = 0$ **(3 marks)**

**26.** $ABCD$ is a trapezium.

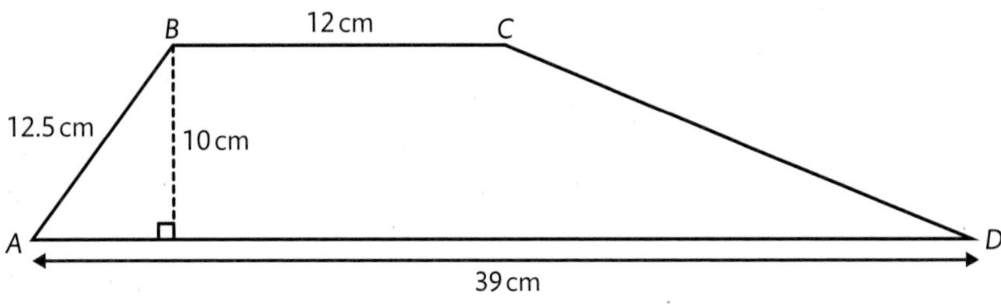


Work out the size of angle $CDA$.
Give your answer correct to 1 decimal place. **(5 marks)**

# Answers

## Page 1 Place value

**Quick quiz:**

1. **(a)** twenty **(b)** one hundred
2. **(a)** 15 **(b)** 1000

**Questions:**

1. **(a)** 4603
   **(b)** Seven thousand, two hundred and thirty-five
2. **(a)** 3084 **(b)** Nine thousand and two
   **(c)** 800
3. **(a)** 3, 6, 9, 18, 24 **(b)** 6578, 6587, 6758, 6775, 6857
4. **(a)** 5, 14, 21, 34, 47
   **(b)** 8569, 8595, 8659, 8956, 8965
5. **(a)** 876 **(b)** 687

## Page 2 Negative numbers

**Quick quiz:**

**(a)** positive **(b)** negative
**(c)** negative **(d)** positive

**Questions:**

1. **(a)** −9 **(b)** −3 **(c)** 45
2. **(a)** 13 **(b)** −12 **(c)** −12 **d)** −28
3. **(a)** −10, −8, −1, 2, 4 **(b)** −32, −15, −14, 28, 40
4. **(a)** 7 °C **(b)** −10 °C
5. **(a)** −10 °C **(b)** 6 degrees **(c)** −5 °C

## Page 3 Adding and subtracting

**Quick quiz:**

**(a)** 11 **(b)** 58 **(c)** 13 **(d)** 35

**Questions:**

1. **(a)** 449 **(b)** 9060 **(c)** 72 374
2. **(a)** 747 **(b)** 1872 **(c)** 1549
3. 176 people **4.** 48 onions
5. **(a)** 340 miles **(b)** 124 miles

## Page 4 Multiplying and dividing

**Quick quiz:**

**(a)** 42 **(b)** 72 **(c)** 4 **(d)** 7

**Questions:**

1. **(a)** 1704 **(b)** 41 817 **(c)** 34 176
2. **(a)** 85 **(b)** 36 **(c)** 381
3. Yes, Devit has enough bread to make 36 sandwiches.
4. 4 minibuses
5. Yes, Nalla has enough thread for the 7 pairs of trousers.

## Page 5 Order of operations

**Quick quiz:**

B – Brackets I – Indices
D – Division M – Multiplication
A – Addition S – Subtraction

**Questions:**

1. **(a)** 13 **(b)** 25
2. **(a)** 10 **(b)** 29 **(c)** 14
3. **(a)** $(5+3)\times 2-1=15$
   **(b)** $12-2\times(3+1)=4$
4. **(a)** $(7\times 9)+1=64$
   **(b)** $32\times(5+10)=480$
   **(c)** $(7-2)+13=18$
5. Brian is correct. Applying BIDMAS, you would calculate $4\times 3$ first giving you 12, then subtract 12 from 20 giving you 8
6. Applying BIDMAS: first you would calculate $10\div 2$ which is 5, then calculate $30+5$ which equals 35
7. $(560\times 20)-5000$

## Page 6 Decimals

**Quick quiz:**

**(a)** 1.3 **(b)** 0.7 **(c)** 0.89 **(d)** 0.41

**Questions:**

1. **(a)** 4 tenths or 0.4 or $\frac{4}{10}$
   **(b)** 8 hundredths or 0.08 or $\frac{8}{100}$
   **(c)** 2 thousandths or 0.002 or $\frac{2}{1000}$
   **(d)** 7 hundredths or 0.07 or $\frac{7}{10}$
2. **(a)** 0.9, 3.62, 4.7, 11.3
   **(b)** 0.2, 0.25, 0.4, 0.5, 0.75
3. 0.79, 0.801, 0.838, 0.86
4. 0.65, 0.7, 0.745, 0.754
5. 0.666, 0.66, 0.606, 0.6
6. $0.404 < 0.44$ or $0.44 > 0.404$

## Page 7 Operations with decimals

**Quick quiz:**

**(a)** 3.6 **(b)** 0.5 **(c)** 6 **(d)** 4

**Questions:**

1. **(a)** 19.73 **(b)** 1.72 **(c)** 14.274 **(d)** 32.1
2. Dunia **3.** 15.76 ounces **4.** £30
5. Callum does not have enough oil for 70 days.

## Page 8 Rounding

**Quick quiz:**

1. 20 **2.** 120 **3.** 1400 **4.** 6

**Questions:**

1. **(a)** 30 **(b)** 5600 **(c)** 197 000
2. **(a)** 15.5 **(b)** 34.57 **(c)** 8.569
3. **(a)** 420 **(b)** 78 **(c)** 7.53
4. **(a)** 14.884 271 25 **(b)** 14.9
5. **(a)** 2.636 580 568 **(b)** 2.6366

## Page 9 Fractions

**Quick quiz:**

**1.** 20 **2.** 20 **3.** 20 **4.** 24

**Questions:**

**1.** e.g. 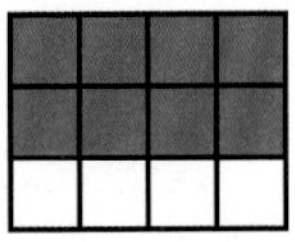 **2.** $\frac{3}{8}$ **3.** $\frac{3}{5}$

**4.** $\frac{1}{2}$ **5.** $\frac{3}{4}$ **6.** $\frac{2}{3}$ **7.** $\frac{1}{5}$

**8.** **(a)** 10 kg **(b)** 9.6 g **9.** 49 cm

**10.** £192 **11.** 42 blue counters

## Page 10 Operations with fractions

**Quick quiz:**

Adding or subtracting fractions: Find equivalent fractions with the same denominator

Multiplying fractions: Multiply the numerators and multiply the denominators

Dividing fractions: Invert the second fraction then multiply

**Questions:**

**1.** **(a)** $\frac{5}{14}$ **(b)** $\frac{6}{11}$ **(c)** $\frac{2}{3}$

**(d)** $\frac{2}{5}$ **(e)** $\frac{11}{42}$ **(f)** $\frac{1}{12}$

**2.** 90

**3.** $\frac{4}{15}$ of $225 = 60$ **4.** $\frac{13}{24}$

## Page 11 Mixed numbers and improper fractions

**Quick quiz:**

**1.** **(a)** 2 **(b)** 2 **(c)** 2

**2.** **(a)** $\frac{15}{2}$ **(b)** $\frac{22}{5}$ **(c)** $\frac{27}{4}$

**Questions:**

**1.** **(a)** $1\frac{9}{10}$ **(b)** 60 **(c)** $6\frac{3}{10}$

**2.** **(a)** $7\frac{31}{40}$ **(b)** $1\frac{19}{21}$ **(c)** $2\frac{1}{3}$

**3.** 45 **4.** 10 **5.** 18 **6.** $40\frac{5}{16}$ kg

## Page 12 Factors, multiples and prime numbers

**Quick quiz:**

**1.** **(a)** 3 **(b)** 3 **(c)** 1 **2.** 12, 15

**Questions:**

**1.** **(a)** 1, 3, 5, 15 **(b)** 1, 2, 3, 4, 6, 8, 12, 24

**(c)** 1, 3, 5, 15, 25, 75 **(d)** 1, 2, 4, 5, 10, 20, 25, 50, 100

**2.** 3, 6, 9, 12, 15 **3.** 6, 12, 18, 24, 30 **4.** 24

**5.** 60 **6.** 31, 37, 41, 43, 47 **7.** 61, 67, 71, 73, 79

**8.** **(a)** One of the following: 4, 5

**(b)** One of the following: 30, 40

**(c)** 29

**9.** **(a)** 72 **(b)** 5 **(c)** 5 or 31

## Page 13 Prime factors, HCF and LCM

**Quick quiz:**

**(a)** $2^3 \times 3^2 \times 5$ **(b)** $5^2 \times 7 \times 11^3$

**Questions:**

**1.** **(a)** $2 \times 2 \times 2 \times 3 \times 3$ **(b)** $2 \times 2 \times 3 \times 3 \times 5$

**2.** **(a)** $3 \times 5^2$ **(b)** 15 **(c)** 450

**3.** **(a)** 20 **(b)** 600

**4.** *For example:* 18 and 45 **5.** £60.25

## Page 14 Estimation and outcomes

**Quick quiz:**

**(a)** 80 **(b)** 200 **(c)** 0.2 **(d)** 0.5

**Questions:**

**1.** 9

**2.** RA, RM, RP, RZ, AM, AP, AZ, MP, MZ, PZ

**3.** **(a)** 4000 **(b)** 4

**4.** **(a)** 75 cm$^2$ **(b)** Underestimate, as the values of $\pi$ and $r$ are rounded down.

**5.** 8000

## Page 15 Indices and roots

**Quick quiz:**

**1.** **(a)** 9 **(b)** 8 **2.** **(a)** 2 **(b)** 3

**Questions:**

**1.** 64 **2.** 1000 **3.** 5

**4.** **(a)** 10 and 15 or 15 and 85 or 100 and 125

**(b)** 100

**(c)** 125 and 61 or 85 and 58 **(d)** 125

**5.** 0.230 752 072 6 **6.** 14 419.006 58

**7.** 2.254 948 339

**8.** Joseph is 36 years old and Nina is 64 years old.

## Page 16 Standard form

**Quick quiz:**

**(a)** $10^3$ **(b)** $10^5$ **(c)** $10^8$ **(d)** $10^9$

**Questions:**

**1.** **(a)** 0.000 78 **(b)** $9.56 \times 10^7$ **(c)** $6 \times 10$

**2.** $45 \times 10^{-4}$, $45 \times 10^{-2}$, $0.0045 \times 10^6$, $45 \times 10^3$, $4.5 \times 10^5$

**3.** No, as 8 cm is greater than 7.5 cm

**4.** $1.37 \times 10^9$ s

## Page 17 Error intervals

**Quick quiz:**

**(a)** 110 **(b)** 90 **(c)** 220 **(d)** 180

**(e)** 10.5 **(f)** 9.5 **(g)** 1.05 **(h)** 0.95

**Questions:**

**1.** **(a)** £7500 **(b)** £8499.99

**2.** **(a)** 25 650 **(b)** 25 749

**3.** **(a)** £115 000 **(b)** £124 999.99

**4.** $78.5 \leqslant A < 79.5$ **5.** $42.65 \leqslant L < 42.75$

**6.** $17.5 \leqslant x < 18.5$ **7.** $16.65 \leqslant y < 16.75$

**8.** $42.445 \leqslant p < 42.455$ **9.** $20.00 \leqslant t \leqslant 20.09$

## Page 18 Exam skills: Number

**1.** **(a)** −7 °C **(b)** 10 degrees **(c)** −3 °C

**2.** £19.63

3. **(a)** 4 tins of sausages and 5 packets of bread rolls
   **(b)** 60 hot dogs

## Page 19 Function machines

**Quick quiz:**

**(a)** 18 **(b)** 2

**Questions:**

1. **(a)** $y = 35$ **(b)** $x = 1$
2. **(a)** $y = 17$ **(b)** $x = 1.5$
3. **(a)** $x \rightarrow \times 4 \rightarrow +2 \rightarrow y$ **(b)** $x \rightarrow -2 \rightarrow \times 4 \rightarrow y$
4. **(a)** $\times 10 \rightarrow +1$ **(b)** $\div 2 \rightarrow -5$, or $-10 \rightarrow \div 2$
5. In the first formula $y = 2x + 6$, in the second formula $y = 2(x + 3)$ which can be expanded to $y = 2x + 6$

## Page 20 Algebraic substitution

**Quick quiz:**

**(a)** 24 **(b)** −12 **(c)** −70 **(d)** 16

**Questions:**

1. **(a)** 22 **(b)** 0 **(c)** 19
2. **(a)** 8 **(b)** −12 **(c)** 17
3. **(a)** 48 **(b)** 57 **(c)** 19
4. **(a)** £85 **(b)** 7.5 hours

## Page 21 Collecting like terms

**Quick quiz:**

$d + d$ $x^2 + x^2$

**Questions:**

1. **(a)** $3d$ **(b)** $5t$ **(c)** $7r$
2. **(a)** $9c$ **(b)** $-4e$ **(c)** $-5g$
3. **(a)** $f + 10$ **(b)** $4x + 6y$
   **(c)** $4x - y$ **(d)** $3 - f$
4. Jane has added all the terms, rather than subtracting *ef*. Answer should be 7*ef*.
5. **(a)** $3m^2$ **(b)** $4a^2 - h$ **(c)** $8x^2 - 7y$
   **(d)** $7p^2 + 5t$ **(e)** $4x^2 - y$ **(f)** $5x^2 + 6y^2$

## Page 22 Simplifying expressions

**Quick quiz:**

1. **(a)** $a \times a = a^2$ **(b)** $ab = a \times b$
   **(c)** $a \times c = ac$ **(d)** $a^3 = a \times a \times a$

**Questions:**

1. **(a)** $5ef$ **(b)** $14t$ **(c)** $15g$
2. **(a)** $6mn$ **(b)** $6ef$ **(c)** $3c^2$
3. **(a)** $8x$ **(b)** $3a$ **(c)** $3y$
   **(d)** $12g$ **(e)** $2a^2$ **(f)** $6t$
   **(g)** 5
4. **(a)** $25x^2y$ **(b)** $2a^3b^2$ **(c)** $3cd^3$
   **(d)** $42g^2h$ **(e)** $7t^7$ **(f)** $15s^3t$
5. Answer should be $7m^2n^2$. Ben has added the indices instead of subtracting.

## Page 23 Writing expressions

**Quick quiz:**

**(a)** 40 **(b)** 8 **(c)** 3

**Questions:**

1. $5x + 3$ 2. $6m + 9n$ 3. $8x + 12y$
4. **(a)** £45$n$ +60 **(b)** £600
5. **(a)** £3.5$n$ **(b)** £875 **(c)** £$n(3.5 - 0.5)$

## Page 24 Algebraic formulae

**Quick quiz:**

**(a)** 5 **(b)** $3x$ **(c)** $3x + 6$ **(d)** $2x - 1$

**Questions:**

1. $(16x + 8)$ cm 2. $T = 8(4x - 6)$
3. $P = 6x + 5$ 4. $A = x^2 + 6x + 7$

## Page 25 Algebraic indices

**Quick quiz:**

**(a)** $a^4$ **(b)** $a^4$ **(c)** $18a^2b$ **(d)** $3a^2b^3$

**Questions:**

1. **(a)** $p^9$ **(b)** $x^5$ **(c)** $y^4$
2. **(a)** $q^6$ **(b)** $y^{12}$ **(c)** $27x^6$
   **(d)** $15x^3y^4$ **(e)** $\frac{5}{3}x^4y^2$
3. $x = 7$ 4. $y = 5$
5. **(a)** $xy$ **(b)** $y^3$ **(c)** $5x^2$
6. $-2, 0.2, 2^{-1}, 2^0$

## Page 26 Expanding brackets

**Quick quiz:**

**(a)** $4x$ **(b)** $5y$ **(c)** $v^2$ **(d)** $4a^2$

**Questions:**

1. **(a)** $3a + 15$ **(b)** $5b - 20$ **(c)** $-4c - 4$
2. **(a)** $e^2 + 2e$ **(b)** $2f^2 - 6f$
   **(c)** $-4g^2 - 8g$ **(d)** $-3h^2 + 3hp$
3. **(a)** $11a - 6b$ **(b)** $8x + 29$ **(c)** $7y - 16$
   **(d)** $-5m^2 + 10m$ **(e)** $x^2 + 8x$
4. $3x \times -5 = -15x$, not $-5$
   $-4x \times +3 = -12x$, not $-7x$

## Page 27 Expanding double brackets

**Quick quiz:**

**(a)** $-2t + 4$ **(b)** $x^2 + 2x$ **(c)** $2d + 22$

**Questions:**

1. **(a)** $x^2 - 6x + 9$ **(b)** $y^2 + 8y + 16$ **(c)** $t^2 - 10t + 25$
2. **(a)** $x^2 - 7x - 18$ **(b)** $x^2 + 7x + 10$ **(c)** $y^2 + 8y - 20$
3. $(x^2 + 5x - 14)$ cm²
4. $\left(\frac{1}{2}x^2 + 7x + 20\right)$ cm²

## Page 28 Factorising

**Quick quiz:**

**(a)** 3 **(b)** 4 **(c)** $x$ **(d)** $y$

**Questions:**

1. **(a)** $3(x + 3)$ **(b)** $4(x - 3)$
   **(c)** $4(x + 2y)$ **(d)** $4(3x - 5y)$
   **(e)** $x(x + 3)$ **(f)** $5x(x + 2)$
2. Answer should be $7x(x - 4)$, as Simon has not factorised completely.

3. **(a)** $6xy(y-2)$ **(b)** $xy(4x+3)$ **(c)** $xy(y^2+3)$

4. $P\,\text{cm} = 2(x-3) + 2(x+10) = 2x - 6 + 2x + 20$
$= 4x + 14$
$= 2(2x+7)\,\text{cm}$

## Page 29 Linear equations

**Quick quiz**

**(a)** 5 **(b)** 3 **(c)** 4 **(d)** −30

**Questions:**

1. **(a)** $\frac{11}{6}$ **(b)** $-\frac{25}{7}$ **(c)** 1
   **(d)** 6 **(e)** $-\frac{7}{3}$ **(f)** 20
2. **(a)** $\frac{7}{10}$ **(b)** 6
3. 6

## Page 30 Rearranging formulae

**Quick quiz:**

**(a)** subtraction **(b)** addition
**(c)** division **(d)** multiplication

**Questions:**

1. **(a)** $x = y - 2$ **(b)** $x = y + 5$ **(c)** $x = 10 - y$
2. **(a)** $d = \frac{n}{4}$ **(b)** $d = 10p$ **(c)** $d = 2c$
3. **(a)** $a = y - t$ **(b)** $b = c - w$ **(c)** $c = k - t$
   **(d)** $g = \frac{n}{5}$ **(e)** $e = fh$ **(f)** $t = ry$
4. $6h = x - 9$
   $h = \frac{x-9}{6}$
   No, Matteo is incorrect.
5. $a = \frac{v-u}{t}$ **6.** $a = \frac{2s}{t^2}$ **7.** $s = \frac{v^2 - u^2}{2a}$

## Page 31 Inequalities

**Quick quiz:**

**(a)** less than **(b)** less than or equal to
**(c)** greater than **(d)** greater than or equal to

**Questions:**

1. 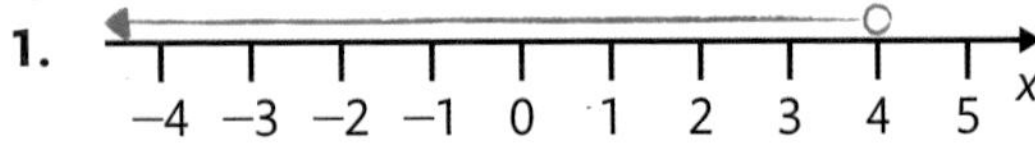

2. 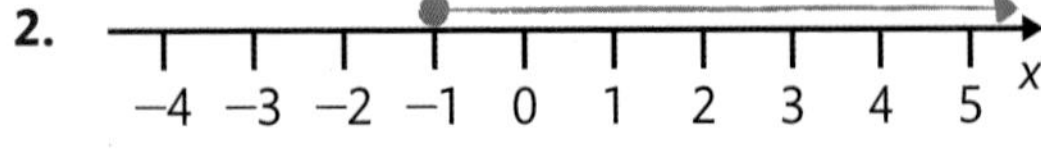

3. 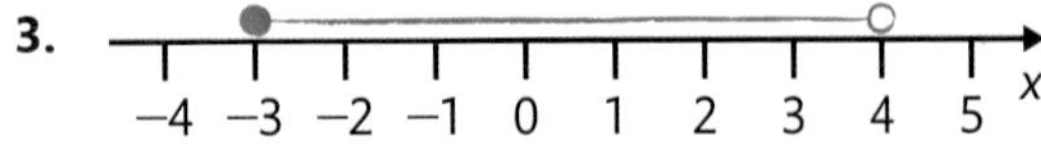

4. −4 −3 −2 −1 0 1 2 3 4 5 x
5. $x \leqslant 3$ **6.** $x \geqslant -2$ **7.** $-2 \leqslant x < 4$
8. $-4 < x \leqslant 3$ **9.** $x = -1, 0, 1, 2, 3$ **10.** $x = -1, 0, 1, 2, 3$

## Page 32 Solving inequalities

**Quick quiz:**

**(a)** $x = 7$ **(b)** $y = 17.5$ **(c)** $t = 2$

**Questions:**

1. **(a)** $x < 9$ **(b)** $x \geqslant 3.5$ **(c)** $x > -1$
2. **(a)** $p < 3$ **(b)** $p > -\frac{1}{2}$ **(c)** 0, 1, 2
3. **(a)** $-1 \leqslant n < 3$ **(b)** −1, 0, 1, 2
4. **(a)** $y \geqslant 3.5$ **(b)** 4
5. **(a)** $x > \frac{11}{3}$ **(b)** 4

## Page 33 Solving sequence problems

**Quick quiz:**

**(a)** 15, 21, 28 **(b)** 25, 36, 49 **(c)** 8, 13, 21

**Questions:**

1. **(a)** $p + 2q$ **(b)** $2p + 3q$
2. 4.5
3. **(a)** 118 **(b)** 40 **(c)** 80
4. No. Substituting $n = 5$ gives $4 \times 5 \times 5 = 100$, so he is not right.

## Page 34 Arithmetic sequences

**Quick quiz:**

**(a)** 11, 14, 17 **(b)** 91, 88, 85 **(c)** 31, 36, 41

**Questions:**

1. **(a)** $5n + 3$ **(b)** No, as $n = 49.75$ is not an integer.
2. $7n - 2$
3. **(a)** No, as 35.333... is not an integer.
   **(b)** $6n + 5$
4. X = 1, 5, 9, 13, 17, 21, ... ; Y = 11, 8, 5, 2, ...
   Since X is increasing and Y is decreasing, the only term that is in both sequences is 5.

## Page 35 Factorising quadratics

**Quick quiz:**

**(a)** $a = -2$ and $b = -4$
**(b)** $a = 2$ and $b = 2$
**(c)** $a = -4$ and $b = 6$

**Questions:**

1. **(a)** $x(x+2)$ **(b)** $x(x-6)$ **(c)** $x(x-9)$
2. **(a)** $(x+5)(x-5)$ **(b)** $(x+7)(x-7)$
   **(c)** $(x+11)(x-11)$
3. If $(x+5)(x+6)$ is expanded, you get $x^2 + 11x + 30$, therefore he did not factorise the expression correctly. The correct answer would be $(x+5)(x+1)$.
4. **(a)** $(x+2)(x+5)$ **(b)** $(x+1)(x+2)$ **(c)** $(x-4)(x-5)$
   **(d)** $(x+7)(x-9)$ **(e)** $(x-3)(x+6)$ **(f)** $(x+8)(x-9)$

## Page 36 Solving quadratic equations

**Quick quiz:**

**(a)** 2 and 10 **(b)** 5 and −3
**(c)** −1 and −4 **(d)** 4 and −5

**Questions:**

1. **(a)** $x = 2$ or $x = -2$ **(b)** $x = 4$ or $x = -4$
   **(c)** $x = 10$ or $x = -10$
2. **(a)** $x = 0$ or $x = 4$ **(b)** $x = 1$ or $x = 10$
   **(c)** $x = -3$ or $x = 4$

**3. (a)** $x = 9$ or $x = -4$ **(b)** $x = 5$ or $x = 3$

**4.** $x = 4$

## Page 37 Simultaneous equations

**Quick quiz:**

**(a)** $x = 6, y = 4$ **(b)** $x = -1, y = \frac{9}{10}$

**Questions:**

**1.** $x = 4, y = 1$ **2.** $x = 5, y = -2$

**3. (a)**

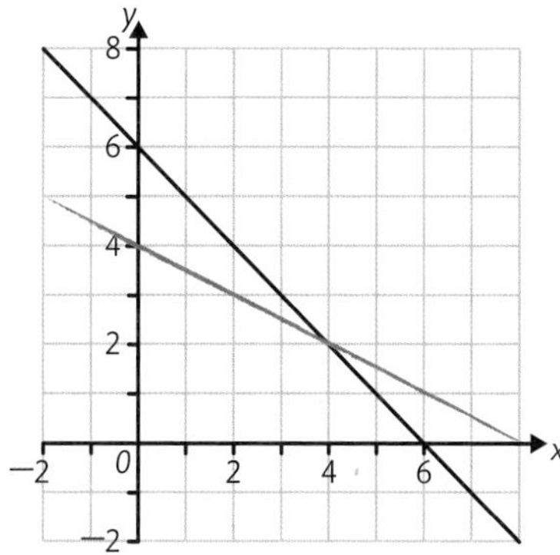

**(b)** $x = 4, y = 2$

**4.** Shirt = £12.50, trousers = £18.00

## Page 38 Gradients of lines

**Quick quiz:**

**(a)** positive **(b)** negative

**Questions:**

**1.** 2

**2.**

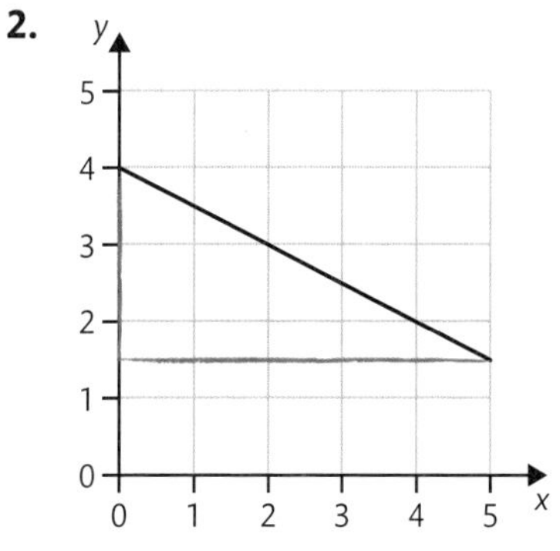

gradient $= \frac{-2.5}{5} = \frac{-25}{50} = -\frac{1}{2}$

**3.** $\frac{3}{4}$ **4.** $-\frac{4}{5}$

## Page 39 Drawing straight-line graphs

**Quick quiz:**

**1.** $m$ **2. (a)** 13 **(b)** −14

**Questions:**

**1.**

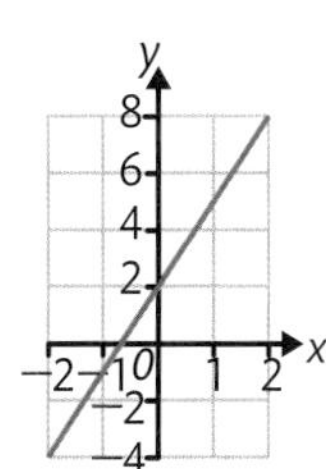

**2.**

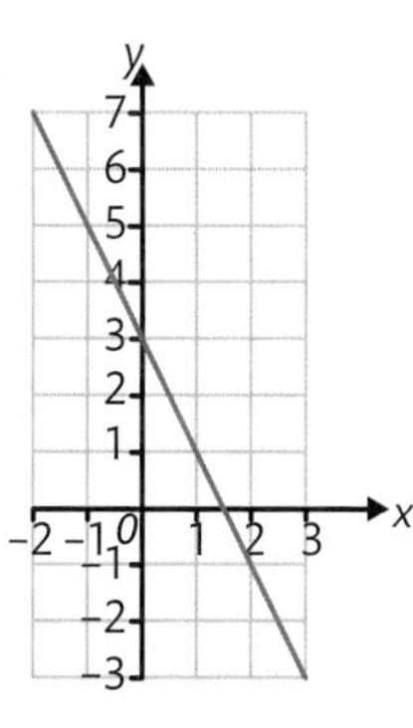

**3. (a)** Gradient = 2, so the water heats up 2 °C every second.

**(b)** $y = 2x + 20$

**4.** $y = -\frac{6}{5}x + 6$

## Page 40 Equations of straight lines

**Quick quiz:**

**(a)** −2 **(b)** −17

**Questions:**

**1.** $y = -5x + 22$ **2.** $y = 2x + 5$

**3. (a)** (1, 7) **(b)** $y = -\frac{2}{3}x + \frac{23}{3}$

**4. (a)** $y = 4x + 8$ **(b)** $3y - 2x = -17$

## Page 41 Parallel lines

**Quick quiz:**

**1. (a)** $y = 2x + 5$

**(b)** $y = -3x + \frac{5}{3}$ or $y = \frac{5}{3} - 3x$

**2.** $\frac{9-5}{12-4} = \frac{4}{8} = \frac{1}{2}$

**Questions:**

**1.** $y = 2x - 2$ **2.** $y = -2x + 3$

**3.** $\mathbf{L_1}$ has gradient 2

$3y - 6x + 4 = 0$ so $3y = 6x - 4$ so $y = 2x - \frac{4}{3}$

$\mathbf{L_2}$ has gradient 2

$\mathbf{L_1}$ and $\mathbf{L_2}$ have the same gradient therefore are parallel.

**4.** Gradient of $\mathbf{L} = 4$

Gradient of $y = 4x + 1$ is 4

Both lines have the same gradients therefore $y = 4x + 1$ is parallel to $\mathbf{L}$.

## Page 42 Real-life graphs

**Quick quiz:**

**(a)** speed **(b)** horizontal line

**Questions:**

**1. (a)** 36 km/h **(b)**

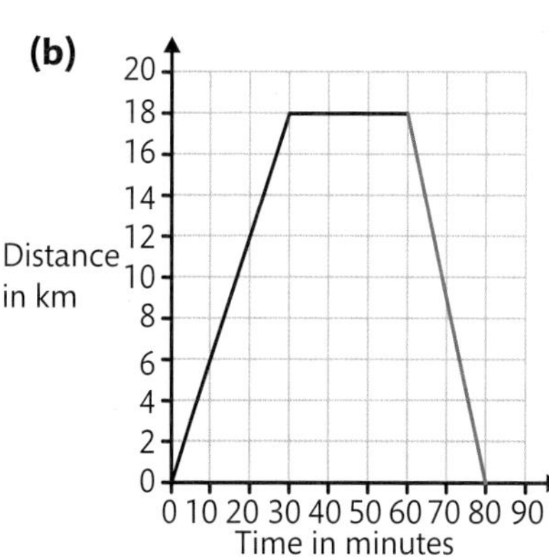


**(c)** 30 minutes

**2. (a)**

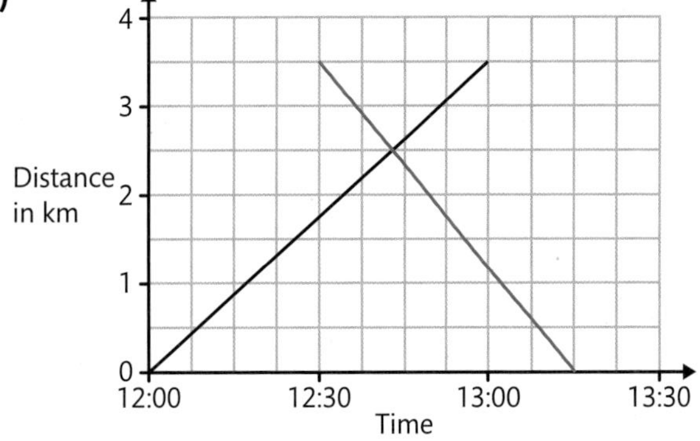


**(b)** 2.5 km

**3. (a) (i)** 32 °F **(ii)** 21 °C **(b)** Manchester

## Page 43 Quadratic graphs

**Quick quiz:**

**1.**

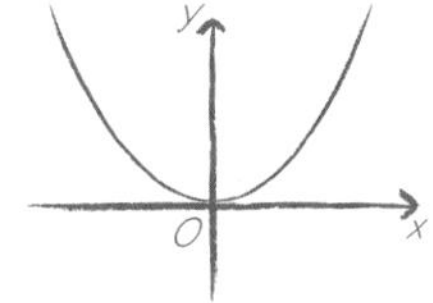

**2.**

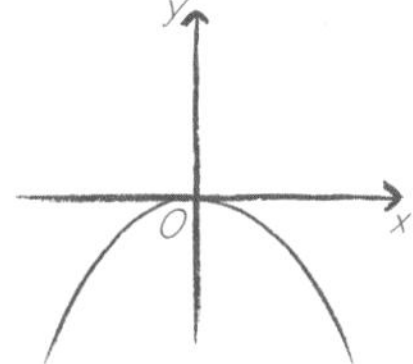

**3.** A quadratic graph has a vertical line of symmetry.

**Questions:**

**1. (a)**

| x | −1 | 0 | 1 | 2 | 3 | 4 | 5 |
|---|---|---|---|---|---|---|---|
| y | 7 | 2 | −1 | −2 | −1 | 2 | 7 |

**(b)**

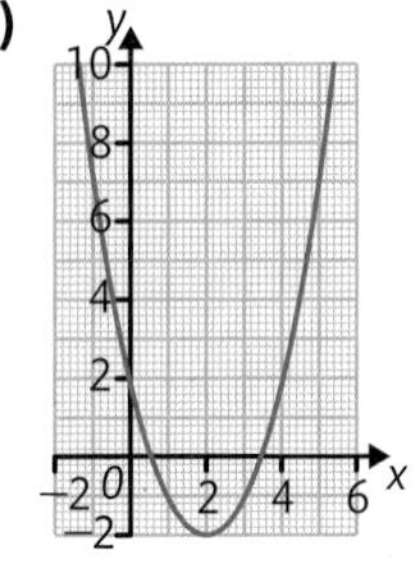

**(c)** (2, −2)

**2.** (2, 3)

**3. (a)**

| x | −4 | −3 | −2 | −1 | 0 | 1 | 2 | 3 |
|---|---|---|---|---|---|---|---|---|
| y | −7 | −1 | 3 | 5 | 5 | 3 | −1 | −7 |

**(b)**

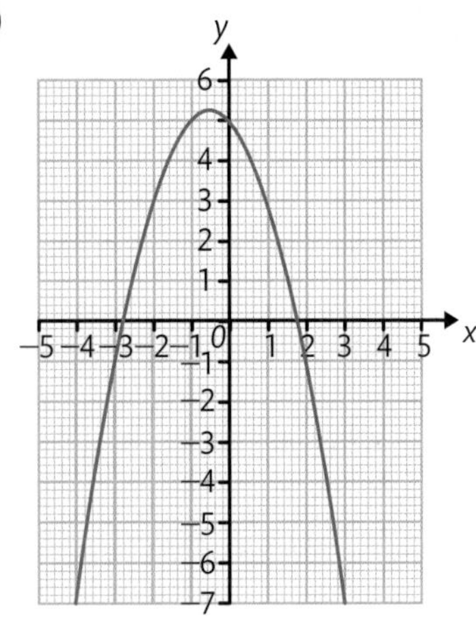

**(c)** (−0.5, 5.25)

## Page 44 Using quadratic graphs

**Quick quiz:**

**(a)** (ii) **(b)** (iii) **(c)** (i)

**Questions:**

**1. (a)**

| x | −2 | −1 | 0 | 1 | 2 | 3 | 4 |
|---|---|---|---|---|---|---|---|
| y | 7 | 2 | −1 | −2 | −1 | 2 | 7 |

**(b) and (c)**

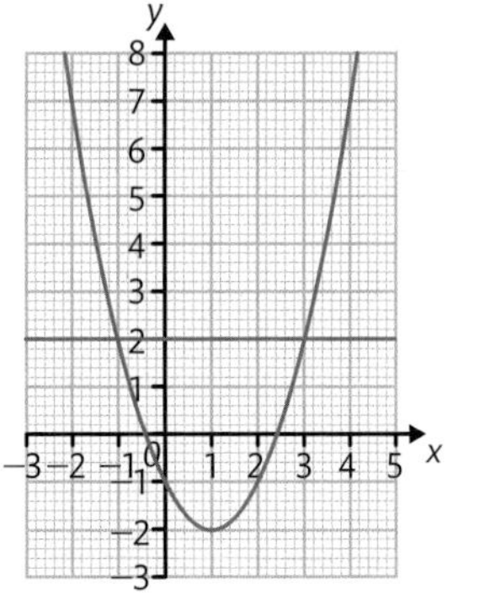

**(d)** (−1, 2), (3, 2)

**2. (a)**

| x | −1 | 0 | 1 | 2 | 3 | 4 |
|---|---|---|---|---|---|---|
| y | 6 | 2 | 0 | 0 | 2 | 6 |

**(b)**

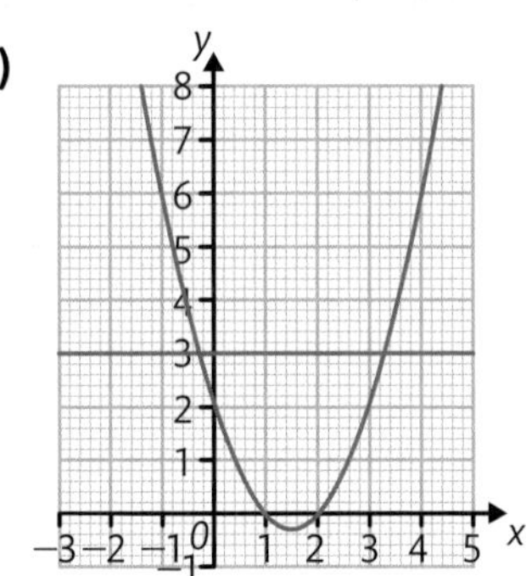

**(c)** $x = -0.3$, $x = 3.3$

## Page 45 Cubic and reciprocal graphs

**Quick quiz:**

From left to right: $y = -\frac{1}{x}$ $y = -x^3$ $y = \frac{1}{x}$ $y = x^3$

**Questions:**

**1. (a)**

| x | −1.5 | −1 | −0.5 | 0 | 0.5 | 1 | 1.5 |
|---|---|---|---|---|---|---|---|
| y | −1.375 | 1 | 1.875 | 2 | 2.125 | 3 | 5.375 |

**(b)**

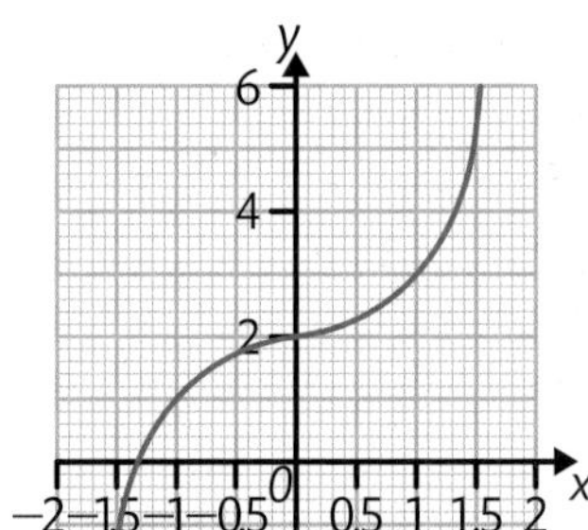

**(c)** −1.26 (or between −1.2 and −1.3)

**2. (a)**

| x | 0.5 | 1 | 2 | 4 | 5 | 8 |
|---|---|---|---|---|---|---|
| y | 8 | 4 | 2 | 1 | 0.8 | 0.5 |

**(b)**

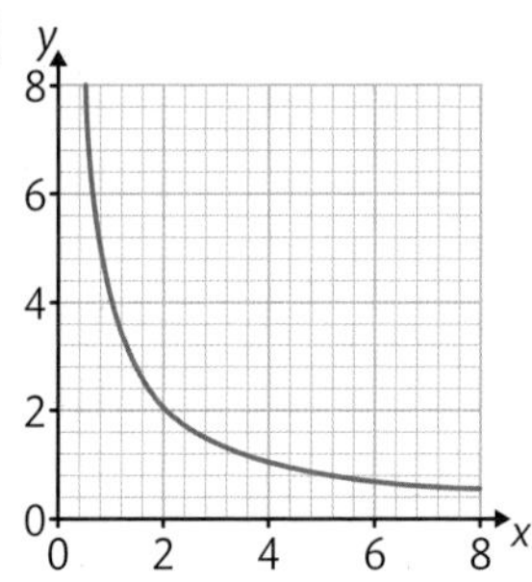

## Page 46 Recognising graphs

**Quick quiz:**

**(a)**
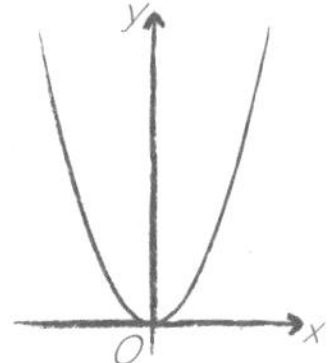

**(b)**
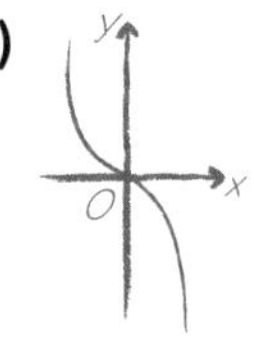

**(c)**
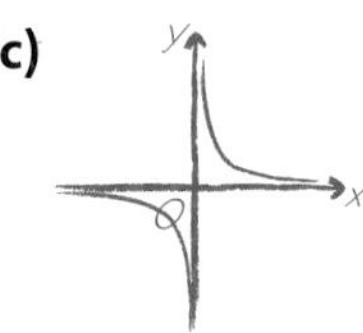

**Questions:**

1. **(a)** B **(b)** C **(c)** E
2. **(a)** D **(b)** E **(c)** C **(d)** B **(e)** A
3. **(a)** B **(b)** C **(c)** E **(d)** A **(e)** D

## Page 47 Algebraic reasoning

**Quick quiz:**

**(a)** $x^2 + 2x$ **(b)** $y^2 - 6y + 9$ **(c)** $t^2 - 8t + 16$

**Questions:**

1.

| | Expression | Formula | Equation | Identity |
|---|---|---|---|---|
| $9x - 3x \equiv 6x$ | | | | ✓ |
| $V = L \times W \times H$ | | ✓ | | |
| $4x + 9 = 15$ | | | ✓ | |
| $2xy + 5x$ | ✓ | | | |

2. $3(x+5) + 4(x+2) = 3x + 15 + 4x + 8 = 7x + 23$
3. $2(y^2 - 3y) - 10(y - 1) = 2y^2 - 6y - 10y + 10$
   $= 2y^2 - 16y + 10$
4. **(a)** Odd. Any integer multiplied by 2 is even. An even number + 1 is always odd. So, $2n + 1$ is odd.
   **(b)** Even. When $n$ is even, $n + 1$ is odd; when $n$ is odd, $n + 1$ is even. An even number multiplied by an odd number always produces an odd number.
   **(c)** Even, because $n + n$ is the same as $2 \times n$ and any integer multiplied by 2 is even.
5. **(a)** $3n + 3$ **(b)** $3n + 3 = 3(n + 1)$ so multiple of 3
6. **(a)** e.g. 40 **(b)** e.g. $2 \times 3 = 6$
7. $(n+1)^2 - (n-1)^2 = n^2 + 2n + 1 - (n^2 - 2n + 1)$
   $= n^2 + 2n + 1 - n^2 + 2n - 1$
   $= 4n$

   4 is an even number therefore $(n + 1)^2 - (n - 1)^2$ is always even for all positive values of $n$.

## Page 48 Exam skills: Algebra

1. **(a)**

| x | −1 | 0 | 1 | 2 | 3 | 4 | 5 | 6 |
|---|---|---|---|---|---|---|---|---|
| y | 9 | 3 | −1 | −3 | −3 | −1 | 3 | 9 |

**(b)**
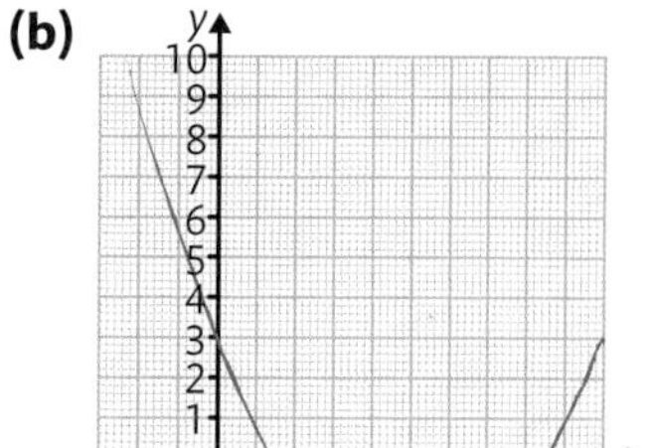

**(c)** $x = 0.7$ and $x = 4.3$ **(d)** (2.5, −3.3)

2. $3(x + 5)$ 3. $x = 5, y = -3$

## Page 49 Ratio

**Quick quiz:**

**(a)** 1:4 **(b)** 2:3 **(c)** 8:3 **(d)** 15:8

**Questions:**

1. **(a)** $\frac{2}{5}$ **(b)** £5 **(c)** 1:2
2. 1.25 kg 3. 120 cm 4. 36%

## Page 50 Direct proportion

**Quick quiz:**

**(a)** 60p **(b)** 30p

**Questions:**

1. **(a)** 540 g **(b)** 25 pancakes
2. **(a)** $y = 31.5$ **(b)** $x = 16$
3. New York 4. 50 g

## Page 51 Inverse proportion

**Quick quiz:**

**(a)** decreases **(b)** decreases

**Questions**

1. $y = 2.4$ 2. 2.4 days 3. 10 days
4. $p = 18$ 5. 960 6. 73.8 amps
7. 36 minutes

## Page 52 Percentages

**Quick quiz:**

**(a)** 100 **(b)** 8 **(c)** 40 **(d)** 10

**Questions:**

1. **(a)** 45 **(b)** 162
2. **(a)** 22.5 kg **(b)** 164 m (3 s.f.) **(c)** £16.45
3. 204 4. £48
5. **(a)** 44% **(b)** 40% 6. 15%

## Page 53 Fractions, decimals and percentages

**Quick quiz:**

| Fraction | Decimal | Percentage |
|---|---|---|
| $\frac{1}{2}$ | 0.5 | 50% |
| $\frac{1}{4}$ | 0.25 | 25% |
| $\frac{3}{4}$ | 0.75 | 75% |

**Questions:**

**1.** **(a)** $\frac{7}{10}$ **(b)** 60% **(c)** 0.375 **(d)** $\frac{9}{10}$

**2.** 0.25, $\frac{3}{10}$, 0.32, 35%, $\frac{2}{5}$ **3.** 0.401, 41%, $\frac{3}{7}$, 0.45, $\frac{2}{3}$

**4.** £1040 **5.** £225

## Page 54 Percentage change

**Quick quiz:**

**1.** 100 **2.** 6 **3.** 20 **4.** 45

**Questions:**

**1.** **(a)** 13.5% (3 s.f.) **(b)** 16.7% (3 s.f.) **(c)** 49.9% (3 s.f.)

**2.** **(a)** 1080 (3 s.f.) **(b)** 195 (3 s.f.) **(c)** £92.08

**3.** Yes, as he reaches 30%.

**4.** Hotel 1 is £7828 and Hotel 2 is £8925, so Hotel 1 is cheaper.

## Page 55 Reverse percentages

**Quick quiz:**

1.12 = an increase of 12% 1.105 = an increase of 10.5%

0.85 = a decrease of 15% 0.972 = a decrease of 2.8%

**Questions:**

**1.** £1200 **2.** £144 **3.** 31 minutes

**4.** Fixed bond: £1930; ISA: £1884. The fixed bond grew more.

## Page 56 Growth and decay

**Quick quiz:**

**(a)** 1.15 **(b)** 0.82 **(c)** 1.0235 **(d)** 0.931

**Questions:**

**1.** £1952.62 **2.** $n = 3$ **3.** £6552

**4.** **(a)** 3.2 m **(b)** 164 cm **5.** 2533

## Page 57 Compound measures

**Quick quiz:**

**1.** two **2.** speed, density

**Questions:**

**1.** 3.75 $m^2$ **2.** 4 hours and 30 minutes **3.** Carina

## Page 58 Speed

**Quick quiz:**

$\text{speed} = \frac{\text{distance}}{\text{time}}$ $\text{distance} = \text{speed} \times \text{time}$

$\text{time} = \frac{\text{distance}}{\text{speed}}$

**Questions:**

**1.** **(a)** 42 mph **(b)** 108 miles

**2.** 53.3 mph (3 s.f.) **3.** No, as Amina's speed is 46.7 mph.

## Page 59 Density

**Quick quiz:**

**(a)** $\text{density} = \frac{\text{mass}}{\text{volume}}$

**(b)** $\text{mass} = \text{density} \times \text{volume}$

**(c)** $\text{volume} = \frac{\text{mass}}{\text{density}}$

**Questions:**

**1.** 5.2 kg/$m^3$ **2.** 5.71 $m^3$ **3.** 157 g

**4.** 11.6 g/$cm^3$ **5.** 19.3 g/$cm^3$ **6.** 11

## Page 60 Proportion and graphs

**Quick quiz:**

**(a)** graph A **(b)** graph C

**Questions:**

**1.** 67.2 **2.** No, Adam drove further.

**3.** **(a)** €78 **(b)** £208

## Page 61 Exam skills: Ratio and proportion

**1.** £367.20 **2.** 2:1 **3.** 20 chocolate biscuits

## Page 62 Angle properties

**Quick quiz:**

**(a)** equal **(b)** equal **(c)** equal

**(d)** 180° **(e)** 180° **(f)** 360°

**Questions:**

**1.** **(a)**

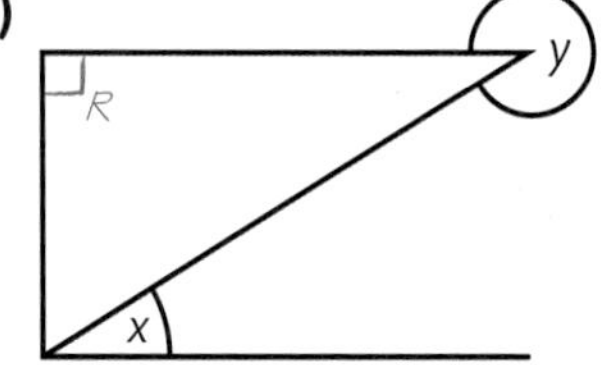


**(b)** **(i)** acute angle **(ii)** reflex angle

**2.** **(a)** 55° because angles on a straight line add up to 180°

**(b)** 160° because angles around a point add up to 360°

**3.** $ABE = 55°$ because alternate angles are equal

$EBF = 55°$ because base angles in an isosceles triangle are equal

$x = 180° - 55° - 55° = 70°$ because angles on a straight line add up to 180°

**4.** $BDC = 360° - 235° = 125°$ because angles around a point add up to 360°

$CBD = 180 - 125° - 48° = 7°$ because angles in a triangle add up to 180°

$x = 180° - 7° = 173°$ because angles on a straight line add up to 180°

## Page 63 Solving angle problems

**Quick quiz:**

**1.** Angle $d$ and angle $f$ are alternate angles.

**2.** Angle $c$ and angle $g$ are corresponding angles.

**3.** Angle $e$ and angle $g$ are vertically opposite angles.

**Questions:**

**1.** $BFG = 70°$ because alternate angles are equal

$FBG = 70°$ because base angles in an isosceles triangle are equal

$BGF = 40°$ because angles in a triangle add up to 180°

$x = 180° - 40° = 140°$ because angles on a straight line add up to 180°

**2.** $DBC = (180° - 50°) \div 2 = 65°$ because base angles in an isosceles triangle are equal

$DBA = 180° - 65° = 115°$ because angles on a straight line add up to 180°

$x = 180° - 115° - 20° = 45°$ because angles in a triangle add up to 180°

3. $AEB = 65°$ because vertically opposite angles are equal
$EAB = 55°$ because alternate angles are equal
$ABE = 180° - 55° - 65° = 60°$ because angles in a triangle add up to 180°
$x = 180° - 60° = 120°$ because angles on a straight line add up to 180°
4. $ADB = 25°$ because base angles in an isosceles triangle are equal
$ABD = 180° - 25° - 25° = 130°$ because angles in a triangle add up to 180°
$DBC = 180° - 130° = 50°$ because angles on a straight line add up to 180°
$x = 180° - 50° - 70° = 60°$ because angles in a triangle add up to 180°

## Page 64 Angles in polygons

**Quick quiz:**

**(a)** 360° **(b)** 180°

**Questions:**

**1.** 150° **2.** 105° **3.** $x = 150°$
**4.** 84° **5.** 22.5°

## Page 65 Constructing perpendiculars

**Quick quiz:**

**(a)** half **(b)** 90°

**Questions:**

**1.**

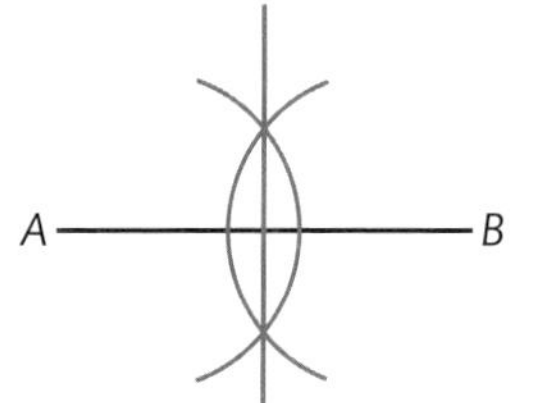


**2.**

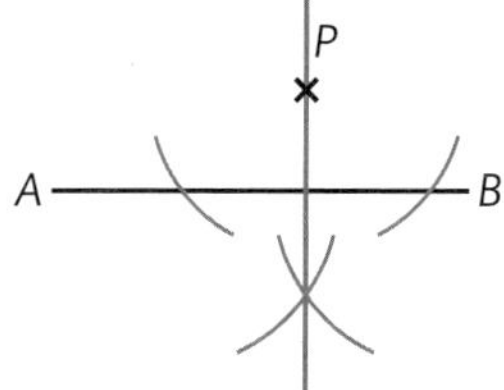


**3.**

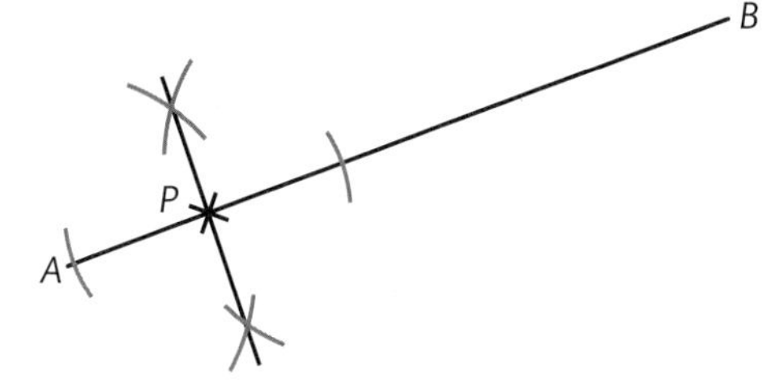


## Page 66 Constructions with angles

**Quick quiz:**

**(a)** equilateral **(b)** bisect, 90° **(c)** bisect, 60°

**Questions:**

**1.**

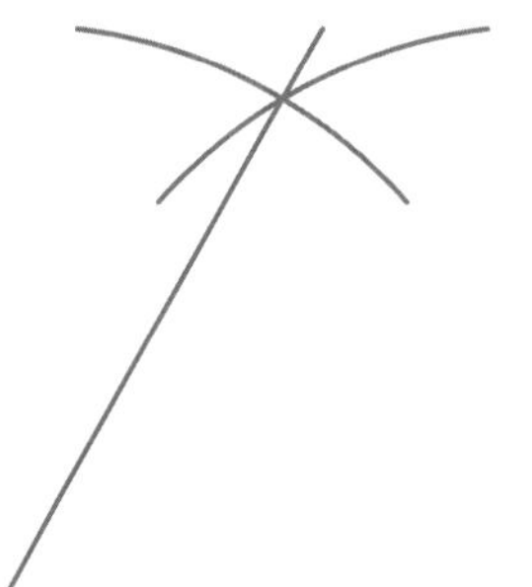

**2.**

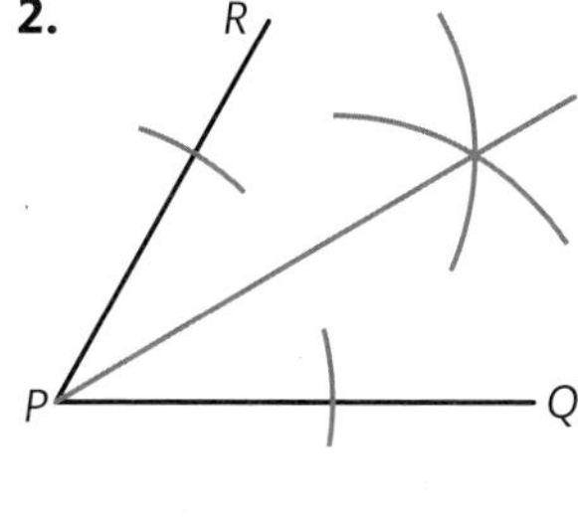


## Page 67 Loci

**Quick quiz:**

**(a)** 30 km **(b)** 400 m **(c)** 2.5 cm

**Questions:**

**1.**

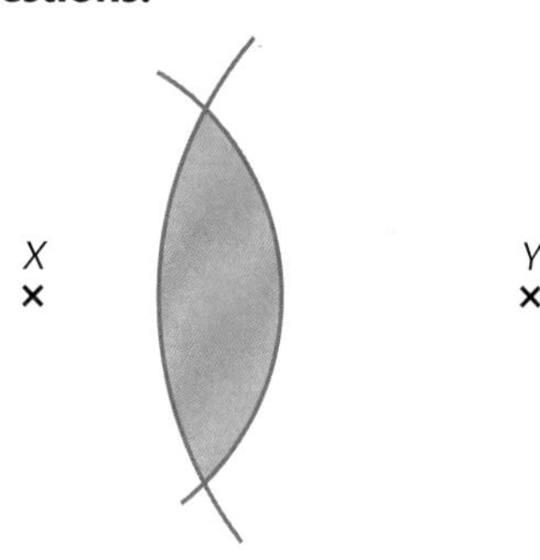


**2. (a)**

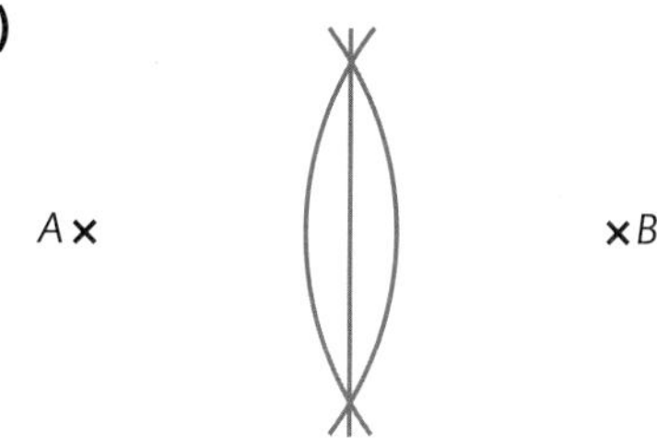


**(b)**

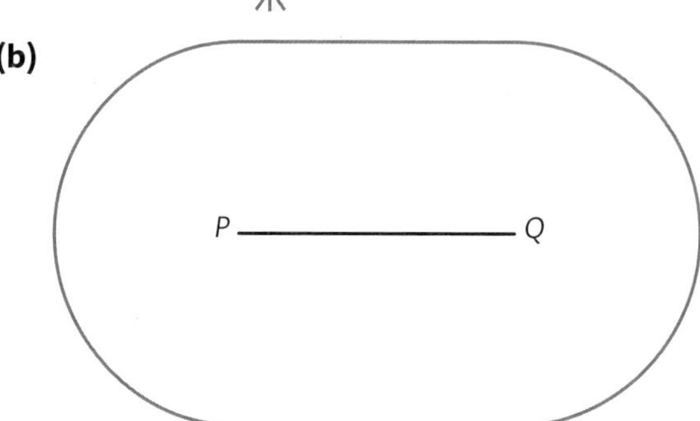


**3.**

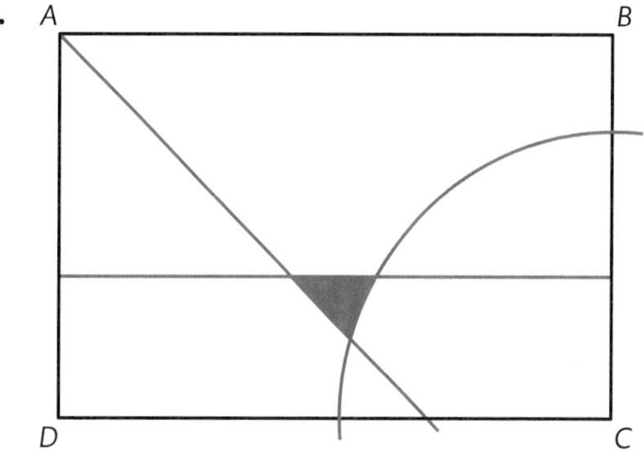


## Page 68 Perimeter and area

**Quick quiz:**

3 + 8 + 3 + 8

**Questions:**

**1. (a)** 24 cm **(b)** 22 cm$^2$
**2. (a)** 28 cm **(b)** 36 cm
**3.** 14 cm$^2$
**4.** Your rectangle can have any of the following dimensions: 2 × 6, 3 × 4, 4 × 3 or 6 × 2
**5.** 10 cm

## Page 69 Areas of 2D shapes

**Quick quiz:**

rectangle → $A = l \times w$

triangle → $A = \frac{1}{2}bh$

parallelogram → $A = bh$

trapezium → $A = \frac{1}{2}(a + b)h$

**Questions:**

1. $40\,cm^2$ 2. $36\,cm^2$ 3. $15\,m^2$
4. $55\,cm^2$ 5. $80\,cm^2$ 6. $22\,m^2$

## Page 70 3D shapes

**Quick quiz:**

cube sphere pyramid

**Questions:**

1.

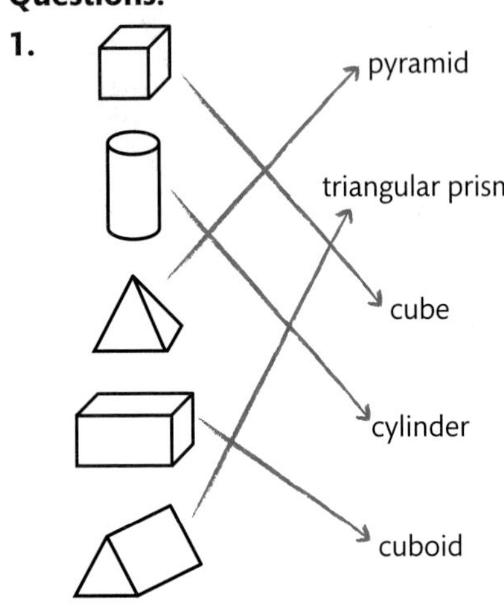


2. **(a)** sphere **(b)** cone **(c)** cylinder
3. **(a)** 6 **(b)** 12 **(c)** 8
4. **(a)** 5 **(b)** 9 **(c)** 6

## Page 71 Volumes of 3D shapes

**Quick quiz:**

**(a)** $l^3$ **(b)** $lwh$

**Questions:**

1. $380\,cm^3$ 2. $3016\,cm^3$ 3. $972\,cm^3$
4. $1005\,m^3$ 5. $160\,in^3$ 6. $905\,m^3$

## Page 72 Surface area

**Quick quiz:**

**(a)** $32\,cm^2$ **(b)** $100\,cm^2$ **(c)** $6\,cm^2$

**Questions:**

1. $382\,cm^2$ 2. $756\,cm^2$ 3. $628\,cm^2$
4. $452\,m^2$ 5. $4156\,cm^2$ 6. $144\,cm^2$

## Page 73 Circles and cylinders

**Quick quiz:**

1. **(a)** $2\pi r$ **(b)** $\pi r^2$ **(c)** $\pi r^2 h$
2. $16\pi\,cm^2$

**Questions:**

1. $9890\,m^2$
2. **(a)** 5.03 m **(b)** 994
3. **(a)** 15.0 cm **(b)** $1570\,cm^2$

## Page 74 Circles, sectors and arcs

**Quick quiz:**

**(a)** circumference = 31.4 cm
area = $78.5\,cm^2$

**(b)** circumference = 94.2 m
area = $707\,m^2$

**(c)** circumference = 126 mm
area = $1260\,mm^2$

**Questions:**

1. **(a)** 4.32 m **(b)** $4.86\,m^2$ 2. 20.9 cm
3. **(a)** 40.8 cm **(b)** $86.4\,cm^2$

## Page 75 Circle facts

**Quick quiz:**

1. straight 2. equal

**Questions:**

1. **(a)** $x = 90°$ **(b)** $y = 38°$
2. $OBC = 90°$ and $OAC = 90°$ because the angle between the tangent and the radius of a circle is 90°
   Shape *OBCA* is a quadrilateral so its internal angles add up to 360°
   $x = 360° - 90° - 90° - 48° = 132°$
3. **(a)** Lines *OA* and *OB* both represent a radius of the circle, so are the same length. Therefore, triangle *OAB* is an isosceles triangle, meaning that angle *OAB* = angle *OBA*
   **(b)** $OAB = 90 - 61 = 29°$
   $OBT = 76 + 29 = 105°$

## Page 76 Transformations

**Quick quiz:**

reflection, rotation, translation, enlargement

**Questions:**

1.

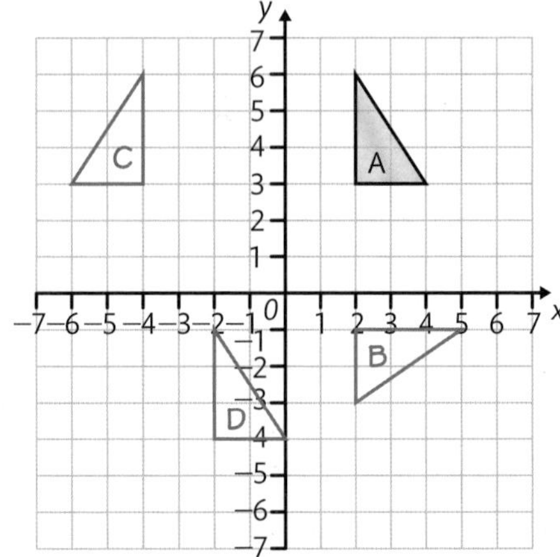


2. **(a)** Rotation 90° anticlockwise about (−1, −2)
   **(b)** Reflection in $y = -x$
   **(c)** Translation of $\begin{pmatrix} 2 \\ -3 \end{pmatrix}$
3. **(a)** Translation of $\begin{pmatrix} 5 \\ -3 \end{pmatrix}$
   **(b)** and **(c)**

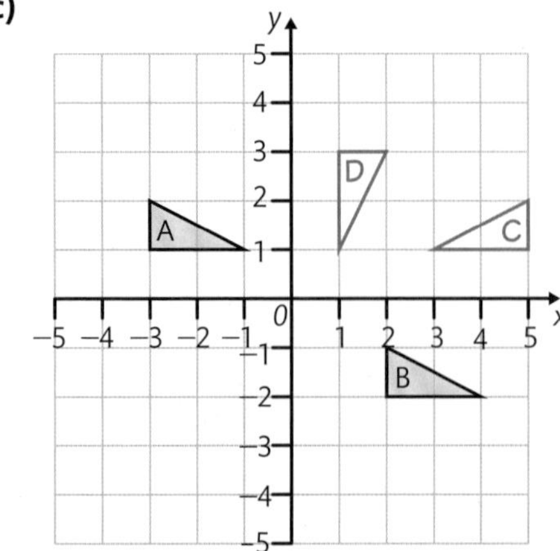

## Page 77 Enlargement

**Quick quiz:**

**(a)** larger **(b)** smaller

**Questions:**

**1.**

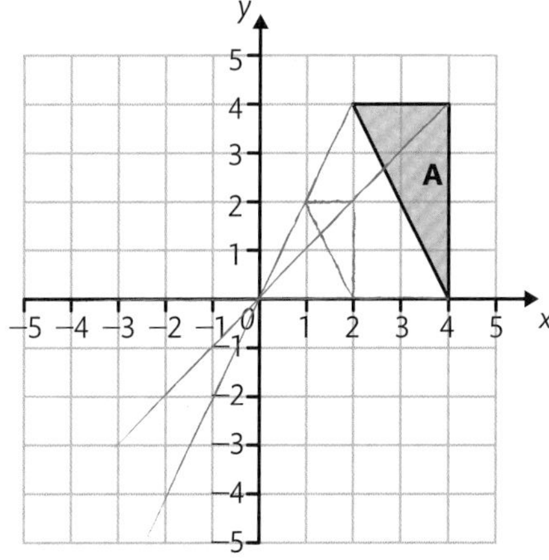

**2.** Enlargement about (1, 3) of scale factor 2

**3.**

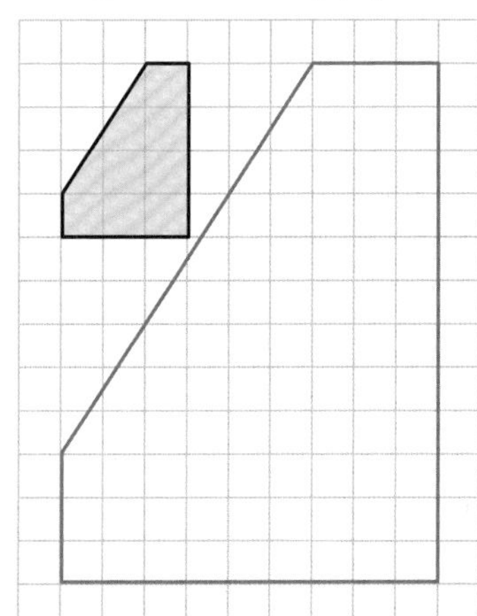

## Page 78 Bearings

**Quick quiz:**

**(a)** north, three **(b)** *A* **(c)** *B*

**Questions:**

**1.** **(a)** 078° **(b)** 044° **(c)** 180° + 44° = 224°

**2.** 233° **3.** 138°

## Page 79 Scale drawings and maps

**Quick quiz:**

**(a)** 90 km **(b)** 3.25 cm

**Questions:**

**1.** **(a)** 328° (accept 326° to 330°)

**(b)** 140 km

**2.** **(a)** 73 km **(b)** 096° or 097°

**(c)**

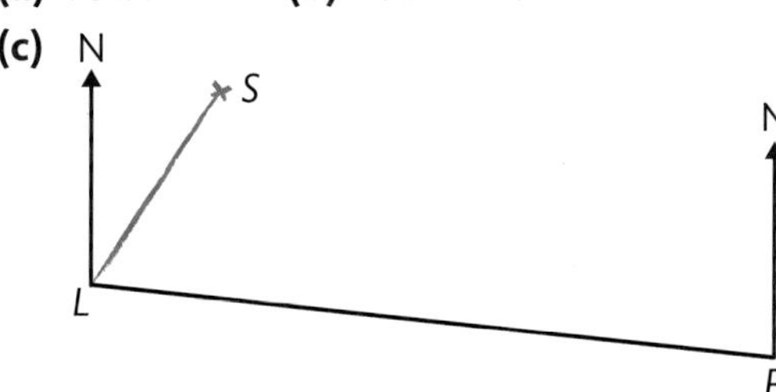


## Page 80 Pythagoras' theorem

**Quick quiz:**

**1.** $a^2 + b^2 = c^2$

**2.**

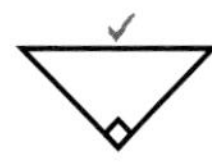

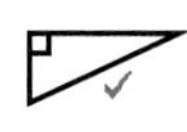

**Questions:**

**1.** **(a)** 7.1 **(b)** 7.4

**2.** 86.5 cm **3.** 2.19 kg

## Page 81 Units of length, area and volume

**Quick quiz:**

**(a)** 10 mm **(b)** 100 cm **(c)** 1000 mm **(d)** 1000 m

**Questions:**

**1.** **(a)** **(i)** 2 000 000 cm³ **(ii)** 4 500 000 m²

**(b)** 45.2 m²

**2.** 227 km **3.** 86.1 cm

## Page 82 Trigonometry: lengths

**Quick quiz:**

**(a)** $\sin\theta = \frac{\text{opp}}{\text{hyp}}$ **(b)** $\cos\theta = \frac{\text{adj}}{\text{hyp}}$ **(c)** $\tan\theta = \frac{\text{opp}}{\text{adj}}$

**Questions:**

**1.** 47.6

**2.** **(a)** 5.32 cm **(b)** 9.61 cm **(c)** 11.7 cm

**3.** 11.9 cm **4.** 42.5 m

## Page 83 Trigonometry: angles

**Quick quiz:**

**1.** 73.8° **2.** 51.3° **3.** 70.1°

**Questions:**

**1.** 34.2° **2.** **(a)** 7.83 cm **(b)** 45.1°

**3.** 38.4°

## Page 84 Trigonometry techniques

**Quick quiz:**

**(a)** $\sqrt{3}$ **(b)** $\frac{1}{\sqrt{2}}$ **(c)** $\frac{\sqrt{3}}{2}$

**Questions:**

**1.** 030°

**2.** $\cos x = \frac{3}{6}$ so $x = 60°$

The ladder is not safe to use.

**3.** 25 m

## Page 85 Time and timetables

**Quick quiz:**

**(a)** 60 **(b)** 24

**Questions:**

**1.** **(a)** 40 minutes **(b)** 75 minutes

**2.** **(a)** 21:15 **(b)** 20:55 **(c)** 21:50

**3.** **(a)** 10:39 **(b)** 35 minutes **(c)** 126 minutes

**4.** **(a)** 11:59 **(b)** 79 minutes **(c)** 12:59

## Page 86 Reading scales

**Quick quiz:**

**(a)**
**(b)**

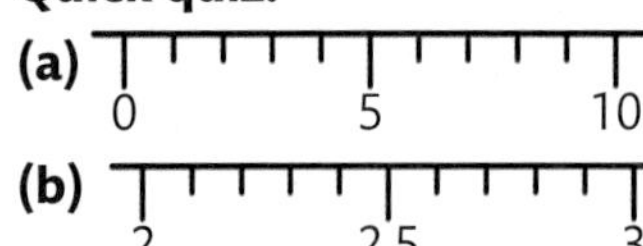


**Questions:**

**1.** **(a) (i)** 76 **(ii)** 52

**(b)**

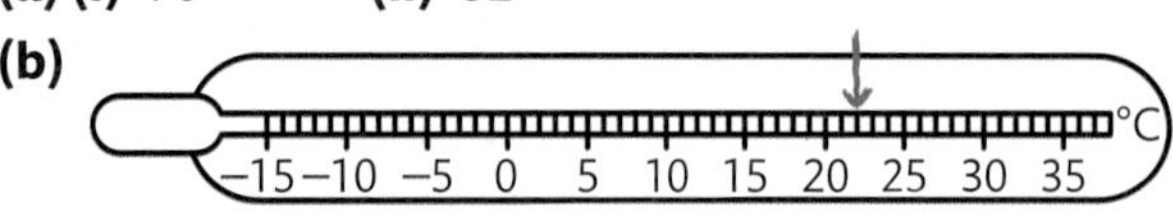


**2.** **(a)** 3.7 **(b)** 2.24

**3.** **(a)**

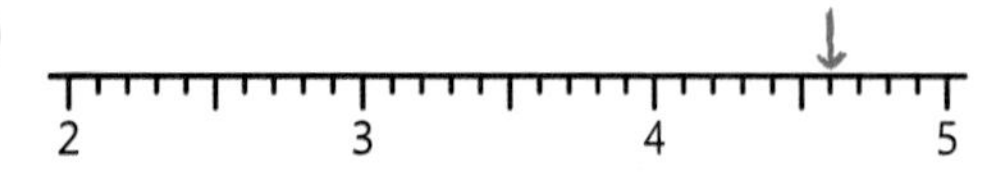


**(b)**

6.1 6.2 6.3

**4.** 35.4

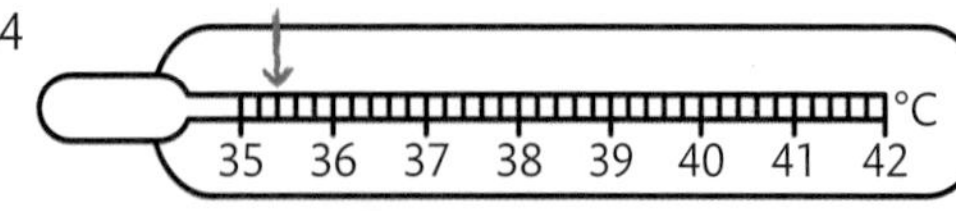


**5.** 2.4

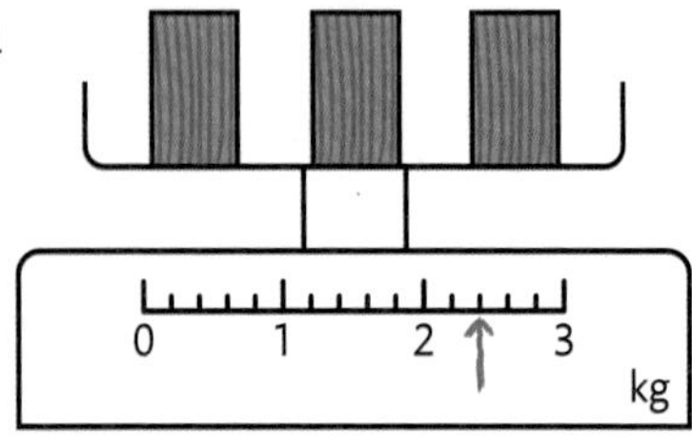


## Page 87 Symmetry

**Quick quiz:**

**(a) and (b)** reflective (line) and rotational

**Questions**

**1.** **(a)** e.g.

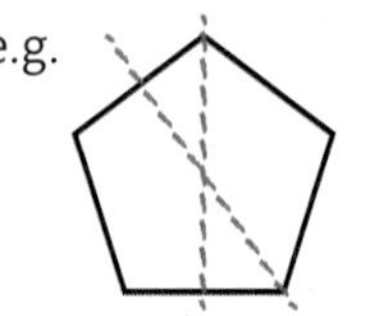

**(b)** 5

**2.** **(a)**

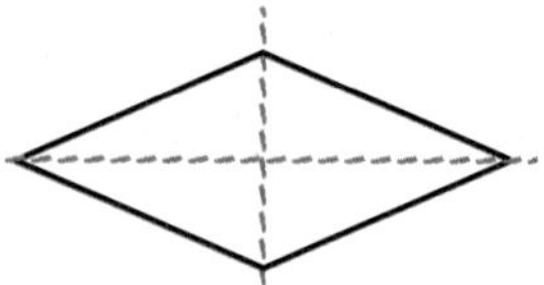

**(b)** 2

**3.** **(a)**

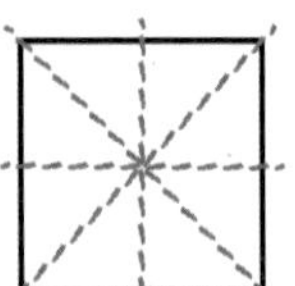

**(b)** 4

**4.** **(a)**

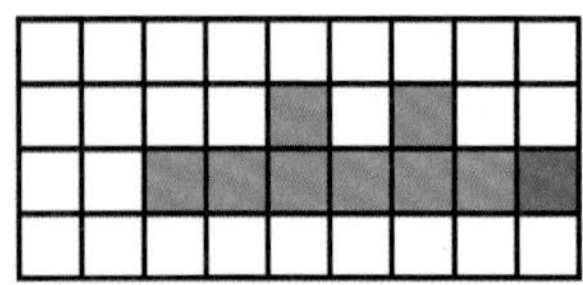

**(b)**

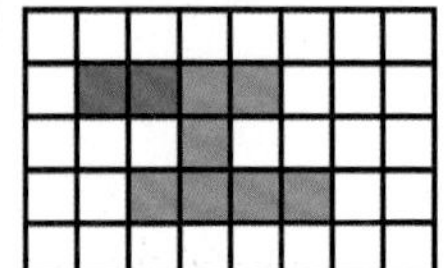

**5.** **(a)** **A** = 0, **B** = 1, **C** = 1, **D** = 0 **(b)** **A**

**6.** **(a)** **A** **(b)** 1

## Page 88 Quadrilaterals

**Quick quiz:**

four, 360

**Questions:**

**1.** square and rectangle

**2.** **(a)** rhombus **(b)** parallelogram

**3.** **(a)** e.g.

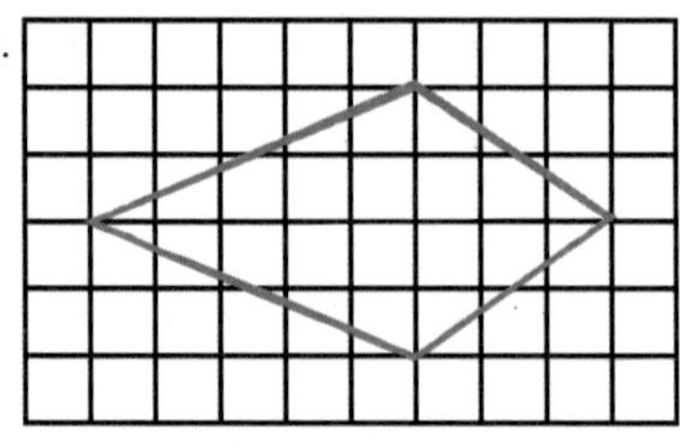

**(b)** e.g.

**4.** **(a)** square, rhombus

**(b)** trapezium **(c)** kite

## Page 89 Plans and elevations

**Quick quiz:**

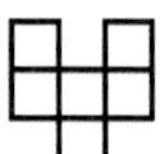

**Questions:**

**1.** **(a)**

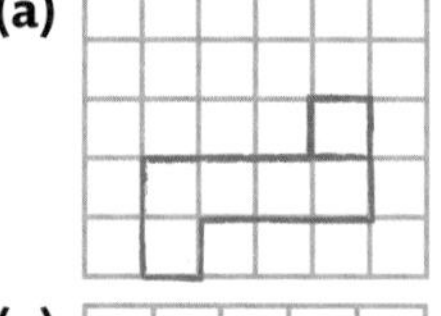

**(b)**

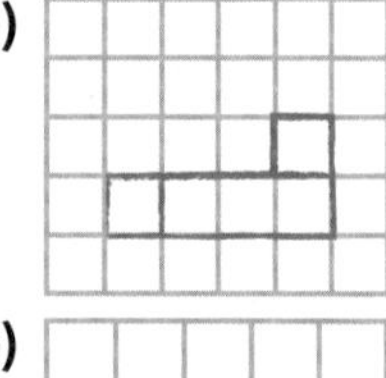

**2.** **(a)**

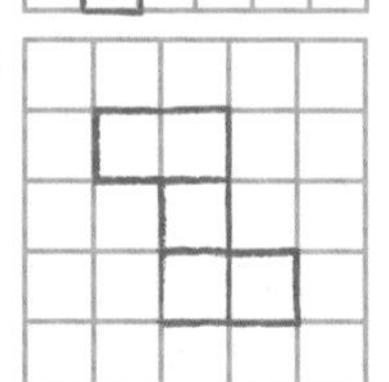

**(b)**

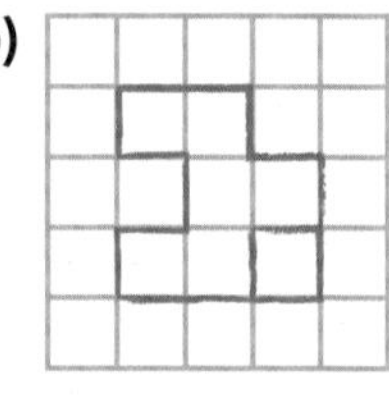

**3.** **(a)**

**(b)**

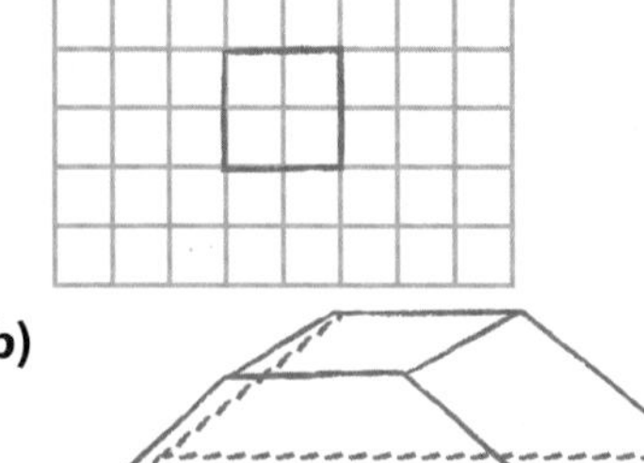

## Page 90 Similarity and congruence

**Quick quiz:**

**(a)** congruent **(b)** similar

**Questions:**

**1.** **(a)** **A** and **G** **(b)** **H**

**2.** **(a)** **A** and **E** **(b)** **D**

**3.** **(a)** **B** and **F** **(b)** **A**

**4.** **(a)** **B** and **D** **(b)** **E**

## Page 91 Similar shapes

**Quick quiz:**

2.5

**Questions:**

1. **(a)** 36 cm **(b)** 20 cm
2. $AB = 45 - 5 - 5 = 35$

   $AD = 30 - 5 - 5 = 20$

   $\frac{EH}{AD} = \frac{30}{20} = \frac{3}{2}$

   $\frac{EF}{AB} = \frac{45}{35} = \frac{9}{7}$

   The ratios of the sides are not the same, so the rectangles are not mathematically similar.
3. 52.5 cm
4. **(a)** 24 cm **(b)** 18 cm

## Page 92 Congruent triangles

**Quick quiz:**

SAS RHS AAS SSS

**Questions:**

1. **(a)** SAS **(b)** SSS **(c)** AAS
2. *BD* is shared

   *BA* = *CD* (opposite sides of a parallelogram)

   *BC* = *AD* (opposite sides of a parallelogram)

   Therefore *ABD* and *BCD* are congruent (SSS).
3. *AB* = *CD* (given)

   Angle *BAC* = *DCA* (alternate angles)

   Angle *ABD* = *CDB* (alternate angles)

   *ABE* and *CDE* are congruent (ASA).
4. *AC* = *BC* (sides of an isosceles triangle)

   Angle *ACD* = *BCE* (shared)

   *CD* = *CE* (given)

   Therefore *ACD* and *BCE* are congruent (SAS).
5. *AD* = *BC* (opposite sides of rhombus)

   *AE* = *EC* (diagonals of rhombus bisect each other)

   *DE* = *EB* (diagonals of rhombus bisect each other)

   Therefore *ADE* and *BCE* are congruent (SSS).

## Page 93 Line segments

**Quick quiz:**

1. $x = 10$ 2. $y = 11.4$

**Questions:**

1. **(a)** (3, 3) **(b)** 4.47
2. **(a)** (4.5, 5.5) **(b)** 7.07
3. **(a)** (1.5, 8) **(b)** 8.06

## Page 94 Vectors

**Quick quiz:**

1. Vectors are quantities that have both magnitude and direction.
2. $\begin{pmatrix} x \\ y \end{pmatrix}$ is called a column vector.

**Questions:**

1. **(a)** $\begin{pmatrix} 1 \\ -5 \end{pmatrix}$ **(b)** $\begin{pmatrix} -7 \\ 7 \end{pmatrix}$

   **(c)** $\begin{pmatrix} 17 \\ -15 \end{pmatrix}$ **(d)** $\begin{pmatrix} -32 \\ 34 \end{pmatrix}$
2. **(a)** 2**a** **(b)** 2**a** + **b** **(c)** **b** − **a**
3. **(a)** −2**a** **(b)** 2**a** + 2**b** **(c)** 4**a** − 2**b**

## Page 95 Exam skills: Geometry and measures

**Questions:**

1. 512 $cm^3$ 2. 18°, 72° and 90° 3. 19.7° (1.d.p)

## Page 96 Introduction to probability

**Quick quiz:**

From left to right:
impossible, unlikely, even chance, likely, certain

**Questions:**

1. 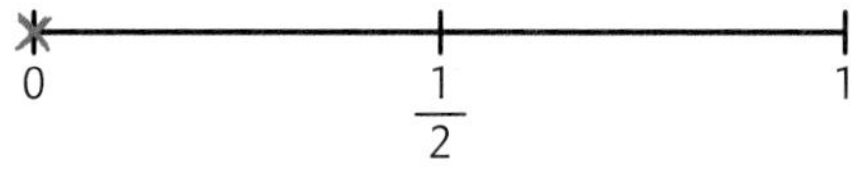

2. even
3. **(a)**

| | 2 | 4 | 6 |
|---|---|---|---|
| 1 | 3 | 5 | 7 |
| 3 | 5 | 7 | 9 |
| 4 | 6 | 8 | 10 |

   **(b)** $\frac{2}{3}$

4. **(a)**

| | | Bag A | | | |
|---|---|---|---|---|---|
| | | 1 | 3 | 5 | 7 |
| Bag B | 2 | 2 | 6 | 10 | 14 |
| | 4 | 4 | 12 | 20 | 28 |
| | 6 | 6 | 18 | 30 | 42 |
| | 8 | 8 | 24 | 40 | 56 |

   **(b)** $\frac{3}{8}$

## Page 97 More about probability

**Quick quiz:**

**(a)** For any event, the total probability of all the possible outcomes adds up to 1

**(b)** 0.65

**(c)** **(i)** $\frac{1}{2}$ or 0.5 **(ii)** $\frac{2}{3}$ or $0.\dot{6}$ **(iii)** $\frac{1}{6}$ or $0.1\dot{6}$

**Questions:**

1. **(a)** 0.15 **(b)** 0.09
2. **(a)** 0.729 **(b)** 0.001
3. $\frac{1}{36}$ 4. $\frac{13}{30}$

## Page 98 Relative frequency

**Quick quiz:**

1. $\frac{2}{5}$ or 0.4
2. As you increase the number or times the coin is tossed, the relative frequency gets closer to the theoretical probability.

**Questions:**

1. **(a)** $\frac{2}{15}$ **(b)** $\frac{4}{5}$ **(c)** $\frac{13}{30}$
2. **(a)** $\frac{1}{2}$ **(b)** $\frac{7}{8}$ **(c)** $\frac{7}{200}$
3. Sarah has the more reliable result as she rolls the dice more times.

## Page 99 Venn diagrams

**Quick quiz:**

both events occurring

**Questions:**

1. **(a)**

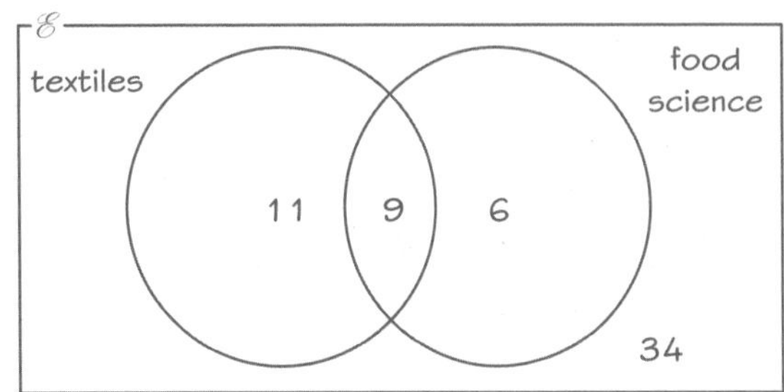


**(b)** $\frac{11}{60}$ **(c)** $\frac{17}{30}$

2. **(a)**

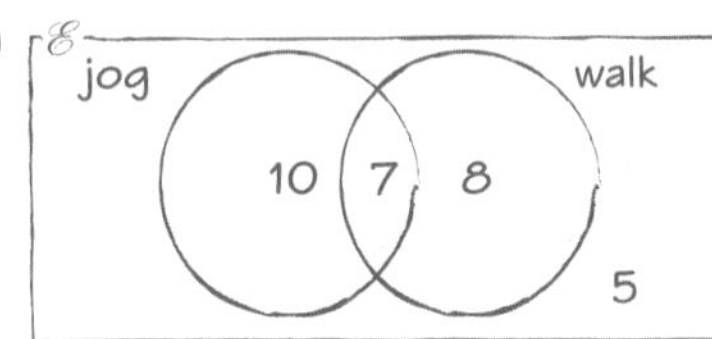


**(b) (i)** $\frac{1}{6}$ **(ii)** $\frac{3}{5}$

3. **(a)**

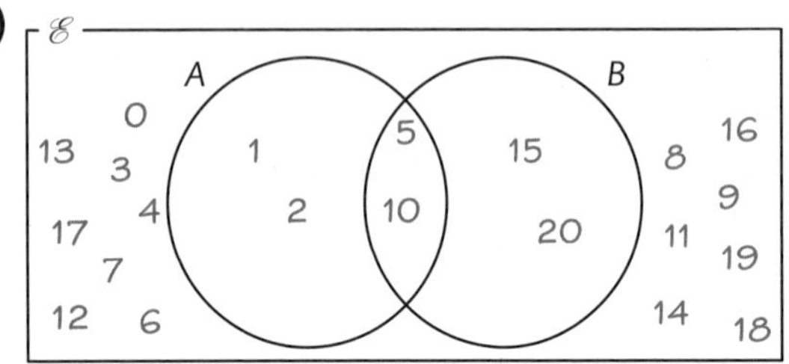


**(b)** 5, 10

## Page 100 Tree diagrams

**Quick quiz:**

tree diagram

**Questions:**

1. **(a)**

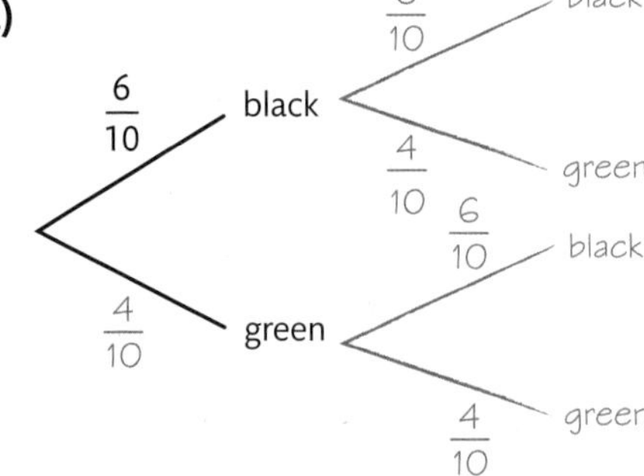


**(b)** $\frac{9}{25}$ **(c)** $\frac{12}{25}$

2. **(a)**

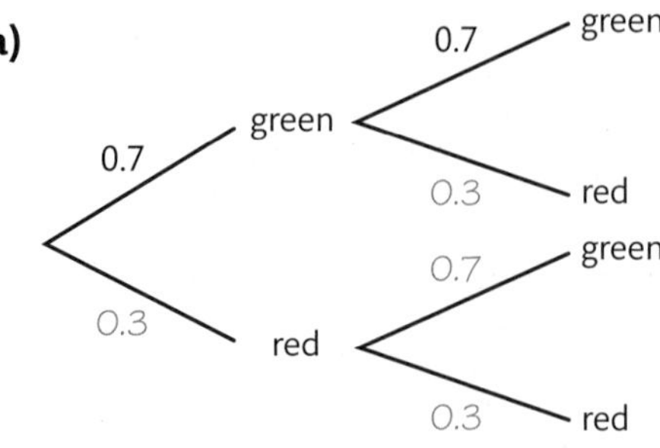


**(b)** 0.49 **(c)** 0.42

## Page 101 Exam skills: Probability

**Questions:**

1. **(i)**

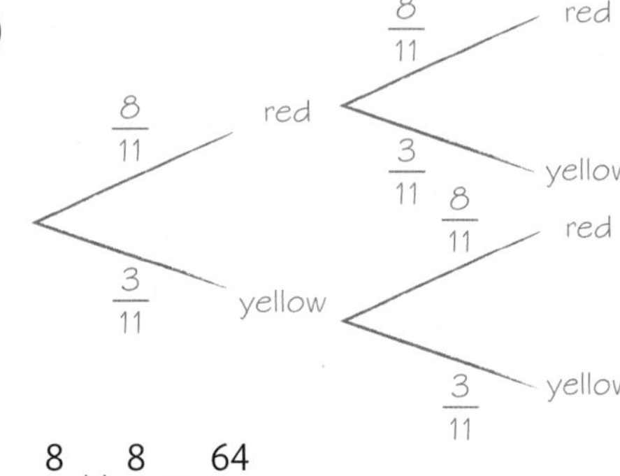


$\frac{8}{11} \times \frac{8}{11} = \frac{64}{121}$

**(ii)** $\frac{48}{121}$

2. **(a)**

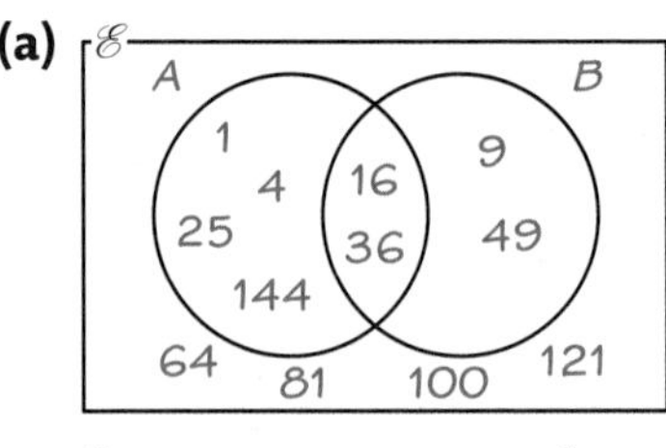


**(b)** $\frac{2}{3}$ **(c)** $\frac{1}{6}$

3. **(a)** 0.2 **(b)** 98

## Page 102 Averages and range

**Quick quiz:**

mode → the number or item which occurs most often

median → the middle number in a set of data, when the data has been written in ascending order

mean → all the values added together and divided by the number of values

range → the difference between the largest and smallest values

**Questions:**

1. **(a)** 4 **(b)** 5 **(c)** 7 **(d)** 11
2. **(a)** 25 cm **(b)** 23 cm **(c)** 21 cm **(d)** 17 cm
3. **(a)** 7 kg **(b)** 6 kg
   **(c)** Uri is correct because the median is not affected by extreme values and 15 kg is an extreme value in this data set.
4. 16 seconds

## Page 103 Pictograms

**Quick quiz:**

**(a)** 10 **(b)** 15 **(c)** 30

**Questions:**

1. **(a)** 12

**(b)**

| Sport | Number of friends |
|---|---|
| Football | ● ● ● |
| Badminton | ● ◖ |
| Tennis | ● ● ◔ |
| Cricket | ○ ○ ◖ |

Key ● represents 4 friends

**(c)** 37

2. **(a)**

| Day | Number of tins |
|---|---|
| Monday | ◇ ◇ ◇ ◇ |
| Tuesday | ◇ ◁ |
| Wednesday | ◇ ◇ ◇ ◇ |
| Thursday | ◇ ◇ ◇ |
| Friday | ◇ ◇ ◁ |

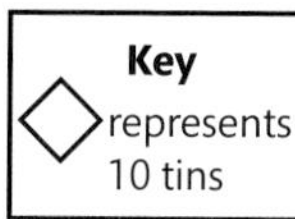


**(b)** 25 tins

## Page 104 Line graphs

**Quick quiz:**

**(a)** 36 **(b)** 18 **(c)** 20.9

**Questions:**

1. **(a)**

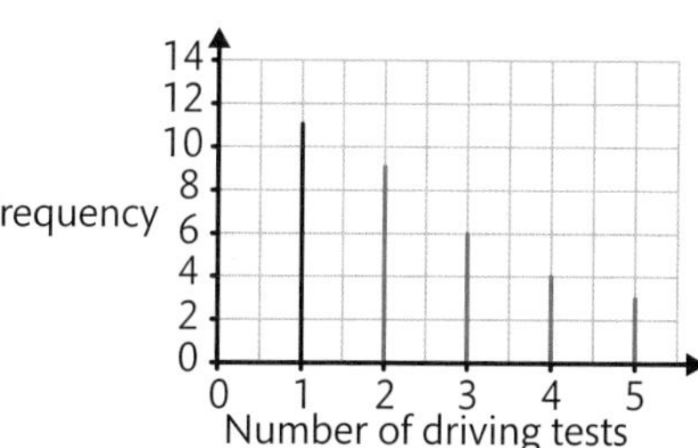


**(b)** 1 **(c)** 2.36

2. **(a)** 162 **(b)** downwards

## Page 105 Pie charts

**Quick quiz:**

**(a)** 240 **(b)** 252 **(c)** 280

**Questions:**

1.

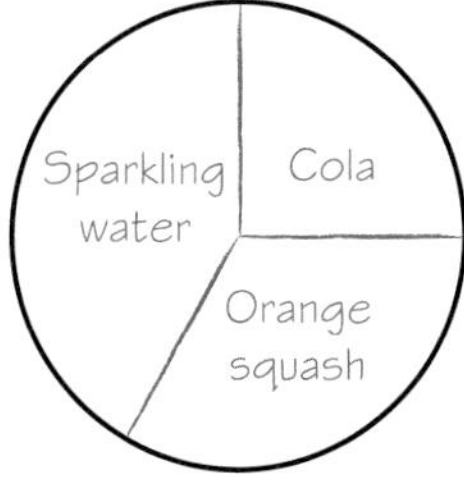


2.

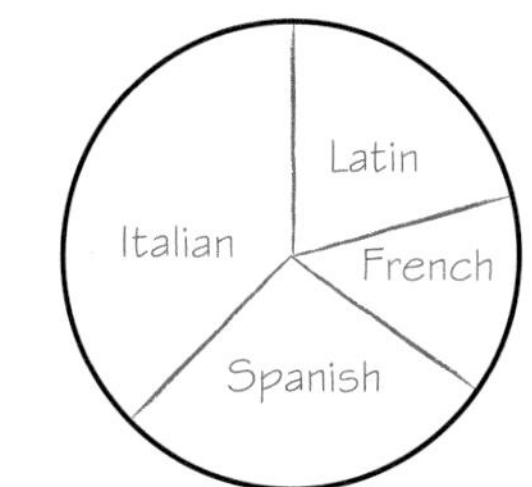


3. **(a)** 9 **(b)** 18 **(c)** 72

## Page 106 Stem-and-leaf diagrams

**Quick quiz:**

**(a)** 1 2 2 3 5 6 9

**(b)** 5 5 6 7 7 8 9

**Questions:**

1.

| | |
|---|---|
| 3 | 7 8 8 |
| 4 | 0 0 1 3 5 7 8 |
| 5 | 1 2 4 6 6 9 |
| 6 | 3 5 8 |

Key 3|7 represents 37 grams

2.

| | |
|---|---|
| 11 | 3 5 9 |
| 12 | 0 3 3 5 7 8 |
| 13 | 7 7 8 9 |
| 14 | 0 1 |

Key 11|3 represents 113 cm

3.

| | |
|---|---|
| 4 | 9 |
| 5 | 3 5 6 6 |
| 6 | 1 2 5 5 6 7 9 9 |
| 7 | 3 9 |

Key 4|9 represents 49

4.

| | |
|---|---|
| 6 | 1 3 8 |
| 7 | 1 4 4 7 8 |
| 8 | 1 2 3 5 6 6 6 8 |
| 9 | 0 1 3 4 |

Key 6|1 represents 61 cm

## Page 107 Scatter graphs

**Quick quiz:**

**(a)** positive **(b)** negative

**Questions:**

1. **(a)** (140, 60)
   **(b)** **(i)** suitable line of best fit **(ii)** positive **(c)** 63 kg
   **(d)** No, as 180 cm is out of the data range / extrapolation.

2. **(a)**

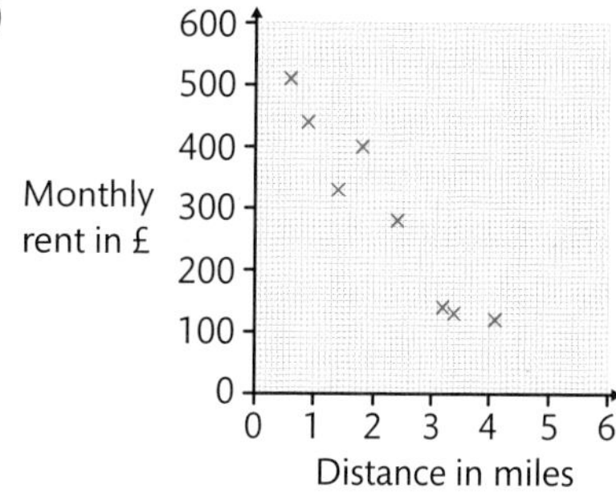


**(b)** Negative, because as the distance from the city centre increases, the rent decreases.
**(c)** about £230
**(d)** Yes, as 2.8 miles is within the data range.

## Page 108 Frequency tables

**Quick quiz:**

**(a)** 5 **(b)** 8 **(c)** 8.4

**Questions:**

1. **(a)** 0 **(b)** 1 **(c)** 1.29
2. **(a)** $20 \leqslant t < 30$ **(b)** $30 \leqslant t < 40$ **(c)** 27.8 minutes
   **(d)** The data is grouped.

## Page 109 Two-way tables

**Quick quiz:**

**(a)** 18 **(b)** 12 **(c)** 16

**Questions:**

**1. (a)**

| | Latin | Spanish | German | Total |
|---|---|---|---|---|
| **Female** | 20 | 4 | 22 | 46 |
| **Male** | 12 | 19 | 13 | 44 |
| **Total** | 32 | 23 | 35 | 90 |

**(b)** $\frac{23}{90}$

**2. (a)**

| | Banana | Orange | Pear | Total |
|---|---|---|---|---|
| **Girls** | 11 | 11 | 13 | 35 |
| **Boys** | 13 | 9 | 3 | 25 |
| **Total** | 24 | 20 | 16 | 60 |

**(b)** 16 **(c)** $\frac{1}{20}$

**3. (a)**

| | Swimming | Badminton | Tennis | Total |
|---|---|---|---|---|
| **Girls** | 17 | 14 | 24 | 55 |
| **Boys** | 15 | 11 | 19 | 45 |
| **Total** | 32 | 25 | 43 | 100 |

**(b) (i)** $\frac{17}{100}$ **(ii)** $\frac{19}{100}$

## Page 110 Sampling

**Quick quiz:**

All the individuals in the population have an equal chance of being chosen.

**Questions:**

**1. (a)**

| | Thriller | Horror | Science fiction | Musical |
|---|---|---|---|---|
| **Tally** | | | | |
| **Frequency** | | | | |

**(b)** For example: 10 people is too small a sample; Friday-night cinema-goers are not necessarily a representative sample.

**2.** Choose 20 random numbers between 1 and 2000. Select the *n*th bolt produced each day for each random number *n* chosen.

**3.** For example: He is only asking his friends at school so the sample is likely to be biased; the sample is too small.

**4** Not a good sample because

Any two from:

- not all residents have an equal chance of being selected
- only asks Wells Street residents
- residents elsewhere cannot give opinions
- residents in one street may have similar interests / views
- Wells Street may not be representative
- the sample is too small.

## Page 111 Analysing data

**Quick quiz:**

On average it takes boys longer to get home than girls.

**Questions:**

**1.** On average, shoe size for the boys is greater than for the girls.

**2.** Amrit is more consistent as the range of his scores is smaller.

**3.** Statement 1 is true: The missing person has an age greater than the mean so the mean value of the new set will be higher.

Statement 2 is false: The median value including the extra person will be at least 32. It could still be 32 but it cannot be less than that as a value has been added that is greater than 32. The old median was between the 15th and 16th values and the new median is the 16th value.

## Page 112 Exam skills: Statistics

**1. (a)**

| Colour | Number of children |
|---|---|
| **Red** | ○ ○ ○ |
| **Yellow** | ○ ○ ◖ |
| **Green** | ○ ○ ○ ○ ○ |
| **Pink** | ○ ◖ |

Key: ○ represents 4 children

**(b)** 10 **(c)** 48

**2. (a)**

| | |
|---|---|
| 1 | 5 8 9 |
| 2 | 0 1 3 4 5 6 8 8 |
| 3 | 1 1 2 3 4 5 6 7 9 |
| 4 | 1 3 6 7 8 9 |
| 5 | 1 |

Key 1|5 represents 15 phone cards

**(b)** 32 **(c)** 36

## Page 113 Problem-solving strategies

**1.** Height of triangle $= 5.2 - 3.8 = 1.4\,\text{m}$

Area of triangle $= 0.5 \times 4 \times 1.4 = 2.8\,\text{m}^2$

Area of rectangle $= 4 \times 3.8 = 15.2\,\text{m}^2$

Total area $= 2.8 + 15.2 = 18\,\text{m}^2$

Number of packs of tiles $= 18 \div 2 = 9$

Cost of tiles $= 9 \times$ £6.50 = £58.50

Discounted price = £58.50 $\times 0.8 =$ £46.80

Taimoor does have enough money.

## Page 114 Solving number problems

**1.** Area of square $= 5.3 \times 5.3 = 28.09\,\text{m}^2$

Area of semicircle $= (\pi \times (0.5 \times 5.3)^2) \div 2 = 11.03\,\text{m}^2$

Total area $= 28.09 + 11.03 = 39.12\,\text{m}^2$

Number of packs required $= 39.12 \div 3.5 = 11.18 = 12$

Cost of wood chips $= 12 \times$ £23.60 = £283.20

Discounted price = 76% of £283.20 = £215.23

Len does have enough money.

**2.** Bank A

## Page 115 Solving graphical problems

**1. (a)** 4.4 gallons

**(b)** No as 427.5 litres is less than 460 litres

**2. (a)**

| x | 0 | 2 | 4 | 6 | 8 | 10 | 12 |
|---|---|---|---|---|---|---|---|
| **A** | 0 | 20 | 32 | 36 | 32 | 20 | 0 |

(b)

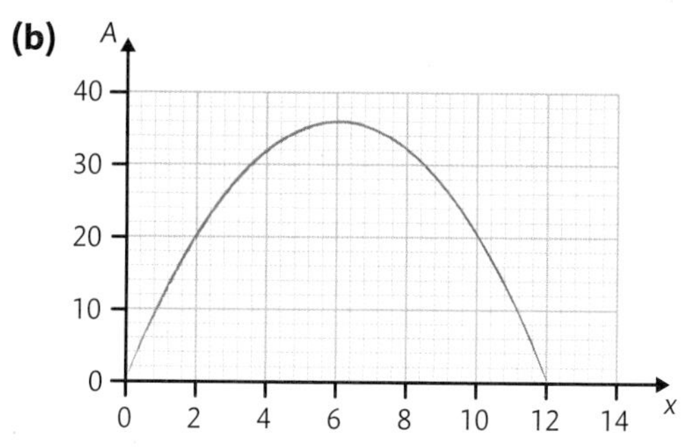


(c) (6, 36) **(d)** The maximum area is 36 m$^2$.

## Page 116 Solving geometric problems

**1.**

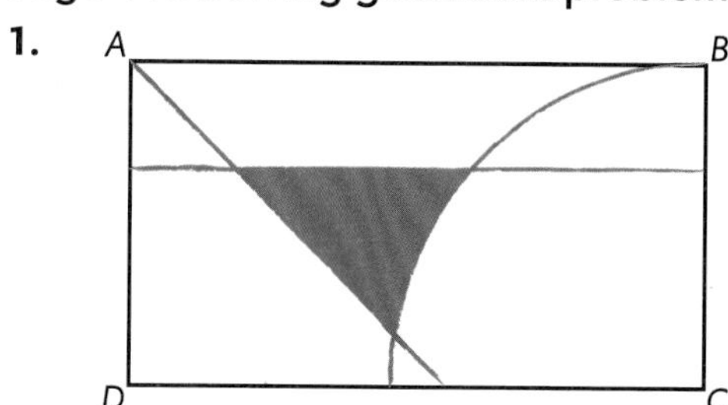


**2.** £659.83

## Page 117 Solving algebraic problems

**1.** 126 cm$^2$

**2.** One tin of paint costs £4.50 and one tin of varnish costs £2.75.

## Page 118 Solving statistical problems

**1. (a)** 5 °C

**(b)** Air temperature drops as height above sea level increases. This is negative correlation.

**(c)** about 2.75 km

**2. (a)**

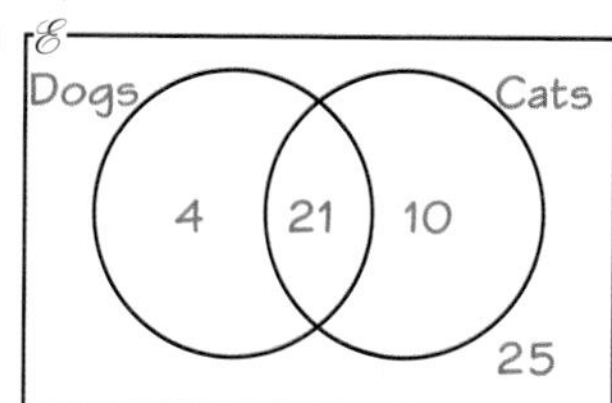


**(b)** $\frac{5}{12}$

## Page 119 Non-calculator practice paper

**1. (a)** 480 cm **(b)** 4.6 kg

**2.** 3 **3.** 3.75

**4.** −3 **5.** 19, 23 **6.** $P = 5x + 1$

**7. (a)** (3, −2)

**(b) (i)**

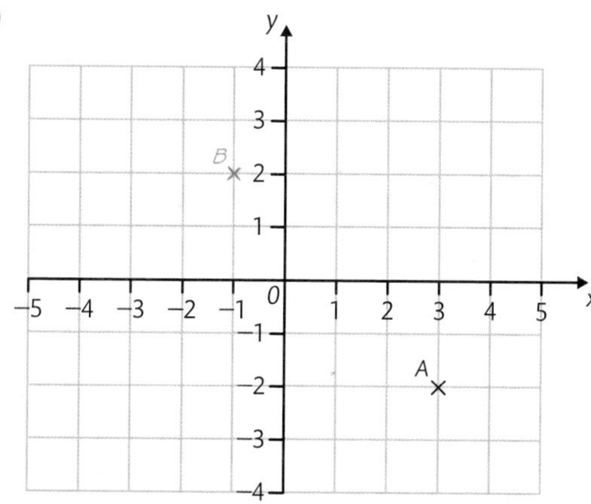


**(ii)** No. (line drawn or algebraic method)

**8.** 28 cm

**9.**

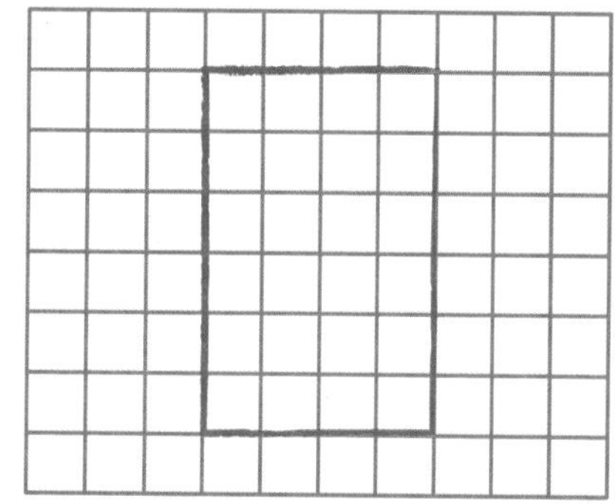


**10. (a)** Asha because the range of her scores is greater.

**(b)** He is not correct because none of his scores are greater than 17.

**11. (a)** 5

**(b)** No, because the total number of people is still less than the number of people that can travel in 5 minibuses.

**12. (a)**

| | Left-handed | Right-handed | Total |
|---|---|---|---|
| **Male** | 16 | 14 | 30 |
| **Female** | 8 | 12 | 20 |
| **total** | 24 | 26 | 50 |

**(b)** $\frac{3}{5}$ **(c)** $\frac{6}{25}$

**13.** 96 cm$^2$

**14.** $\frac{4}{7} = \frac{36}{63}$; $\frac{5}{9} = \frac{35}{63}$; $\frac{4}{7}$ is bigger

**15.** $\frac{3}{5}$ **16.** £700 **17.** $\frac{1}{3}$ **18.** £105

**19.** 275 g flour, 50 g butter, 200 ml milk and 5 tablespoons of sugar

**20.** Lesedi 29.469 **21.** $6 \times 10^{-3}$

**22. (a)** $\frac{21}{32}$ **(b)** $\frac{7}{15}$ **(c)** 4 **(d)** $\frac{1}{9}$

**23.** $2^4 \times 3$ **24.** 22%

**25.** Angle $FBC = 65°$ (alternate angles)

Angle $BFC = 65°$ (base angles in isosceles triangle are equal)

$x = 50°$ (angles in triangle add up to 180°)

**26.** Area of floor $= (5 \times 4) - (2 \times 2.5) = 15\text{ m}^2$

Martina needs 6 litres of paint to paint 15 m$^2$. $\left(\frac{15}{2.5}\right)$

She has $5 \times 1.5$ litres $= 7.5$ litres

Martina has enough paint.

**27. (a)** 44 **(b)** Yes, it will increase the mean.

**28.** £110

## Page 122 Calculator practice paper

**1.** 0.35 **2.** 5000

**3. (a)** $20mn$ **(b)** $p^3$ **(c)** $4x$

**4.** 8

**5.** 32

**6. (a)** $\frac{37}{60}$ **(b)**

Prawn, Chicken, Cheese, Egg

**7. (a)** $\frac{7}{15}$ **(b)** 4:1

**8.** 17 **9.** 389 cm$^3$

**10. (a)** 12 **(b)** 17

**(c)**

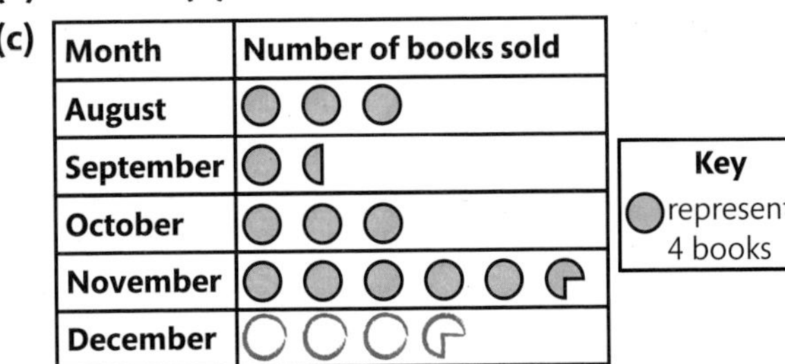

| Month | Number of books sold |
|---|---|
| August | |
| September | |
| October | |
| November | |
| December | |



**11.** Angle $BCA = 76°$ (angles on a straight line add up to 180°)
Angle $BAC = 56°$ (angles in a triangle add up to 180°)
No

**12.** about 7.2 m

**13. (a)** 36 **(b)** 32 **(c)** 31 or 37

**14.** Pens 4 U, as £12.45 < £14.40 **15.** £8.58

**16.**

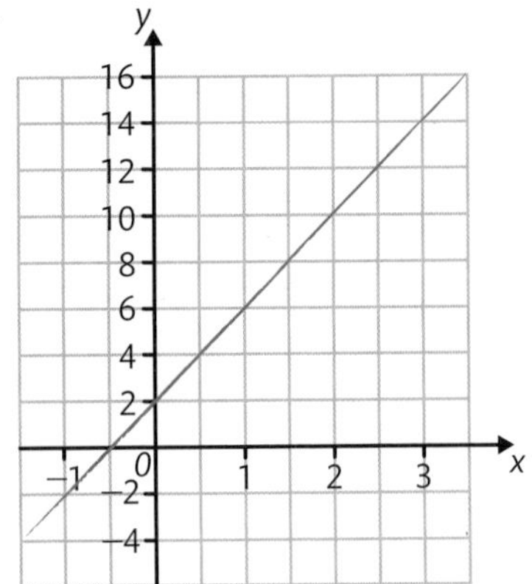


**17. (a)** $6(x - 2)$ **(b)** $3ab(a + 4b)$

**18. (a)** 0.0058 **(b)** $2.94 \times 10^8$

**19. (a)** 0.15 **(b)** 24

**20. (a)** $6n - 1$ **(b)** No, as $n$ is not an integer.

**21.** In Wolverhampton, 1 litre is £1.094.
In Washington D.C., 3.875 litres is \$2.85, so 1 litre is \$2.85/3.875 = \$0.735.
£1 = \$1.45, so \$0.735 = £0.51
Petrol is better value for money in Washington D.C.

**22. (a)** 7.8 cm **(b)** 4.1 cm

**23.** Wolves Bank = £37 142.28 and Bankworld = £37 055.85
Wolves Bank offers the better deal.

**24.** $8.335 \leqslant n < 8.345$ **25.** −8 and 5 **26.** 27.1°

---

Published by BBC Active, an imprint of Educational Publishers LLP, part of the Pearson Education Group, 80 Strand, London, WC2R 0RL.

www.pearsonschools.co.uk/BBCBitesize



Edited, typeset and produced by Elektra Media Ltd
Illustrated by Elektra Media Ltd
Cover design by Andrew Magee & Pearson Education Limited 2019
Cover illustration by Darren Lingard / Oxford Designers & Illustrators

The right of Navtej Marwaha to be identified as author of this work has been asserted by him in accordance with the Copyright, Designs and Patents Act 1988.

First published 2019

22 21 20 19
10 9 8 7 6 5 4 3 2 1

**British Library Cataloguing in Publication Data**
A catalogue record for this book is available from the British Library

ISBN 978 1 406 68566 4

**Acknowledgements**
**BBC:** 1–17, 19–47, 49–56, 58–59, 62–84, 87–94, 96–100, 102–105, 107–111, 114–118 © 2019



Printed and bound in Slovakia by Neografia.

The Publisher's policy is to use paper manufactured from sustainable forests.

**Notes from the publisher**

1. While the publishers have made every attempt to ensure that advice on the qualification and its assessment is accurate, the official specification and associated assessment guidance materials are the only authoritative source of information and should always be referred to for definitive guidance. Pearson examiners have not contributed to any sections in this resource relevant to examination papers for which they have responsibility.

2. Pearson has robust editorial processes, including answer and fact checks, to ensure the accuracy of the content in this publication, and every effort is made to ensure this publication is free of errors. We are, however, only human, and occasionally errors do occur. Pearson is not liable for any misunderstandings that arise as a result of errors in this publication, but it is our priority to ensure that the content is accurate. If you spot an error, please do contact us at resourcescorrections@pearson.com so we can make sure it is corrected.

**Websites**
Pearson Education Limited is not responsible for the content of third-party websites.